Developments in Geotechnical Engineering 19

STABILIZED EARTH ROADS

Further titles in this series

Volumes 1, 2 and 3 are out of print

Developments in Geotechnical Engineering 19

STABILIZED EARTH ROADS

by

Á. KÉZDI

Member of the Hungarian Academy of Sciences
Professor of Civil Engineering
Technical University of Budapest

ELSEVIER SCIENTIFIC PUBLISHING COMPANY

Amsterdam – Oxford – New York – 1979

The distribution of this book is being handled
by the following publishers

for the U.S.A. and Canada

Elsevier/North-Holland, Inc.
52 Vanderbilt Avenue
New York, New York 10017, U.S.A.

for the East European Countries, China, Korean People's Republic,
Cuba, People's Republic of Vietnam and Mongolia

Akadémiai Kiadó, The Publishing House of the Hungarian Academy of Sciences, Budapest

for all remaining areas

Elsevier Scientific Publishing Company
335 Jan van Galenstraat
P.O. Box 211, 1000 AE Amsterdam, The Netherlands

Library of Congress Cataloging in Publication Data

Kézdi, Árpád.
   Stabilized earth roads.

   (Developments in geotechnical engineering; 19)
   Revised and updated translation of Stabilizált
földutak.
   Bibliography: p.
   Includes index.
   1. Soil stabilization. 2. Roads – Foundations.
3. Roads, Earth. I. Title. II. Series.
TE210.0.4.K4713 1978 625.7′4 78 – 6185
ISBN (vol. 19) 0 – 444 – 99786 – 5
ISBN (series) 0 – 444 – 44662 – 5

Printed in Hungary

Preface to the English editon

It is a source of great satisfaction to me that my book on Stabilized Earth Roads is now published in English, on the heels of the Hungarian and German editions. This will result in a much wider distribution of its content.

The methods of stabilization described have been developed and proved over the last twenty years: stabilization has been employed for pavements and also as an element of the pavement in layered constructions. It has been my intention to present the physical and chemical processes taking place in soil stabilization in order to provide a sound basis for these methods and to contribute to the better understanding of the field as a whole.

If I have succeeded in this it will undoubtedly be of assistance to civil engineers engaged in road building programmes and, I would like to hope, will contribute towards developing road systems for the benefit and mankind.

In the preface to the first Hungarian edition I thanked Béla Nagyváti and László Farkas for their help. It is with deep regret that I have to say that they have since died — their contribution to this book will nevertheless always be acknowledged with my sincere thanks.

Budapest, October 1978   Árpád Kézdi

Preface to the Hungarian edition

I am extremely pleased that this manuscript "Stabilized Earth Roads" has been published, since I believe the contents mark the end of an epoch of road-construction-oriented soil stabilization in Hungary: unfortunately the period of preparatory work, experimentation, and accumulation of experience far exceeded the estimated time. It was more than 30 years ago that stabilization based on the principles of soil mechanics was first mentioned in the Hungarian literature,[1] whereafter repeated efforts were made to introduce a mass construction of stabilized earth roads in this country. This book, the first comprehensive survey of soil stabilization theory and practice, has the main objectives of presenting the physical, chemical, and Soil Mechanics principles of soil stabilization to the reader, and describing as well as evaluating the experiences thus collected through the correlation of these principles. I do not intend to offer a detailed instruction or design and construction manual, this latter being the responsibility of the government authorities in charge of our road construction projects. However, I feel that formulating such information can be greatly aided by a careful study of the material presented here. This volume is intended to complete the research work started in 1948 by Prof. Dr. József Jáky in the Laboratory of Soil Mechanics at the Budapest Technical University, with the moral and financial support of the Hungarian Academy of Sciences, and directed by the Author since 1950; a great number of the research results have been presented in this book. The laboratory work and in-situ operations along test sections must be replaced now by investigations on the routine-type mass construction of stabilized earth roads. I am quite convinced that the prerequisites of such mass construction projects are available in Hungary, being joint effort, good organization, and precise control. Thus, I trust that our competent authorities will soon realize the great importance of this case on which any further development of our agriculture is critically dependent.

My work being completed, I should like to express thanks and gratitude to my colleagues. Béla Nagyváti, research engineer, prepared the manuscript and, even

[1] JÁKY, J.: Talajmechanikai vizsgálatok az útépítésre tekintettel (Investigations on soil mechanics with respect to road construction). Magyarország Útügyi Évkönyve, 1934.

JÁKY, J.: Az alsóbbrendű utak kiépítésének szükségessége (The need of secondary road constructions). Budapest 1938.

important, participated actively and enthusiastically for 17 years in the research work referred to and contributed greatly to the results achieved. His efforts in reviewing this volume must similarly be acknowledged. Dr. Jenő Járay, who also read this manuscript, is another Hungarian pioneer of soil stabilization who, with his excellent professional comments and observations, eliminated a great many errors. Thanks are due to Tibor Buócz for reviewing Chapter 6.

László Farkas, research associate, also rendered great assistance for 17 years in our stabilization research, and his extremely careful precision as well as eager activity always warranted the most accurate implementation of the experiments.

Thanks go to Mrs. F. Panrok for the high-speed but precise and careful typing work, a very great assistance.

Finally, many thanks are deserved, by "Akadémiai Kiadó", the Publishing House of the Hungarian Academy of Sciences, for their patience and the faultless accomplishment of publication,

The Author

Contents

1. Introduction

1.1 The importance of stabilized road construction

Since ancient times, mankind has used the natural soil surface for transport and communication. The soil surface roads have been compacted by human and animal traffic, the wheels of team hauled vehicles, and tracks were developed almost spontaneously, as a natural result. These road surfaces were then broadened, covered with rocks and gravel, and thus made suitable for the scarce traffic of early times. Periodically, however, they were transformed into masses of mud by the spring and autumn rains, whereas in the summer season the carts created clouds of dust.

Social development could not longer tolerate such road conditions and, about 150 years ago, roads passable under any weather conditions gradually started to evolve. Thus were born, first gravel topped "Macadam" roads, then, only in the last few decades, the asphalt, concrete, and other high load bearing capacity roads. Durable, smooth pavings, resistant to increased loads and variable climatic conditions, were then constructed in order to exploit the many openings in travel offered by motor vehicles, the herald of communication, and to enable heavily loaded transport to travel safely at a speed previously incredible.

The historically developed routes of the past, following almost precisely the gradients and other terrain features, had to be abandoned, and road design and construction adopted engineering principles identical to those accepted earlier only for railways. However, in addition to the road network completed with high grade paving against considerable costs, the agricultural and other connecting feeder links remained in their original soil surface condition since the financial resources of the communities concerned did not permit such major investments, although these roads had to withstand excessive transportations at intervals e.g. during the harvest season. Since the ordinary soil roads were only passable during certain periods, part of the crop was destroyed or suffered great losses in value, so that transport along these poor tracks has led to tremendous extra costing. Owing to the lack of permanently passable roads the rural population was practically barred from culture, and the exchange of industrial and agricultural commodities was rather difficult. Without first creating the elementary transport and communication, any improvement in living standards cannot even be considered. Similarly, construction of at least the main routes of a national

13

road network is the starting point for development in any economically under-developed country.

Accordingly, a demand for the construction of inexpensive roads satisfying moderate traffic requirements but readily built and economically passable throughout the year has emerged everywhere in the world. This demand, however, could not be satisfied either by the 150 years of traditional stone roads or by recently developed construction techniques. Due to the excessive investment and maintenance costs, and the lack of sufficient road construction capacity, new methods had to be sought and new building materials introduced. Thus, the engineers returned to the ancient road "building material": soil, available everywhere. But this return was at a much higher level than previously since scientific research to clarify the soil properties, and the development of Soil Mechanics have meanwhile taught us how to change the characteristics of in-situ soils using certain treatments, thus enabling us to render soil suitable for permanent road purposes. By treating natural soils, or by the addition of certain materials to the soil, we can produce new substances which, if correctly built-in and maintained, will permanently resist traffic and climatic effects, i.e. they can be considered as stable.

The degree of stability and load bearing capacity depends mainly on the shear strength which, in turn, is the function of the type and condition of the soil. Thus, owing to the continuous variation of the soil condition, the shear strength of natural soil roads reveals significant fluctuation during the year, and is certainly not stable.

If, for example, sand or clay is used in communication and transport roads as the direct running surface, these soils will withstand wide variations in weather conditions, load and road vehicle traffic. Under wet conditions sand has an adequate cohesion due to the capillary stresses, whereby it has a sufficient load bearing capacity. Under dry weather conditions, however, its particles disintegrate, the load-bearing capacity of the soil over the surface reduces to almost zero, it cannot withstand loading, and the wheels sink in. The sand volume hardly changes with the variation of the moisture content. The clay, on the other hand, develops considerable cohesion in dry condition, and has a high-load bearing capacity which, however, rapidly decreases with increased moisture content, so that under wet weather conditions it transforms into soft mud as a result of moisture and the kneading action of wheels. Then, when it is dried again, it will undergo excessive shrinkage. Thus sand and clay are not stable and, alone, neither is suitable for the construction of permanent soil roads. However, if granular soil is spread on clay, or if loose sand is mixed with some cohesive soil, both will be stronger having an increased load-bearing capacity, and a material will be obtained which, in the case of sufficient compaction, combines the favourable characteristics of both components, and, under moderate traffic conditions, will supply a paving passable in any weather. This is the ancient and simplest form of soil stabilization.

Soil stabilization means, therefore, increase of the shear strength of that soil corresponding to the given requirements, and its stabilization independent of the weather conditions or the traffic turnover.

Accordingly, stabilization includes strength and durability increase alike, with certain selected soil properties playing a similarly important role such as the elimination of shrinkage, frost hazards, or high compressibility, and their maintenance at this improved level. It is desirable that any such improvement — increased strength or durability — should be expressed quantitatively, i.e. by the numerical value of the physical properties. Thus, depending on its material and strength, a stabilized soil may be suitable for representing part of the load bearing structure of roads.

Soil stabilization always involves certain treatment of the soil which again always involves remixing or the admixture of other soil types or foreign matter, and the compaction of the mixture. Thus soil stabilization must not be confused with soil solidification aimed at increasing the strength of in-situ soil masses in natural condition, generally without any interference with their structure. Soil stabilization, on the other hand, produces new materials which resist weather and traffic effects if correctly used and maintained, and allow transport and communication in all weather conditions.

The economic significance of stabilized earth roads can be readily verified even in the case of the simplest stabilization techniques referred to above. Figure 1 illustrates the variation of the unconfined compression strength of sand and clay in the function of water content. Since the traction force requirement depends mainly on the depth of the wheel tracks which, in turn, is inversely proportional to the unconfined compression strength, the specific traction force can be illustrated the function of the water content by a curve having an opposite character.

Remembering that under poor road conditions not only the traction force but also the transport speed will be radically reduced, then the daily transport output would develop as a function of the condition of earth road more or less according to Fig. 2.

However, if the soil is stabilized meaning that its strength is maintained at an approximately constant value then the output will be continuously indicated by the dash-dotted line. The significance of this result is best illustrated by the fact that the transport of the majority of agricultural products in many countries has to be done during the rainy season.

Data supplied by a transport cost analysis are still more convincing.

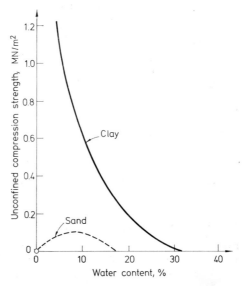

FIG. 1. Unconfined compression strength of sand and clay as a function of water content

15

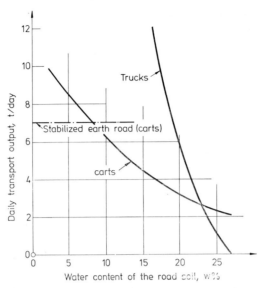

FIG. 2. Daily transport output as a function of the
road condition (water content of the soil)

Let us examine, for example, the correlation between transport cost and resistance forces and so introduce the following symbols:

Gross weight of the transport means	Q (kN)
Deadweight of the transport vehicle	βQ (kN)
Delivery distance	h (km)
Daily payment for (operational cost of) the transport means	B (monetary unit per day)
Daily working time	T (hours per day)
Transport rate	v (km per h)
Loading time	t_l (hours)
Discharge time	t_e (hours)
Specific resistance	μ
Traction force	V

Using the above symbols, the time required for one return journey of the transport vehicle will be, if the to and fro rates are identical, or v (km/h) indicates the average transport speed

$$t_f = \frac{2h}{v} + t_l + t_e$$

The number of return journeys per day:

$$n = \frac{T}{\dfrac{2h}{v} + t_i + t_e}$$

The weight delivered daily:

$$q = \frac{Q(1 - \beta)\, T}{\dfrac{2h}{v} + t_l + t_e}$$

Thus the cost of transporting 1 kN goods will be

$$k^{(\mathrm{m\cdot unit/kN})} = \frac{B}{q} = \frac{B\left(\dfrac{2h}{v} + t_l + t_e\right)}{Q(1 - \beta)\, T} \tag{1}$$

Let us indicate the $t_l v$ and $t_e v$ quantities by symbols h_l and h_e, respectively, meaning the mileage the vehicle would cover during the time of loading and discharge, and consider the fact that the gross weight depends on the traction force or haulage capacity of the vehicle. Thus, assuming a horizontal road, we get

$$V = \mu Q \quad \text{and} \quad Q = V/\mu$$

After substitution and rearrangement:

$$k^{(\mathrm{m\cdot unit/kN})} = \frac{\mu}{v}\left[\frac{B}{v} \frac{(2h + h_l + h_e)}{V(1 - \beta)\, T}\right] = C\,\frac{\mu}{v} \tag{2}$$

For the case of the same vehicle and a given delivery distance, the value of C (the term in brackets) will be constant, and thus the transport cost is proportional to the resistance force, and inversely proportional to the transport speed. Since the resisting force will decrease and the transport speed increase with road stabilization, the transport cost will be favourably affected by the variation of both factors. For a numerical estimation of the savings, the costs have been calculated in the case of a horse-team cart and a truck. The results are shown in Fig. 3.

The difference between the costs of transporting along normal and stabilized earth roads, respectively, is very evident. Along a muddy or sandy road, for example, at $\mu = 140$ N/kN the transport speed will be 2 or 3 km/h whereas over a smooth stabilized earth road the same figure is $v = 6-7$ km/h At the same time the transport cost will decrease from 80 to 15 m · unit/kN. When transporting by truck, the cost reduction will be as much as 74 per cent, If the transport cost difference is calculated for the two cases, then multiplied by the total weight of goods

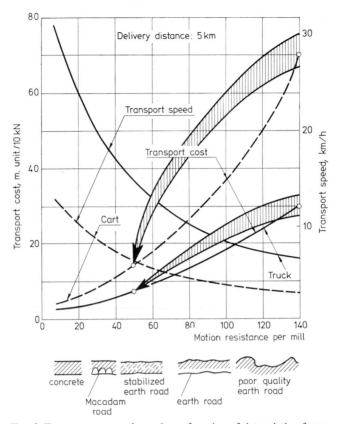

FIG. 3. Transport cost and speed as a function of the resisting force

to be transported annually and divided by the length of the delivery distance, we get the amount that might be spent each year on the construction and maintenance of 1 km stabilized earth road, or the construction cost at which stabilization is still economic, as well as the amount of annual savings. For example, Fig. 4 illustrates the construction and maintenance costs as well as the savings of a road system for a 4000 ha agricultural enterprise. The relevant calculations are reckoned with the crop losses due to transport standstill (which would, however, be eliminated by the construction of stabilized roads, as well as the reduction of the transport costs).

I have deliberately presented these economic investigations and examples at the beginning, since I wanted to emphasize that the construction of stabilized earth roads is one of the critical problems of agriculture. Concrete and Macadam roads, flexible pavements etc., i.e. high-cost road surfaces capable of satisfying considerable load-bearing capacity and traffic requirements — are economic only above a certain volume of traffic. Roads with less traffic do not return the costs of stabilization for economic reasons, although if left in an ordinary soil

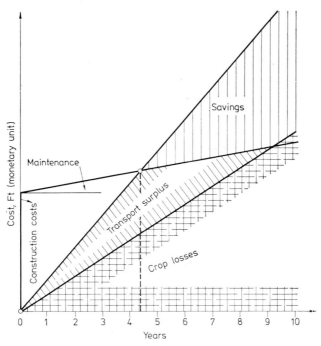

Fɪɢ. 4. Construction and maintenance costs of a stabilized road system for a 4000 ha farm, and the savings due to such a project

road condition, the excessive haulage costs, the increased wear on the vehicles, and only seasonal accessibility would cause tremendous financial losses annually. In Hungary, the majority of low traffic turnover roads (about 90 per cent) are in the agricultural areas. Since they are not stabilized, the transport cost per unit product in agriculture is two or three times higher than in the industry. About 55 to 60 per cent of agricultural operations are represented by material handling, thus a considerable part of the production costs is due to transport expenditure.

In addition to primary economic reasons, the mass construction of stabilized soil roads is necessitated in many countries by political and technical motivations as well. A favourable political and economic effect of road network construction is its promoting the concentration of building projects with the related contribution to the development of civilized urban settlements and the reduction of scattered communities (Figs 5 and 6). This is particularly true for developing countries. Due to technical development, the transport means of large-scale agricultural production have undergone some significant changes. Earlier, the transport agriculture had been almost exclusively the team-drawn carts, but the horse stock decreased at a rapid rate for operational reasons. In Hungary, for example, the one horse per 6.3 ha (figure of 1935) decreased by 1975 to only one per 28 ha, and

FIG. 5. Ordinary earth road in good weather

FIG. 6. Stabilized earth road

they have been replaced by machines, particularly as keeping requires the produce of 1 ha arable land per horse.

Weather conditions limit the use of mechanical transport considerably. In rainy autumnal seasons, for example, agriculture suffers harvest losses worth several millions as a result of transport problems. The development of intensive agricultural production does not allow the departure from the best transport times and methods to result in reduction in produce and quality impairment, transport and other agricultural operation peaks, and finally a considerable cost increase.

The heavy-duty transport means of the large-scale agricultural enterprises can only accomplish their tasks independently of the existing weather conditions, if the main low-traffic roads are stabilized and their continuous maintenance is ensured.

Consequently, agricultural development necessitates the improvement of transport and communication. Similarly, improvement of the settlements' road network is another urgent task. Forestry development, too, requires inexpensive road constructions. However, all these tasks can only be accomplished by soil stabilization. Although these requirements could undoubtedly be much better satisfied by high-quality concrete, asphalt, or Macadam roads, the raw material stock available (rock, gravel, cement, bitumen, etc.), the economics involved and the labor situation, etc., do not permit any such solution, the problem is never asked whether we construct Macadam road or a stabilized earth road, but so, whether we are able to construct stabilized roads or nothing. The answer is made obvious by the fact that we have to effectively pay the costs of road construction regardless of whether we actually build the roads or not, though the expenditures in surplus transport costs, crop losses, vehicle wear and breakdown, etc., resulting from a lack of roads are much greater.

1.2 Historical background

The history of stabilized earth roads has its roots in the distant past. Certain types had already been known in ancient Mesopotamia and Egypt. Greece and the Roman Empire used lime stabilization. As mentioned previously, in the Middle Ages and subsequently the modest need for roads did not bring about any a cause for development, and so this began only in the 19th century with the beginning of Macadam road-constructions. Rubble was first used in 1858, and a steam roller in 1860.

In Europe the foundation based and water bound Macadam roads received no competition for almost a whole century. The first highways of the United States, too, have been constructed using European methods. However, it was soon discovered there that the rate of road construction could not keep pace with the increasing demand, and that the construction costs were growing inadmissibly high, because of the manual labour and vast material handling and transport needs. Moreover, the roads thus constructed did not meet the requirements of the continuously increasing and accelerating traffic, and were ruined faster than they could be repaired. New economic methods had to be developed, therefore, to enable high-speed construction of durable roads. In the field of urban roads and highways, this development has led to the introduction of concrete and black pavings, and in the case of secondary roads to the regular use of stabilized soil.

It was in 1906 when the United States conducted the first experiments with sand-clay mixtures. The favourable results motivated subsequent construction projects using various mixtures. It was at this time that cement, bitumen, and certain chemicals were first employed for soil-stabilization purposes, and a number of different stabilization techniques were elaborated. The initial success aroused the interest of the machine industry, too, and the machines designed for earth stabilization have greatly rationalized the operations involved. The building industry, on the other hand, was particularly hesitant at the beginning, as the new "building material" was regarded as a competition, but as soon as it was realized that the extension of the road network would also offer advantages to that branch, they undertook a major role in development.

In Europe, at the beginning of the century when, in terms of the requirements, number, speed, and loading of the vehicles, a relatively dense road network was available, no large-scale road constructions seemed necessary. The result was that the sceptical professionals rejected the idea of stabilized-road constructions, claiming that such roads would only be useful in underdeveloped regions, poor in transport and communication routes. Therefore, it was not until the 'thirties, when the vast increase of the motor vehicle traffic had begun, and Soil Mechanics entered the field of road construction in Europe, that the idea of stabilization was accepted. During the Second World War, all the countries involved introduced earth stabilization by tar or cement, mainly for airport and runway constructions. After the war, a number of European countries continued earth stabilization but, by that time, for road construction (mainly for secondary, settlement roads), bicycle, or pedestrian roads, and as highway base courses.

Soil stabilization as a science started to evolve about 40 years ago, and today it is generally accepted that the last 20 — 25 years have seen the most important development in road and airport construction. It helps countries and regions to emerge from mud and dust, to reach for a higher economic and cultural level, and to join the economic and cultural system of the developed world. Today, stabilized roads are built all over the world from the Sahara desert to the Arctic regions, from the highly civilized to the economically most underdeveloped countries.

In Hungary, the case of stabilized earth roads was able to progress only after the Second World War, although Prof. Dr. József Jáky, Member of the Hungarian Academy of Sciences, recognized their tremendous significance much earlier, and in 1934 (Jáky, 1934) and later in 1937 and 1938, he repeatedly called the attention of the competent authorities to the subject, exerting every effort to promote the introduction of this road type here. Finally, in the postwar years, again upon an initiative by Prof. Jáky, systematic laboratory-scale research work was started. Part of the results was published (Kézdi, 1951). Stabilization was successfully used in the foundation of higher-order pavings (Járay), and the Geotechnical Department of the Budapest Technical University constructed test sections of soil cement roads. Similar extensive research was conducted by the Road Research Institute of Hungary (Gáspár, 1954, 1959, 1965, etc.), the conditions of general introduction were elaborated and standards, as well as design principles, have been published.

1.3 Stabilized road construction methods

Improvement of the physical properties of soils, and the stabilization of the favourable properties are feasible in several different ways. These methods can be classified from a number of aspects. Here only two classification types will be described, mainly to explain the sequential lay-out of this book.

The first classification type is based on the character of the techniques and, accordingly, three main categories can be distinguished:

(1) Mechanical methods
which ensure soil stability without the addition of any foreign material. Thus the soil properties can be improved

22

— by reducing the void volume of the in-situ soil or the fillup soil delivered to the site, that is, by the compaction of the soil;

— by drainage and the maintenance of the water content at a constant level (by means of adequate facilities), and

— by the admixture of different soil types. It must be noted here that these techniques are usually combined since, for example, compaction is needed in almost every case.

(2) Physical methods

The practical physical reactions leading to stabilization include

— temperature change (e.g. the temperature decrease and solidification of the hot bitumen mixed to the soil);

— hydration (bondage and hardening due to the hydration of Portland cement);

— evaporation (e.g. the drying out of a bitumen emulsion reinforced soil);

— adsorption.

(3) Chemical methods

The chemical reactions used so far for soil stabilization are

— ion exchange (changing the adsorption complex of the soil particles by base exchange);

— precipitation (mixing two solutions will produce a new compound capable of exerting a stabilization effect);

— polymerization (under certain conditions the interaction of several simple compounds will produce new, large-molecule compounds exerting a stabilizer action), and

— oxidation.

These methods and their most important characteristics are reviewed in Table 1.

Another type of classification may be based on the purposes for which the various methods can be used. In this case the following categories can be distinguished:

(1) General improvement of the soil properties without the addition of any foreign matter. Methods in this group increase strength, reduce compressibility and permeability, favourably affect volume variations, expansion, resistance to frost effects, and plastic deformation. The most important such technique is compaction.

(2) Improvement of an important soil property. Most frequently increased strength and durability are aimed at, and are made feasible by the use of a number of additives (cement, lime, bitumen, etc.), or chemically.

(3) The achievement of water impermeability.

This is best accomplished by the use of hydrocarbon based additives or, perhaps, by means of a water impermeable membrane.

(4) Dust removal or erosion protection, made feasible by the addition of various salts and other chemicals.

The adaptability of the various techniques is commented on in Table 1.

Table 1

Effect on the soil

Stabilization type	Method	Mechanism	Classification and evaluation basis	Addition weight %	Soil-type			
					rough granular	fine granular	low plasticity heavy	high plasticity heavy
Mechanical	Compaction	Reduced volume will increase friction resistance and interparticle attraction; more advantageous soil structure	Dry volume weight, water content, strength experiments e.g. CPR	—	B			
						A–JG B–RG		
							A	
								B
	Mixing	Internal resistance increase by improved grain distribution	Grain distribution, compaction and load bearing experiments	—	A			
						A		
							C	C
Cementation	Cement	Cement hydration, puzzolana effect, clay mineral modification	Durability, frost resistance, strength	3–8	A			
				5–9		A		
				9–12			A	
				10–16				B
	Lime	Coagulation, puzzolana effect of lime, clay mineral modification	Durability, strength		C	C		
				2–6			A	
				2–8				A
	Lime and fly ash	Puzzolana effect by lime, silicate and aluminate effect, clay mineral modification	Durability and strength	3–5% lime	A			
				10–20% fly ash		A		
				5–9% lime			B	
				10–25% fly ash				C

physics properties

Compactness	Plasticity	Permeability	Water uptake	Volume change	Durability	Compression strength	Bending strength	Young modulus	Special advantage
+	0	−	0	0	0	0		++	
+	0	−	0	0	0	0		++	Inexpensive, easy control
+	0	− − −	−	−	++	++	+	++	
+	0	− −	−	− −	++	++	+	++	
+++	0	−	0	0	0	++	+	++	
+++	0	− −	0	0	0	++	+	++	Improves useless soils
+	− −	− − −	−	− −	+++	+++	+++	+++	
+−0	− −	− − −	−	− − −	+++	+++	+++	+++	Strength increase in short time
0−+	− −	−	− − −	− − −	+++	+++	+++	+++	
−	?	0− −	− −	− −	++	+++	++	++	
−	− − −	−	− − −	− − −	+++	+++	++?	+++	Rapid clay plasticity decrease insensitive to interval between mixing and compaction
− −	− − −	+	− − −	− − −	+++	+++	++?	+++	
−	− −	− − −	−	− − −	+++	+++	+++	+++	
−	− −	− − −	−	+++	+++	+++	+++	+++	No time-factor effect
−	− − −	−	− − −	++	++	++	++	++	

Table 1 (Cont.)

Stabilization type	Method	Mechanism	Classification and evaluation basis	Addition weight %	Soil-type			
					rough granular	fine granular	low plasticity heavy	high plasticity heavy
Cementation	Bitumen asphalt and tar	Grain coating and adhesion, water uptake delay	Viscosity and strength	3–6%	A			
				3–6%		A		
				5–9%			B	
								C
Modification	NaCl and CaCl₂	Base exchange, freezing point decrease	Compactness and moisture		C			
				0.36–1%		A		
				0.25–1%			V	
	Organic cation compounds	Modified water repellent clay	Water uptake, compression, volume change		C	C		
				<1%			A	
								A
	Cement	Base exchange, hydration	Consistency limit, strength, grain distribution		C	C		
				1–4%			A	
				2–6%				B
	Lime	Base exchange, material modification, puzzolana reaction	Consistency limit, strength		C	C		
				1–4%			B	
				2–6%				A
	Bitumen	Grain coating, water uptake delay	Water uptake, compression, volume change	1–4%	B			
				1–4%		A		
				1–4%			B	
								C
Others	Phosphoric acid, calcium acrylate, aniline furfural resin, etc.			Still under research, application and economics greatly depend on the local conditions				

Compactness	Plasticity	Permeability	Water uptake	Volume change	Durability	Compression strength	Bending strength	Young modulus	Special advantage
−−+	+?	−−−	−−−	−−	+++	++	++	++	
−−+	+	−−−	−−−	−−	+++	++	++	++	Water seal
−	−?	−	−−−	−−	++	+	+	+	
?	−	−	0	0	++	+	0	+	Inexpensive
?	−	+−−	0	0	+	+	0	+	
0	−	−?	−−−	−	++	++	++	++	Maintenance of the condition in the time of production
0	−	−?	−−−	−−−	++	++	++	++	
0	−−	−−−	−−	−−	++	++	++	++	
0	−−	+	−−	−−	+	+	+	+	
−	−−	−−+	−−	−−	++	++	++	++	Assistance for earth-work construction using soaked soils
−	−−−	−	−−−	−−−	++	++	++	++	
+	+?	−−−	−−+	0	+	0	0	0	
+	+?	−−−	−−	0	++	+	+	+	
−−	−?	−	−−	−	++	+	+	+	

Key to symbols

A	= excellently suitable	PG	= poorly graded
B	= adaptable	0	= no change
C	= impracticable	−	= slightly decreasing
+++	= greatly increasing	−−	= decreasing
++	= increasing	−−−	= greatly decreasing
+	= slightly increasing	?	= not sufficiently known
WG	= well graded		

From economic and engineering aspects, several of the above methods can usually be adapted and expedient for the solution of a problem. With respect to the soil, the following factors should be considered in order to select the best method:

— properties of the soil in natural condition,
— properties expected from the stabilized soil,
— effects on the stabilized soil after stabilization.

In the latter category the most important role is played by the character, magnitude, and frequency of the force effects, that is, by traffic itself, and by the meteorological effects, such as drying out, wetting, frost, leaching, etc. Additionally oxidation, harmful chemical effects of ground water, and bacterial actions may occur.

The careful testing and determination of the above factors represent the Soil Mechanics design and planning of stabilization. Considering the results, the most suitable stabilization method is then chosen, along with the determination of the mixture ratio, the quantity of the foreign matter to be added, etc. Properties of the soil in a natural condition can be readily determined with the laboratory techniques of Soil Mechanics. The properties to be modified can be identified if the final objective of the stabilization is precisely known. The character and extent of modification, on the other hand, are determined by the effects on the soil after the completion of construction.

Soil Mechanics design should take into account the following circumstances:

(a) Road character: the order, earthwork, and tracing of the road;
(b) Soil conditions: quality, load-bearing capacity, physical and chemical characteristics, and behaviour upon water effects of the soil, availability of other soil types;
(c) depth, fluctuation, and chemical properties of the ground water;
(d) meteorological and hydrological conditions; the amount, frequency, and type of precipitation, surface waters, temperature and its fluctuation, frost data, etc.;
(e) the character, distribution, frequency and magnitude of the traffic, the loading, speed, and type of the vehicles, etc.

Stabilized soil can be used as both the load bearing surface of roads like a pavement, and the foundation or bed of higher value pavings.

As pointed out earlier, soil stabilization can only give permanent results if both its design and implementation are performed professionally. This applies to careful Soil Mechanics testing, reliable construction with strict adherence to the technology specified, and the Soil Mechanics control of the latter alike.

Hence the problems of stabilized earth roads will be discussed in the following order:

In Chapters 2–7, we discuss the physical and chemical aspects of stabilization, including general issues, basic notions, examinations and testing, then the various

28

methods and procedures enumerated above. In the same section the Soil Mechanics design problems of soil stabilization as well are also dealt with.

In Chapter 8, road planning and design problems, including the force effects acting upon the road surface, the stresses in both soil and cover, tracking and drainage problems, cross-section development, design and dimensioning of pavings and other surfaces are expounded.

Finally, in Chapter 9 construction itself is explained, paying particular attention to the problems of mechanization.

1.4 Recommended literature

The literature of soil stabilization is extremely rich in professional papers, almost impossible to survey, and in studies on the individual problems involved, but comprehensive publications simply cannot be found. However, some of the articles referred to record unfortunately such laboratory achievements or in-situ results that cannot be generalized, and whose data are hardly adaptable or seem deficient. Publications often advertise a machine type, material, or method, so they present certain features much more favourably than is the general case. Thus literature should be studied with some caution. The papers referred to in this volume are listed in the bibliography at the end, but some comprehensive publications are presented below. Since the problems of stabilization are discussed extensively, they are recommended to all those interested in the field. The monographs dealing with the various techniques considered in this volume are mentioned at the relevant point in the text.

WINTERKORN, H. F.: Principles and Practice of Soil Stabilization. In: J. Alexander: Colloid Chemistry, Vol. VI, Reinhold Publishing Corp. New York, 1946.

Proceedings of the Conference in Soil Stabilization, Massachusetts Institute of Technology, Cambridge, Mass. 1952.

Soil and Soil-Aggregate Stabilization Symposium, Highway Research Board, Bulletin 108, Washington DC, 1955.

GÁSPÁR, L.: Problems of the Hungarian Soil Road System — Mérnöki Továbbképző Int. 3391, Budapest, 1955 (in Hungarian).

GÁSPÁR, L.: Soil Stabilization I—II. Útügyi Kutató Int. 8, Budapest 1959 (in Hungarian).

LAMBE, T. W.: Soil Stabilization, Chapter 4, in: Leonards G. A.: Foundation Engineering, McGraw-Hill, New York, 1960.

JOHNSON, A. W.—MORELAND, H.—DAVIDSON, D. T.—HANDY, R. L.: Soil Stabilization, Section 21 in: Woods, K. B.—Berry, D. S.—Goetz, W. H.: Highway Engineering Handbook, McGraw-Hill, New York, 1960.

HERPAY, I.—PANKOTAI, G.: Agricultural Road Construction. Mezőgazdasági Kiadó, Budapest, 1963 (in Hungarian).

WINTERKORN, H. F.: Soil Stabilization, Mimeographed Lecture Notes, Princeton University, Princeton N. J., 1963.

(BEZRUK, V. M. – KNAZYUK, K. A.) Безрук, В. М. – Князюк, К. А.: Устройство цементно-грунтовых покрытий. Дориздат Москва, 1952.

Straßenbau von A – Z, bearbeitet für die Forschungsgesellschaft für das Straßenwesen eV, Band I – IV, Bielefeld, 1958.

JESSBERGER, H. L.: Grundlagen und Anwendung der Bodenstabilisierung, VDI Verlag GmbH, Düsseldorf, 1967.

LINEMANN, K. (Ed.): Erdstabilisierung in Theorie und Praxis, VEB Verlag für Bauwesen, Berlin, 1966.

BRAND, W.: Der Einfluss von Kalziumhydroxid auf die Eigenschaften der Böden im Straßenbau. Dissertation; Rheinisch-Westfälische Technische Hochschule, Aachen, 1962.

GILLILAND, J. L. – HUNTER, H. M.: Rapid method for estimating cement content of soil-cement and blended cements. Bull. American Soc. Test. Mater. 1952 (180) 29 – 30.

HERZOG, A. – MITCHELL, J. H.: Reactions accompanying the stabilization of clay with cement. A paper presented at the 42nd annual meeting of the Highway Research Board, Washington, D. C. 1963.

KÉZDI, Á.: Fragen der Bodenphysik. VDI-Verlag, Düsseldorf, 1976.

LEADABRAND, J. A. – NORLING, L. T.: Simplified Methods of Testing Soil-Cement-Mixtures. In: Highway Research Board, Bulletin 122. Washington, D. C. 1956.

PATTON, J. – REEDER, W.: New indicator for titration of calcium with (ethylene-dinitrilo) Tatra-acetate. Analyt. Chem., 1955, **28** (6), 1026–8.

WINTERKORN, H. F.: Soil Stabilization. In: Foundation Engineering Handbook (ed. by Winterkorn, H. F. and Hsai-Yang Fang). Van Nostrand Reinhold Co., New York, 1975.

2. Physical and chemical aspects of soil stabilization

2.1 Fundamental definitions of soil physics

2.1.1 Physical characteristics of soil

The expected physical properties of soils can be best characterized with respect to stabilization by the particle distribution curve and the Atterberg limits (liquid limit and plastic limit). These properties can be easily determined by routine experiments and, in general, are quite sufficient for deciding the most important problems[2]. Soil classification, too, is based on these properties. From the distribution curve data and the Atterberg limits, certain classification indices can be derived which inform empirically on the suitability of the soils for the various stabilization purposes and their load-bearing capacity in compacted condition.

The shape of the grain-distribution curve may be characterized, in addition to the usual uniformity coefficient (U), by the grain-size factor (Dos Santos, 1953). This quantity (Fig. 7) is the sum of the grain-distribution curve ordinates which, starting from the $d = 9.42$ mm particle diameter, can be measured along the centre line of the log 2 width bands down to a diameter of $d = 0.001$ mm. By means of the grain-size coefficient (c) the average particle diameter can be calculated:

$$d_a = 9.42/2^c \tag{3}$$

The soil behaviour resulting from water effects can be described by the effective grain size obtained from the surface equality. It is the diameter of a sphere which in the case of a set of equal spheres, supplies a surface identical to that given by the mixed grain set under test. Its numerical value can be determined by using the equation

$$\frac{1}{d_e} = \int_0^1 \frac{\mathrm{d}S}{d} \cong \sum \frac{\mathrm{d}S}{d} \tag{4}$$

For its graphic definition, the S ordinates of the grain-distribution curve, pertaining to d, are plotted in the function of $1/d$, and the surface below the curve

---

[2] The general problems of soil physics are naturally not discussed in this volume, but reference is made to author's work "Handbook of Soil Mechanics" (Vol. I, Soil Physics), Elsevier Scientific Publishing Company, Amsterdam, 1973. The laboratory and in-situ methods of investigation are described in Vol. II of the Handbook.

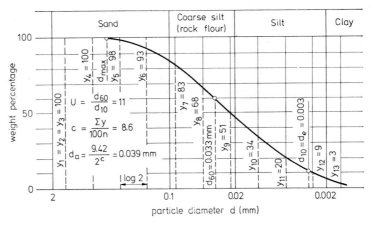

FIG. 7. Definition of the grain-size coefficient

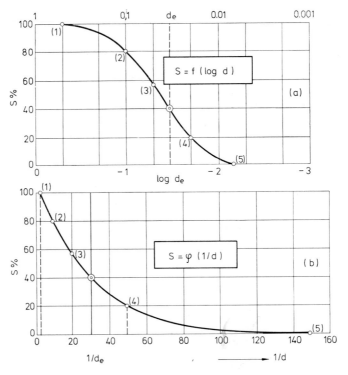

FIG. 8. Effective grain-size determination. (a) Grain-size distribution curve in semi-log presentation; (b) Weight per cent of smaller particles as a function of the reciprocal of grain diameter

thus obtained is then transformed into an identical area square of unit height (100 per cent) whose width represents the $1/d_e$ value (Fig. 8).

From a grain-size distribution viewpoint, the soil is more suitable for stabilization the higher its uniformity coefficient, that is, the greater its graduation. This is due mainly to the fact that soils consisting of mixed grains can be much better compacted, and their dry volume weight due to compaction is generally higher than that of the uniform particle soils. The more compact the stabilized soil layer (the earth-road surface), the greater its strength, load-bearing capacity and durability, and the lesser its traction-force requirement, water permeability, and the depth of the wheel tracks. The compact condition, as seen later, is the fundamental prerequisite of a successful stabilization.

On the practically feasible degree of compaction value, Fig. 9 offers information after Kabai (1972). In the co-ordinate system defined by the uniformity coeffi-

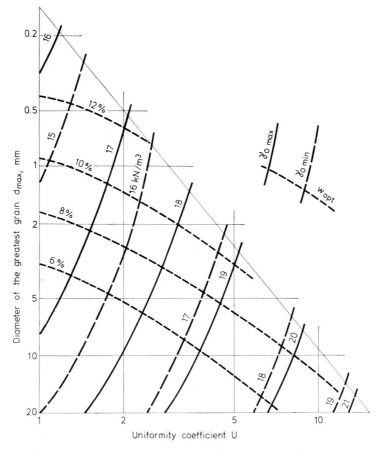

FIG. 9. Optimum moisture content and maximum dry density for granular soils

cient and the d_{10} grain diameter, the maximum dry density feasible by the given compaction work and the optimum moisture content of compaction can be expressed by definite curves (see also Kézdi, 1976).

With respect to soil stabilization, the particles are best classified in the following categories by size:

coarse grains	$d > 2$ mm
medium-size grains	$2 - d \geq 0.1$ mm
fine grains	0.1 mm $\geq d$

Composition according to these particle categories can be illustrated in a triangle as that of Fig. 10. If the occurrence of the individual fractions amounts to 100 per cent, then the soil can be indicated at a vertex of the triangle. Points in the areas *a, b, c* adjacent to each vertex, cut off the 50 per cent lines, indicate the coarse, medium, and fine grain soils, respectively, while points *k* of the central striated triangle indicate mixed soils. Figure 11 illustrates the particle distribution curves of some soil types. The points representing these soils in the triangle diagram are also shown in Fig. 10.

An important fact relating to grain distribution with respect to stabilization is whether the curve is uniform and smooth course corresponding to that of a probability curve, or reveals an irregular composition. In the former case the soil is considered to be well graded, and in the latter poorly graded, as shown in Fig. 12. The grain distribution of poorly graded soils cannot be evaluated precisely by triangular diagrams.

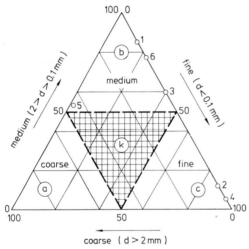

FIG. 10. Triangular diagram illustration of the soil composition by fractions

Natural soils are usually mixtures of three media having different states of the matter. Apart from the clays and fine silts consisting of very fine particles where the electrical and chemical effects over the grain surface are the critical factors, the behaviour of a set will be governed by the size of the solids, water particles, and air-filled voids, as well as the relative volume of these phases, and less dependent on the material of the solid particles. The volume and weight relations of the three different consistency media are expressed numerically by several characteristic properties in soil mechanics. The most frequently used characteristics and

34

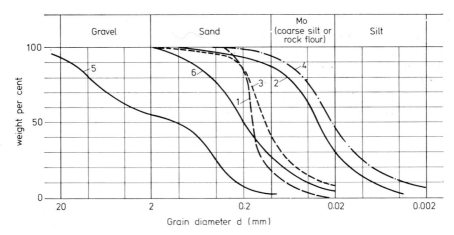

Fig. 11. Characteristic grain distribution curves (Hungarian soils). (1) Fine yellow sand from Felgyő, $U = 2.4$; (2) Lean yellow clay from Érd, $I_p = 16$ per cent, $U = 4.9$; (3) Fine sand with rock flour Budapest Teve Str., $U = 6.8$; (4) Lean brown clay, Budapest Hűvösvölgy, $L_p = 17$ per cent, $U = 9.7$; (5) Pit ballast, Budapest Ferihegy; (6) Silty sand, Budapest Ferihegy, $U = 5$

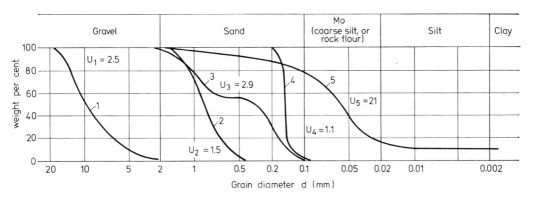

Fig. 12. Grain-size distribution curve forms. (1) Well-graded Danube gravel, screened, Budapest; (2) Normal probability curve: well-graded sand (coarse pit sand, Pécsvárad); (3) Danube sand, poorly graded and deficient particle distribution, Budapest; (4) Fine sand consisting of almost identical size grains, Kecskemét; (5) Grain-size distribution curve of a Budapest lean clay (Hűvösvölgy), intersecting several grain-size fractions

their definitions, and the relations suitable for their calculation are summarized in Table 2, using the symbols of Fig. 13.

As shown in the figures, if the specific-gravity values of the three media are considered as constant — a justified assumption in the case of affine soils — then instead of using the many characteristics of the table, the s, v, and l volume percent-

Table 2

Physical characteristics of the soil composition by phases

Serial number	Characteristic	Symbol	Definition	Practical calculation
1	Water content	$w\%$	$\dfrac{V_w\,\rho_w}{V_s\,\rho_s}\,100$	$\dfrac{G_f - G_0}{G_0}\,100$
2	Void ratio	ε	$\dfrac{V_l + V_w}{V_s}$	$\dfrac{V - G_0/\rho_s}{V_s}$
3	Porosity	$n\%$	$\dfrac{V_l + V_w}{V}$	$\dfrac{V - G_0/\rho_s}{V}\,100$
4	Degree of saturation	S	$\dfrac{V_w}{V_l + V_w}$	$\dfrac{w\rho_s}{\varepsilon\rho_w}$
5	Density	ρ g/cm³	$\dfrac{V_w\,\rho_w + V_s\,\rho_s}{V}$	$G_f/V;\ \dfrac{\rho_s(1 + w)}{1 + \varepsilon}$
6	Dry density	ρ_t g/cm³	$\dfrac{V_s\,\rho\,V_s}{V}$	$G_0/V;\ \dfrac{\rho_s}{1 + \varepsilon}$
7	Density in saturated state	ρ_g g/cm³	$V_l = 0$ $\dfrac{V_w\,\rho_w}{V}$	G_g/V $\rho_s(1 + w)\bigg/\left(1 + w\,\dfrac{\rho_s}{\rho_w}\right)$

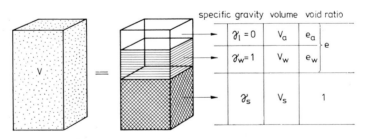

	specific gravity	volume	void ratio
	$\gamma_l = 0$	V_a	e_a
	$\gamma_w = 1$	V_w	e_w
	γ_s	V_s	1

FIG. 13. Symbols of the numerical data characteristic of the solid, water, and air quantities

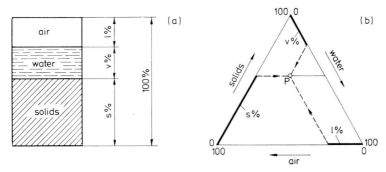

Fig. 14. Triangular diagram illustrating the solid, liquid, and gaseous phase volume ratios.
(a) Volume per cent; (b) triangular diagram

ages of Fig. 14, are alone sufficient whose sum is

$$s^{\%} + v^{\%} + l^{\%} = 100 \qquad (5)$$

which means that only two are independent of each other. Between these three characteristics and the data of Table 2 the following simple relations exist:

water content $\qquad w = \dfrac{v\gamma_v}{s\gamma_s}$

void ratio $\qquad e = \dfrac{1 - s}{s}$

porosity $\qquad n = 1 - s \qquad (6)$

degree of saturation $\qquad S = \dfrac{v}{1 - s}$

density $\qquad \gamma = v\gamma_v + s\gamma_s$

dry density $\qquad \gamma_0 = s\gamma_s$

Calculation of the volume percentages from measurement result and the characteristics referred to earlier is by the following equations:

$$v = \frac{G_n - G_0}{V\gamma_v} \qquad v = ws\frac{\gamma_s}{\gamma_v} = w\frac{\gamma_0}{\gamma_v}$$

$$s = \frac{G_0}{V\gamma_s} \qquad s = \frac{\gamma_0}{\gamma_s} = \frac{1}{1 + e} = 1 - n \qquad (7)$$

37

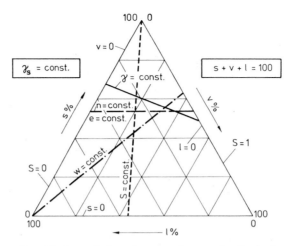

FIG. 15. Interrelations between the usual soil physics
characteristics and the volume percentages on the basis
of the auxiliary lines in the triangle diagram

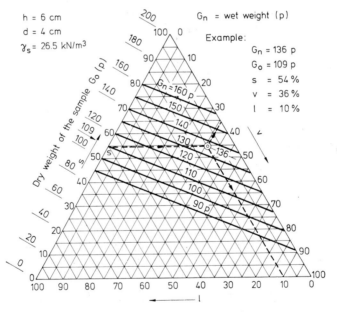

FIG. 16. Determination of the volume percentages by means
of the triangular diagram, on the basis of measurement data
(with the wet and dry weight, respectively, of the cylindrical soil
sample of a given volume known)

In the above formulae

G_n is the weight of a soil sample in the wet — natural — condition,
G_0 is the weight of the sample in the dried state,
V indicates the volume of the soil sample.

Description of the soil condition by the above volume percentages can be excellently illustrated using the triangular diagram technique as shown principally in Fig. 14. Relations with the commonly used characteristics of Table 2 can be simply read from the auxiliary lines as plotted in the diagram of Fig. 15. This diagram can be made suitable for the determination of the v, l, and s values from measurement data: in Fig. 16, for example, based on the wet and dry weight, respectively, of the usual $h = 6$ cm high and $d = 4$ cm diameter cylindrical soil samples the v, l, and s values can be read off the diagram, while if the auxiliary lines of Fig. 15 are also indicated, then w, n, e, S, γ, γ_0 and γ_t can also be read. It should be noted here that this diagram is adaptable not only for the description of the soil condition, but it also renders assistance in following the variations thereof (collapse, shrinkage, compaction, etc.), and in illustrating any property dependent on the soil composition. Relevant examples will be given with the explanation of the individual stabilization methods.

In soil stabilization, however, it is not only these three components which must be taken into consideration. In an examination of the behaviour of mixtures, the following distinctions should be made:

— granular mixture (set of particles larger than $d = 0.1$ mm, usually with a prespecified composition);
— dry cohesive soil (set of particles smaller than $d = 0.1$ mm which in dry condition has an adequate strength but when wet has adequate plasticity);
— stabilization matter (additive for the production of chemical or physical bonds);
— water (with a quality usually stipulated for the various methods).

On the relative volume and weight of the above materials, various calculations must be performed. The paragraphs below derive the relevant equations.

The symbols are presented in Fig. 17. Above all, the void ratio of the granular skeleton must be known, since any stabilization method supplies the most economic and technically best solution if the total quantity of the different substances added to the granular soil is sufficient to fill up the voids of the granular mixture. Thus using the symbols of Fig. 17 we obtain

$$ e = \frac{V - \dfrac{G_s}{\gamma_s}}{\dfrac{G_s}{\gamma_s}} \; ; \qquad n = \frac{V - \dfrac{G_s}{\gamma_s}}{V} \tag{8} $$

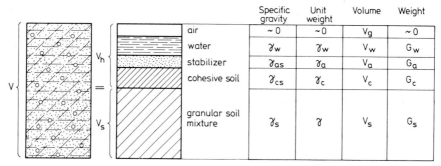

	Specific gravity	Unit weight	Volume	Weight
air	~ 0	~ 0	V_g	~ 0
water	γ_w	γ_w	V_w	G_w
stabilizer	γ_{as}	γ_a	V_a	G_a
cohesive soil	γ_{cs}	γ_c	V_c	G_c
granular soil mixture	γ_s	γ	V_s	G_s

FIG. 17. Composition of a stabilized soil. Symbols

According to the previous condition, $V_g = 0$, and the pores of the granular skeleton are filled up by the mixture of cohesive soil, stabilizer, and water. To indicate the specific stabilizer quantity let us introduce

$$a = \frac{G_a}{G_s}$$

Let us indicate, furthermore, the ratio of the water added and the stabilizer volume by α, and that of the total volume of stabilizer and water in the voids of the granular material to the total void volume by β, that is

$$\alpha = \frac{\text{added water volume}}{\text{stabilizer volume}} = \frac{V_w}{V_a}$$

where the weight ratio is given by

$$\frac{G_w}{G_a} = \alpha \frac{\gamma_w}{\gamma_a}$$

and, on the other hand,

$$\beta = \frac{\text{added water + stabilizer volume}}{\text{total void volume}} = \frac{V_w + V_a}{V_h} = \frac{V_w + V_a}{V - V_s}$$

Thus the total stabilizer and water volume can be calculated from equation

$$\beta V_h = \beta n V$$

The problem in connection either with laboratory investigations or during actual construction is usually the task, at given α and β values, of calculating the quantities required for the production of a V-stabilized soil volume. Let us assume that the granular matter is available in dry condition, while the cohesive soil has a w

40

water content. Thus the total V_w water quantity will consist of two parts: the V_w'-added water amount, and the V_w'' water in the cohesive soil. According to the above definitions

$$[V_a + V_w' = \beta\, nV; \quad V_w'/V_a = \alpha$$

thus the necessary stabilizer volume for the production of a stabilized soil mass of n porosity and V total volume will be

$$V_a = \frac{\beta\, nV}{1 + a} \tag{9}$$

whereas the weight of the stabilizer

$$G_a = \frac{\beta\, nV}{1 + a}\, \gamma_a \tag{10}$$

The cohesive-soil-plus-water volume is

$$V_w - \beta V_w = (1 - \beta)\, nV$$

and since the ratio of the water volume (quantity V_w'') in the cohesive soil to the volume of the solid particles forming the cohesive soil is given by

$$w\, \frac{\gamma_c}{\gamma_w}$$

we may write

$$V_c + V_w'' = (1 - \beta)\, nV$$

and

$$\frac{V_w''}{V_c} = w\, \frac{\gamma_c}{\gamma_v}$$

giving the dry weight of the required material quantity is

$$G_c = V_c \gamma_c = \frac{(1 - \beta)\, nV}{1 + w\gamma_c}\, \gamma_c \tag{11}$$

Thus the water in the mixture consists of two parts: one is the extra added quantity, and the other is introduced with the cohesive soil. Accordingly, the total water weight is

$$G_w = (V_w' + V_w'')\, \gamma_n = \alpha\, \frac{\beta\, nV}{1 + \alpha}\, \gamma_w + \frac{(1 - \beta)\, nV\, \gamma_c}{1 + w\, \gamma_c/\gamma_w} =$$

$$= \gamma_w\, nV \left[\frac{\alpha\beta}{1 + \alpha} + \frac{(1 - \beta)\, w\, \gamma_c/\gamma_w}{1 + w\, \gamma_c/\gamma_w} \right] \tag{12}$$

In the case of $\beta = 1$ no cohesive soil is added, while if $\beta = 0$, then a mechanical soil stabilization is involved.

Example

Let us calculate the material requirement of the cylinders to be prepared for a cement stabilization test.

The porosity of the skeleton is $n = 26$ per cent, $\alpha = 1.4$; a total of 5 cylinders are prepared, with $\beta = 0$, 0.25, 0.50, 0.75 and 1.00

Specific gravity of the cement,	γ_a	$= 3.15$ p/cm³
Specific gravity of the cohesive soil,	γ_c	$= 2.68$ p/cm³
Water content of the cohesive soil, w		$= 20$ per cent
Specific gravity of the granular soil, γ_s		$= 2.65$ p/cm³
Cylinder dimensions: diameter		$= 15$ cm
height		$= 30$ cm
Cylinder volume,	V	$= 30 \times 15^2\, \pi/4 = 5301$ cm³

The weight of cement, dry cohesive soil, and water, respectively, to produce one cylinder, is

$$G_a = \frac{\beta\, nV}{1+a}\, \gamma_a = \frac{0.26 \cdot 5300}{2.4} \cdot 3.15\, \beta = 1808\, \beta\, ,$$

$$G_c = \frac{(1+\beta)\, nV}{1 + w\, \gamma_c/\gamma}\, \gamma_c = \frac{(1-\beta)\, 0.26 \cdot 5300}{1 + 0.2 \cdot 2.68/1.00} \cdot 2.68 = 2404(1-\beta)\, ,$$

$$G_v = \left[a\, \frac{\beta\, nV}{1+a} + \frac{(1-\beta)\, nV\, w\, \gamma_c/\gamma_w}{1 + w\, \gamma_c/\gamma_w} \right] \gamma_w = \frac{1.4 \cdot 0.26 \cdot 5300}{2.4}\, \beta +$$

$$+ \frac{0.26 \cdot 5300 \cdot 2.68 \cdot 0.20}{1 + 0.2 \cdot 2.68}\, (1-\beta) = 80.4\, \beta + 481\, (1-\beta) = 323\, \beta + 481$$

The quantity of granular material required for each cylinder is

$$G_s = (1-n)V \cdot \gamma_s + 0.74 \cdot 5300 \cdot 2.65 = 10\,393\ \text{p}$$

The weight quantities required for the composition of the cylinders are summarized in Table 3 and illustrated graphically in Fig. 18.

Table 3

Composition of cement soil cylinders

Cylinder No.	β	Granular soil	Cohesive soil	Cement	Water	Total weight	Wet unit weight, p/cm³	Dry unit weight, p/cm³	a, per cent
1	0	10 399	2400	0	491	13 291	2.51	2.43	0
2	0.25	10 399	1800	452	579	13 231	2.50	2.38	3.7
3	0.50	10 399	1200	905	648	13 153	2.48	2.36	7.3
4	0.75	10 399	600	1358	736	13 094	2.46	2.33	12.3
5	1.00	10 399	0	1810	805	13 015	2.45	2.30	17.4

If the soil is stabilized by a material which does not react with water, then the calculations develop as follows:

The water content will be (related only to the amount of cohesive soil):

$$w = \frac{V_w \gamma_w}{V_c \gamma_c} = \frac{G_w}{G_c} \qquad (13)$$

The specific stabilizer quantity is

$$a = \frac{V_a \gamma_a}{V_c \gamma_c} = \frac{G_a}{G_c} \qquad (14)$$

Thus the volume weight of the total mixture is

$$\gamma = \frac{G}{V} =$$

$$= \frac{V_n \gamma_n + V_c \gamma_c + V_a \gamma_a + V_s \gamma_s}{V} \qquad (15)$$

The volume of the voids is

$$V_h = nV = \frac{G_w}{\gamma_w} + \frac{G_c}{\gamma_c} + \frac{G_a}{\gamma_a} =$$

$$= G_c \left(\frac{w}{\gamma_w} + \frac{1}{\gamma_c} + \frac{a}{\gamma_a} \right) \qquad (16)$$

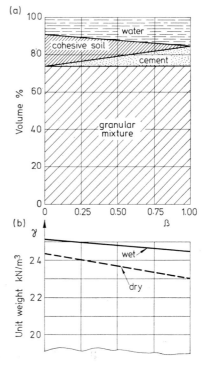

Fig. 18. (a) Percentage composition by volume of cement soil cylinders; (b) Variation of the dry and wet volume weights

while the weight of the dry cohesive material:

$$G_c = \frac{nV}{\dfrac{n}{\gamma_w} + \dfrac{1}{\gamma_c} + \dfrac{a}{\gamma_a}} \qquad (17)$$

the water weight

$$G_w = wG_c \qquad (18)$$

and the stabilizer weight

$$G_a = aG_c \qquad (19)$$

Of the physical properties of the soil, the Atterberg limits are also very important for soil stabilization. The liquid and plastic limits should be determined according to standard specifications, always with fractions separated from particles larger than $d = 0.42$ mm. The soil suitable for earth-road construction is often produced

43

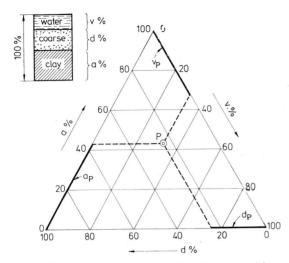

FIG. 19. Triangle diagram illustrating the composition of saturated clays on the basis of the volume percentage of coarse and fine particles, and water

by mixture, and this is why Section 1.3.4 deals with the Atterberg limits of mixtures. However, it must be pointed out that the triangle diagram presented in Fig. 14 is not suitable for a consistency-limit test, since the points indicating saturated soils are all located on the v axis, and so another method must be sought. Since the behaviour of a mixed soil is governed by its fine fraction, it is best to determine the volume per cent of the coarse and fine particles, and that of the water. These values can then be illustrated in a triangle-diagram form, as presented in Fig. 19.

The clay-fraction limit was assumed to be $d = 0.002$ mm and, since a saturated soil was being dealt with, the v-value also determined the void volume of the soil. Depending on the quantity of the coarse grains (here larger than $d = 0.002$ mm), the grain assembly may have one of two characters. If there is too much clay, then the coarse grains float in the clay-water matrix, and the behaviour of the set will be governed almost exclusively by the clay fraction. If, however, a and v are small, then the coarse grains form a more or less solid skeleton.

If the void ratio of the coarse grains related to their loosest condition (e_0) is known, then their critical quantity will be, on the basis of equation

$$e_0 = \frac{1 - d}{d},$$

equal to

$$d = d_0 = \frac{1}{1 + e_0}, \tag{20}$$

i.e.

$$a_0 + v_0 = 1 - \frac{1}{1 + e_0} = \text{constant}$$

If this value is plotted in the diagram shown in Fig. 19, it can be readily decided, for any (a, v, d) triplet, whether or not a skeleton is being referred to ($d_0 \lessgtr 1$) $(1 + e_0)$.

44

2.1.2 Soil classification

From stabilization aspects, in addition to the general soil classifications (e.g. Hungarian Standard MSZ 4487, USC, see Handbook of Soil Mechanics, Vol I, 5.5) it is rather expedient to classify the recovered soils according to the HRB (Highway Research Board) classification prepared specially for road construction purposes. This classification requires only the grain-size distribution curve and the Atterberg limits of the fractions passing through the 0.42 mm sieve. The class into which the soil can be fitted according to its data is found by proceeding along the tabulated figures from the left to the right. The system would distinguish 7 soil groups (from A-1 to A-7) including a total of 12 sub-classes. Table 4 illustrates division into the main groups, while Table 5 that into sub-classes. These tables

Table 4

Soil classification into main categories

General classification	Granular soils grains $< d = 0.074$ mm $S_{max} = 35\%$			Cohesive soils grains smaller than $d = 0.074$ mm $S_{min} = 35\%$			
Soil class	A-1	A-3	A-2	A-4	A-5	A-6	A-7
Grain distribution							
$d < 2$ mm							
$S\%\ d < 0.42$ mm	max 50	min 51					
$d < 0.074$ mm	max 25	max 10	max 35	min 36	min 36	min 36	min 36
Properties of grains smaller than $d = 0.42$ mm $\quad w_L\%$				max 40	min 41	max 40	min 41
$\quad I_p\%$	max 6	0		max 10	max 10	min 11	min 11
Soil index			max 4	max 8	max 12	max 16	max 20

NOTE: Search for the first column from the left to the right into whose class the soil under test may be fitted on the basis of its physical properties.

need no explanation as only the relevant index must be determined. This number (sometimes called the group index) is used for the qualification of the soil as a basis within its own group, but is never used as a basis for the classification of a soil into a group. The latter is by the experimentally determined values of grain distribution and Atterberg limits. The higher this index, the poorer the soil quality. Its value depends on the weight per cent of the fraction passing through the 0.076 mm mesh, the liquid limit, and the index of plasticity, according to the equation

$$N_i = 0.2\,a + 0.005\,ac + 0.01\,bd \qquad (21)$$

45

Table 5

Soil classification into sub-classes

	Granular soils							Cohesive soils			
	A-1		A-3	A-2				A-4	A-5	A-6	A-7
Soil class	A-1-a	A-1-b		A-2-4	A-2-5	A-2-6	A-2-7				A-7-5 / A-7-6
Grain distribution $S\%$											
$d < 2$ mm	max 50										
$d < 0.42$ mm	max 30	max 50	min 51								
$d < 0.074$ mm	max 15	max 25	max 10	max 35	max 35	max 35	max 35	min 36	min 36	min 36	min 36
Properties of grains smaller than $d = 0.42$ mm											
$w_L\%$				max 40	min 41	max 40	min 41	max 40	min 41	max 40	min 41
$I_p\%$	max 6	max 6	0	max 10	max 10	min 11	min 11	max 10	max 10	min 11	min 11
Soil index	0	0	0	0	0	max 4	max 4	max 8	max 12	max 16	max 20
Usual type of the characteristic components	Rubble, gravel and sand		Fine sand	Gravel with silt or clay and sand				Silts		Clays	

NOTE: Search for the first column from the left to the right into whose class the soil under test may be fitted on the basis of its physical properties. If in the last column, for example, $I_p < 30\%$, then A-7-6, while if $I_p > 30\%$ then A-7-5 is indicated.

a = weight per cent of the grains smaller than $d = 0.074$ mm, expressed in S minus 35 but max 40 positive integer (thus if $S \geq 75$, then $a = 40$, and if $S \leq 35$, then $a = 0$)

b = weight per cent of the grains smaller than $d = 0.074$ mm, expressed in S minus 15 but max 40 (if $S \geq 55$, $b = 40$, and if $S \lesssim 15$, $b = 0$)

$c = w_f\% - 40$ but max 20 (if $w_f \geq 60$, $c = 20$, and if $w_f \leq 40$, $c = 0$)

$d = I_p\% - 10$ but max 20 (if $I_p \geq 39$, $d = 20$, and if $I_p \leq 10$, $d = 0$).

Tables 4 and 5 reveal that groups A-1 to A-3 contain the granular, while groups A-4 to A-7 the cohesive soils. In the Casagrande diagram the latter are located as shown in Fig. 20. Soils in the individual groups feature the details described below.

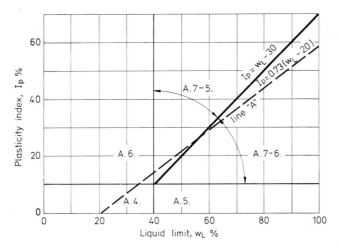

FIG. 20. Location of the individual soil classes in the Casagrande plasticity diagram

Group A-1: Well-graded mixture of rubble or gravel, coarse and fine sands, and barely- or non-plastic binder, including the various pure rubble, gravel, or coarse sand types.

Sub-class A-1-a: Mainly rubble or gravel, with or without well-graded fine-grain binder.

Sub-class A-1-b: Mainly coarse sand, with or without well-graded fine-grain binder.

Group A-3: Typically a fine-grain river, beach, or wind-blown sand, without silt or clay particles, or with little non-plastic silt grains, including poorly graded fine-grain alluvial sand deposits with a little coarse sand or gravel.

Group A-2: Many alternatives of the granular materials, transitional between groups A-1 and A-3 on one hand, and the cohesive soils in groups A-4 to A-7 on the other. Every material containing a max 35 per cent of particles smaller than

47

0.076 mm, and which cannot be classified into groups A-1 and A-3 because of its fine grain content or plasticity, should be classified into this category.

Sub-classes A-2-4 and A-2-5: The soils in this category contain a max 35 per cent of particles smaller than 0.076 mm, and their grains smaller than 0.42 mm exhibit A-4 and A-5 properties. They include silty gravels and sands with a plastic index higher than the A-1 limit, and fine sands whose non-plastic silt content exceeds the limit of Group A-3.

Sub-classes A-2-6 and A-2-7: Sands with a fine-grain fraction consisting of plastic clay exhibiting A-6 and A-7 properties, respectively, and with an index between 0 and 4.

Group A-4: Slightly or non-plastic silts, usually with at least 75 per cent of particles smaller than 0.076 mm particles, including the fine silts and the mixtures consisting of a maximum 64 per cent gravel-sand fractions retained by the 0.076 mm screen. Their index number may vary between 1 and 8.

Group A-5: Typically, the materials in this category are similar to those in A-4, but usually contain much mica and diatoma-earth, rendering them much more elastic and giving a higher liquid limit. Their index is in the $1-12$ range.

Group A-6: Plastic clays, with a weight per cent of the particles smaller than 0.076 mm usually exceeding 75 per cent. Fine clay and sand mixtures may also be classified into this group, if a max 64 per cent of the material retained by the 0.076 mm screen is gravel and sand. Their volume change is usually excessive, and their index varies between 1 and 16.

Group A-7: Again plastic clays, but of a high liquid limit characteristic of Group A-5. Elastic materials, with an excessive volume change, and an index between 1 and 20.

Sub-class A-7-5: Soils with a plasticity index rather low as compared to their liquid limit.

Sub-class A-7-6: The same, but with a relatively high plasticity index, and excessive volume change.

With regard to airport soil stabilization, mention is deserved by the CAA (Civil Aeronautics Administration) system (USA), classifying the soils on the basis of grain distribution, Atterberg limits, volume change characteristics, and the numerical value of the California Bearing Ratio (CBR).

2.1.3 Testing of stabilized soils

The following paragraphs describe a few soil test procedures that must be performed in connection with a number of soil-stabilization methods. They include strength, durability and freezing tests, determination of the water absorption, and testing the extent of pulverization. These examinations are best performed with a uniformly prepared soil. An expedient method of preparation is described below.

First the sample is granulated prepared so that it can be crumbled, in order it may be air or stove dried, if necessary, but the temperature must not exceed 50 °C.

This is followed by crushing the clods with a rubber-covered pestle, until the grainsize conforming to the test requirement and soil type is reached. Next the weighed sample is passed through a screen of the specified mesh, and the retained fraction is retained after recording its weight. From the fraction passed through a representative sub-sample is taken and its water content determined. If several soils are to be mixed for the test purpose, then the quantity of the individual components, determined with the water content taken into consideration, is carefully weighed, and the components are mixed until a uniform mixture is obtained. For this purpose a mechanical mixer or a spatula can be used.

The next step is to mix a precalculated quantity of the soil dried as described above, with water and the stabilizer. The methods of addition and mixing are explained in the descriptions of the various procedures.

Compacted cylindrical specimens of the material thus prepared are then made for testing. Compaction may be by either a static or a dynamic force. Dynamic compaction is preferred in general, although the static method used in Great Britain is better in principle, since in this case the dry unit weight of the specimen is easier to predetermine precisely.

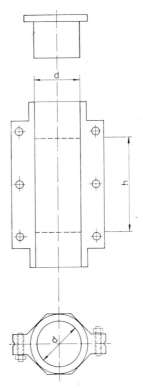

Fig. 21. Mould for the preparation of soil cylinders compacted by static pressure. Cylindrical mould and pressure caps

Preparation of samples compacted by static pressure requires moulds as shown in Figs 21 and 22. Specimen dimensions are determined by the soil type: in the case of coarse grain soils $d = 15$ cm, while the same figures for medium and fine-grained soils are 10 and 5 cm, respectively. Height is always twice the diameter. An insert is placed in the bottom part of the mould then, with the specified dry unit weight known, the soil-mix quantity calculated using the above equation follows and is worked in with a steel rod. Next, the surface is levelled, the second insert positioned, and the mould placed into the press where it is subjected to a pressure of 250 kp/cm². The sample must be compressed at a rate of about 1 mm/min to make the plug-edges contact the cylinder. After pressure release and plug removal, the sample is pressed out of the mould. Finally, the specimen is weighed with an accuracy of 1 pond, then exposed to the treatment required by the test.

Often the sample must be placed into wet surroundings; for this purpose the equipment presented in Fig. 23 is well adaptable. Here, however, care must be

4 Kézdi: Stabilized

FIG. 22. Photo of mould

used to prevent the temperature from fluctuating more than $+2\,°C$. After storage the specimen weight must be checked again and recorded.

Strength is usually characterized by an unconfined compression test and, perhaps, the Brasilien or splitting test; both are performed as described in the Handbook of Soil Mechanics, Vol. 2. Figure 24 illustrates broken soil-cement samples. For the unconfined compression test the British Standard B.S. 1924/1957 makes use of the strain-control method, where the loading force must be continuously increased to reach a deformation rate of 1.25 mm/min. The force is measured by an annular dynamometer, and the maximum value is recorded.

Samples compacted by a dynamic effect (impact energy) are produced with the Proctor device, as described in detail in the Handbook of Soil Mechanics, Vol. 3.

The durability test is aimed at testing the reaction of the stabilized soil to the effect of repeated drying and wetting. Here the American Standard (ASTM D559-44) specifies preparation by dynamic compaction. Dimensions of the samples tested are identical to those of the specimens used for the Proctor compaction test. Before preparation of the mixtures, all particles of a diameter greater than 2 cm are removed from the sample. Compaction is done according to the standard

Proctor process, except that the surface of each compacted layer is roughened prior to the application of the next by scratching a square grid of lines 3 mm wide and 3 mm deep, having approximately 6 mm spacings. During compaction the water content of a representative sample is determined. Each test requires two cylinders: one for testing the weight and water-content variations, while the second is used for weight-loss determination. The ready-made cylinders are weighed, then stored in wet surroundings for 7 days. Weight and dimensions are checked each day of the treatment period, for the calculation of the water content and volume changes. Following the 7-day treatment, the samples are submerged in tap water for 5 hours at room temperature, leaving a water layer of 2 cm above them. After removal the weight and dimensions of specimen No. 1 are checked, then both cylinders are placed into a desiccator at 70 °C for 42 hours. This is followed by another weight check, then specimen No. 2 is brushed by two strong strokes of a wire brush at each side and, finally, a third weighing is performed to determine the weight loss.

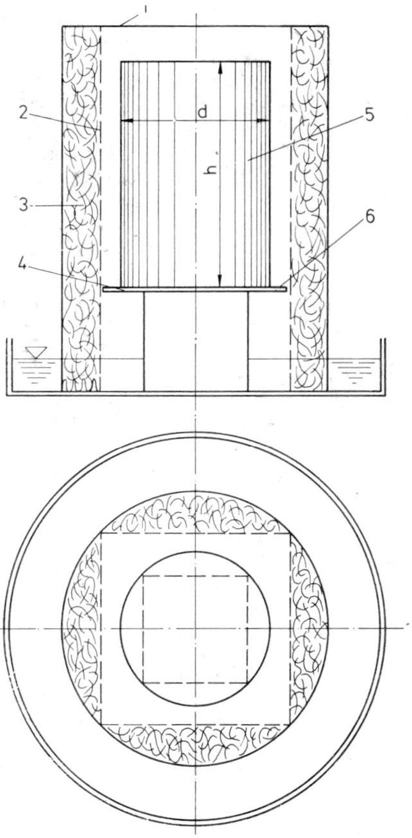

FIG. 23. Equipment providing for a wet area around the sample. 1 — tinplate cylinder; 2 — screen cloth prism; 3 — wet cotton; 4 — filter paper; 5 — soil sample; 6 — glass plate

The operations enumerated represent a single durability test cycle. 12 cycles are usually completed. The volume, water content, and weight variations are expressed as a percentage of the original dry weight.

An objection to this test might be that the use of a wire brush would introduce an individual subjective factor. Another drawback is its long time: a single such test takes several weeks. The results are usually illustrated as shown in Fig. 25. Cylindrical soil samples after the test are presented in Fig. 26.

The freezing test (ASTM D-559-44) is similar to the procedure described above, but drying and wetting are replaced here by freezing and thawing, respectively. Following the treatment, the specimens are placed, with a wet surrounding, into a freezing chamber of -23 °C temperature for 22 hours. Removal is followed by weighing, then the samples are placed into a wet atmosphere for another 22 hours

Fig. 24. Broken soil cement samples

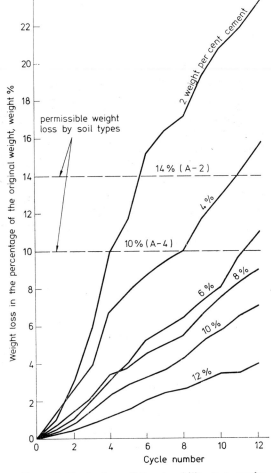

Fig. 25. Illustration of the durability test results

Fig. 26. Cement soil cylinders after durability test

Fig. 27. Cement soil cylinders after freezing and thawing test

at room temperature. Weighing then wire brushing, follow as in the durability test, as does the plotting of the test results. Soil cylinders after the experiment are shown in Fig. 27.

The water-absorption test makes use of the samples produced under static pressure, after a precise determination of their composition. The ready-made samples are weighed, then their entire surface is coated by hot paraffin, applied with a soft brush. Another weighing follows, then the samples are stored in a cool room, for a period conforming to the test purpose. Finally a third weighing is performed, and only those samples may be used for testing whose weight loss does not exceed 2 p.

Prior to the test itself, the paraffin is removed from both ends of the cylinder, taking great care not to disturb or damage the soil there, nor the paraffin over

53

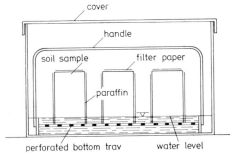

cover

handle

soil sample   filter paper

paraffin

perforated bottom tray   water level

FIG. 28. Water-absorption test

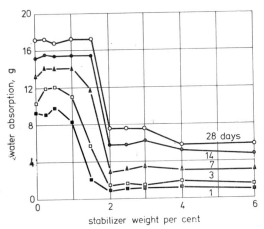

FIG. 29. Water absorption test results

the cylinder surface. The free surfaces are covered by precisely fitting filter papers, then the specimen is placed onto a handle equipped perforated tray like that in Fig. 28, and this assembly is weighed with a 0.2 p accuracy if fine, 1 p accuracy if medium, and with a 5 p precision if coarse-grained soil is tested. Thereafter the specimen is placed into a water tank, leaving a water depth of 2 mm (4, and 6 mm respectively) above the bottom of the cylinder, and then the tank is hermetically sealed. After 1, 3, 7, 14 and 28 days the tray is removed, the water droplets dried off with blotting paper, and the tray + sample-assembly weighed. The results represent the variation of the amount of absorbed water. Data processing is exampled in Fig. 29.

In each soil-stabilization process the soil must be pulverized to enable its satisfactory admixture with the stabilizer. The better the pulverization and mixing, the higher the quality of the stabilized soil. The extent of pulverization can be expressed numerically on the basis of the following test.

About 1 kg quantity (G_1) is taken from the soil pulverized in the course of actual construction or laboratory preparation, placed onto a 5 mm mesh sieve, and carefully vibrated to prevent excessive disintegration of the clods. The weight of the material retained by the sieve (G_2) is then checked, and then the clods crushed, to separate all particles smaller than 5 mm. The sample is then sieved again, and the fraction retained weighed (G_3). The measure of pulverization is

$$p\% = \frac{G_1 - G_2}{G_1 - G_3} 100 \qquad (22)$$

For dimensioning stabilized soil roads, the Young modulus of both the pavement and the subgrade must often also be known. No such quantity should be determined by a static experiment, since the surface is stressed by the repeated pulsation-type loading exerted by traffic and, from a stress viewpoint, the more-or-less elastic deformations produced during transient short-time loadings will be representative. Thus, with respect to the limited speed of the vehicles travelling along earth roads, these deformations and Young moduli can be best determined by repeated compression tests. The representative pavement and subsoil samples are placed into the compression test equipment, exposed to alternative loadings and release within the stress range expected in actual practice, then the extent

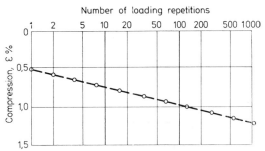

FIG. 30. Compression upon repeated loadings as the linear function of the log of loading repetitions

of compression and expansion, respectively, is measured. Experiences show that the deformations will be fully elastic even after a relatively small number of repetitions, and the $\Delta p / \Delta \varepsilon$ value remains almost constant, while the absolute compression will slightly increase. If the total specific compression is illustrated as a function of the log of loading repetition, then an almost straight line will be obtained, as exampled in Fig. 30.

Although a number of other test methods are also used in connection with stabilized soil roads, these are rather general soil mechanics or road construction-type examinations. The most frequent procedures thereof include
— CBR determination,
— compaction test,
— plate test,
— measurements with the Benkelman beam,
— chemical examinations.
Other tests are performed in connection with a certain individual stabilization technique. These will be discussed together with the corresponding method.

The behaviour of stabilized soils upon traffic effects may accordingly be determined by a number of different laboratory and in-situ investigations as well as through theoretical research. However, all these tests can only render an approximate picture of any such behaviour as it is affected by several factors. In the evaluation of the test results, on the other hand, the experiences collected on actual roads must be strongly relied upon but not completely, since the effects involved are not controllable. Experimental road sections must be therefore constructed on the one hand, where the surface behaviour can be readily evaluated on the basis of the accurate measurements of traffic, weather, and load-bearing capacity factors, although in this case also the internal and external effects cannot be varied optionally. Therefore, on the other hand, the round-about test machines located in laboratories protected from unfavourable weather conditions have been introduced, whereby all the relevant phenomena can be checked upon and measured, and the different variables may be adjusted. Thus the surface behaviour can be accurately observed, the correctness of the accepted dimensioning method controlled, and the effects of traffic, precipitation, etc., investigated. Such machines have been designed by a number of research institutes. The most up-to-date constructions operate with a wide track and a vehicle equipped with both running and driven wheels, like the Road Research Laboratory (UK) unit. The Budapest Technical University constructed a much more modest machine of this type, with limited applicability but still suitable for investigating on a number of problems. Its schematic illustration is presented in Fig. 31.

The substructure is a trough of 40 cm width accommodating the surface and subsoil to be tested, with an average depth of 30 cm and a slight slope beneath. The trough containing the

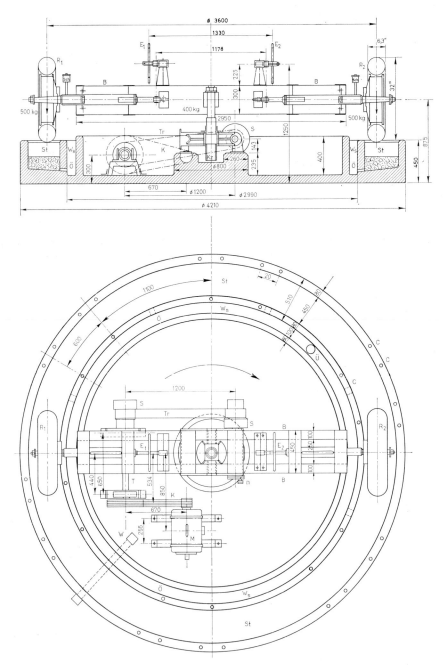

FIG. 31. Round-about test machine for the examination of stabilized soils. M = motor; E = V-belt drive; T = transmission shaft; t = speed adjustment discs; H = driving belt; G = cross-beam; K = king-pin; k_1, k_2 = wheels; S_1, S_2 = lubrication glands; F_1, F_2 = radial wheel setting cranks; Cs = water inlet duct; A = flooding ports; C = gauge pins; f = overpill; n = revolution counter

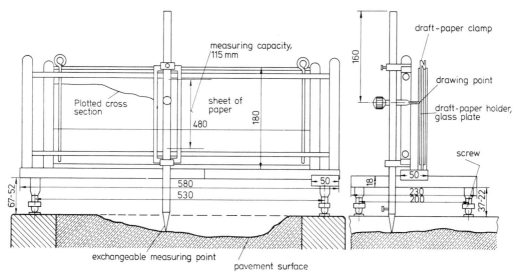

FIG. 32. Profilometer for plotting the cross section of the track

surface layer is connected to an outer trough by steel pipes embedded in concrete, in order to create also the conditions most unfavourable for the surface: if the inner trough is filled with water, the surface will be subject to an upward water pressure. Fill-up is achieved using a rubber hose passed through a duct, while a constant water level is maintained by an over-flow.

The cross-beam is actuated by an 8 HP electric motor fed with a three-phase AC of 380 V, 13 A, and 50 cps. To reduce $n = 1430$ rpm speed of the motor, a high gear-ratio V-belt drive (E) drives a transmission shaft (T), wherefrom the worm (H) driving the vertical axis gear of the kingpin is driven by a rubber belt. The transmission shaft and the worm spindle have three different diameter discs (t), so rotation may be at three different speeds, expressed in approximative peripheral speeds of $v = 15, 20$ and 25 km/h. The machine is equipped with a revolution counter (n).

The mechanism itself consists of a beam (G) having two U-steels welded together, supported at the centre by a king-pin (K), and at the two ends by wheels mounted to the shaft. The total weight of the beam is 1400 kg of which 400 kg are transmitted to the king-pin, and 500 kg to each wheel. Positioning of the wheels over the track is by a threaded mechanism via the rotation of wheels F_1 and F_2.

Onto the shaft, both automobile and cart wheels may be mounted, according to the following specifications:

Automobile wheels: dia 22″, width 6.3″, pressure 4 atm;

Cart wheels: dia 87 cm, iron-rim width 6 cm. When testing stabilized soil road surfaces, after determining the physical properties of the soil type under test, the mixture ratio to be used is determined, then a compacted gravel substrate is placed into the trough, and the pavement built up it. The trough is divided into 6 sections, so that 6 different soil mixtures may be tested simultaneously.

After the wheels have penetrated into the surface to a measurable depth, the track cross section is plotted by means of a "profilometer" designed specially for this purpose. The schematic diagram and operation of the profilometer are illustrated in Fig. 32. In actual

57

testing, after sufficient revolutions, the surface was exposed to different effects including precipitation, upward flooding, etc.

The test results supplied by the machine are reported on in the text with the description of the various stabilization methods.

2.2 Interactions of soil components

2.2.1 Properties of water

Prior to discussing the various stabilization methods in detail, the characteristic properties of the individual phases involved must be investigated. Furthermore, since in the connections between solid particles, a critical role is played by water, some characteristics of water should be discussed. Although the water in the soil always contains dissolved substances, it is still best to examine first the properties of clean water, and then to determine how the various dissolved materials and contact surfaces modify them.

Water is a peculiar substance. Under normal temperature and presssure conditions it ought to be a gas like H_4S_2, H_4Se, or H_4Te, but it is still a liquid and, as such, reveals in certain tests an order similar to the crystalline state, just like the solids.

These peculiar properties of water are due to the structure and character of its molecules. The water molecule, similarly to the H_2F_2 and HCN molecules, has an electric polarity which means that the positive and negative charge centres do not coincide within the molecule. In addition, the hydrogen atoms can interact with the neighbouring molecules and create so-called hydrogen bonds, even although they each pertain to a certain molecule. The energy of one mole (6.02×10^{23}) hydrogen bond is of the order of 6000 calories. Owing to these hydrogen bonds the molecules of the liquid water are not independent of one another, but each is bonded to the next. In the course of molecular movement, these bonds must be continuously broken and restored. Due to the structure and polarity of the hydrogen molecules the liquid water volume, too, has a structure or at least contains secondary

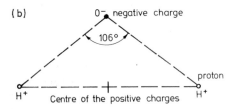

FIG. 33. (a) Triangular H_2O molecule shape due to the polarizability of the oxygen ion; (b) The dipole thus developed in the state of equilibrium

structural units whose presence can be readily demonstrated by X-rays. However, this structure changes if ions, other molecules, or dispersed particles are added to the water. The extent of this structural change is characterized by the heat quantity released or absorbed when ions or molecules are dissolved, or solid particles wetted. If, for example, 1 pond of bentonite is moistened with 0.3 pond of water, then about 20 cal heat will be produced which, as related to one mole of the water participating in the interaction, represents 1200 calories, that is, one-fifth of the hydrogen bond energy. It is fully justified, therefore, to speak in such cases only about the modification of, or an interference with the original structure of water, and not the production of another new structure.

A classical water molecule model is presented in Fig. 33. If the presence of electrostatic forces is considered alone, and if it is assumed that the electron shell of the oxygen ion can be deformed to a certain extent, then the most stable position of the H_2O molecule can be determined as follows:

One electron charge equals $e_0 = 4.77 \times 10^{-10}$ electrostatic units. The potential energy value can be expressed, if the H-ions and the oxygen nucleus are located along the same straight line (as indicated by the black circles in Fig. 33), by the repulsion force of the positive particles:

$$+ \frac{2 \times 6 \, e_0^2}{r} + \frac{e_0^2}{2r} \tag{23a}$$

and the attraction between the electron shell and the H-ions:

$$- \frac{2 \times 8 \, e_0^2}{r} \tag{23b}$$

When the H-ions are displaced in the direction of the arrow, then the repulsion will be

$$\frac{2 \times 6 \, e_0^2}{r''} + \frac{e_0^2}{2r'} \tag{23c}$$

while the attraction will remain the same as above. In the case of only slight displacements, r'' increases faster than r' decreases. A state of equilibrium, that is, minimum potential energy is obtained when, due to the position of the H^+ ions the value of 2α is between $100°$ and $110°$. The actual situation is best approximated by assuming $2\alpha = 106°$. In this structure, the nuclear positive and electronic negative charges do not coincide, so a dipole is produced. The dipole moment of water, that is, the product of the magnitude and separation of the actual positive and negative charges is equal to 1.7 to 1.87×10^{-18} electrostatic units, the oxygen-ion radius is about 1.32×10^{-8} cm.

If in a medium the significant force effects act in definite directions, like the hydrogen bonds, then the density of that medium is usually lower than when these

Table 7

Some characteristic properties of water
and other materials having a similar chemical structure

Material	Mole weight	Melting point*	Boiling point*
H_2O	18.02	0.0	100
H_2S	34.08	-82.9	-61.8
H_2Se	80.98	-64	-42
H_2Te	129.63	-51	-4

* in °C, at a pressure of 1 atm.

forces are uniformly distributed in space. In water, hydrogen bonds prevail, so its density is the lowest among all the affiliated compounds. Thus the molecular weights of H_2O, SiO_2, and Al_2O_3 are 18.02, 60.06, and 101.94, respectively, while their densities, i.e. ice − quartz − corundum, equal 0.917, 2.65, and 4.0; if the volume of the H^+, Si^{4+}, and Al^{3+} ions is neglected, then 1 pond of oxygen atoms will occupy a volume of 19.65 cm^3 in the case of ice, while the same figures for quartz and corundum are 11.35 and 8.5 cm^3, respectively. Obviously, therefore, the oxygen ions are located much more loosely in ice and, consequently, in water than in quartz or corundum. Further consequences of the geometric and electrical properties of the water molecule, and of its suitability for the production of hydrogen bonds, are explained in Table 7.

If the intermolecular forces in the various compounds are of about the same order of magnitude, then the melting and boiling points will be higher for an increased molecular weight. This rule is precisely followed by H_2S, H_2Se, and H_2Te. The abnormal behaviour of water is due to its strong, oriented intermolecular bonds. The melting point of normal materials increases with an increasing pressure, whereas that of the water first decreases, up to a pressure of as much as 2050 kp/cm^2, and increase only thereafter. The normal substances expand when melted, whereas at the normal melting point the volume of ice is 10 per cent larger than that of the liquid water. It could be stated that water would only assume normal characteristics if external hydrostatic pressures large enough to break the internal bonds between the molecules are exerted.

From certain aspects the mutual attraction and bonding of water molecules may be considered as though these molecules were under an internal pressure of a few 1000 atm. However, this analogy is not quite valid as the internal bonds are oriented, while the hydrostatic pressure would generate the same stress at every point and in each direction. If an external pressure is employed, it is not simply superimposed to the calculated internal pressure, but this increased pressure causes the molecules to approach each other while the oriented bonding forces are deformed. As a result of these deformations the structure is finally broken, explaining the behaviour of water under the effect of a variable temperature and pressure. This behaviour is illustrated in Fig. 34, where water is shown to have 5 different solid ("ice") states.

The internal stresses of a liquid body may be considered as the state of equilibrium between the dispersive and cohesive forces or, in other words, as thermal (kinetic) stress + repulsive stress = cohesion + external pressure. For many real liquids, the intermolecular attraction and repulsion vary equally within the wide range of volume variation due to an external pressure, whereby the resultant internal stress remains unchanged even if the external stress has been changed considerably.

The water molecules, however, do not only associate to larger structural units maintained by hydrogen bonds, but they also undergo dissociation: H^+, OH^-, and O^{--} ions are produced. Although the dissociation affects only a very small number of molecules, the production of H^+ and OH^- ions is rather significant, particularly because in a liquid aqueous medium the product of the H^+ and OH^- ion concentrations is always constant at a given temperature, regardless of whether these ions were produced by the dissociation of water molecules or of dissolved acids and bases. The acids may be regarded as being produced from HOH by the replacement of OH^- with other anions, and the bases as being produced by the exchange of H^+ with other cations. Since the (H^+) (OH^-) concentration product is constant at a given temperature, the dissolution of an acid in water will reduce the OH^- concentration, while that of the base reduces the H^+ concentration. At 22 °C the mean value of the safd product is 10^{-14}, and since in a pure neutral water the hydrogen and hidroxyl ion concentrations are identical, both have a value of 10^{-7}. The acidity or alkalinity of the solution can be characterized by the hydrogen-ion concentration, although, as is well known, the negative log of this figure is preferred (pH) for practical reasons. At an increasing temperature the kinetic energy of the molecules and, consequently, the dissociation similarly increases. The $K = CH^+ \cdot COH^-$ value is, therefore, highly temperature-dependent. The variation is illustrated in Fig. 35.

This figure also displays the variation of the hydrogen-ion concentration (CH^+; $-\log CH^+ = pH$) of neutral water, again as a function of temperature. This temperature effect explains why hydrolysis has its maxi-

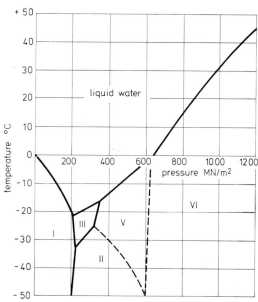

FIG. 34. Phase diagram of the single-component H_2O system

mum intensity under tropical and subtropical conditions.

Owing to their dipole moment, the water molecules are strictly oriented in an electrical field. This order is brought about against the effect of the molecules' kinetic energy, thus it decreases the actual field strength, as a function of the intensity and concentration of the dipoles per unit volume, and as that of the kinetic energy acting against the former. The measure of this effect is the dielectric constant D: if a material of a dielectric constant D is situated between two point charges e_1 and e_2, at a distance r from each other, then the intercharge strength will decrease from e_1e_2/r^2 to e_1e_2/r^2D.

The dielectric constant of the water is 81 at 18 °C, and decreases with an increased temperature. Because of this high value, water can readily dissolve strong electro-

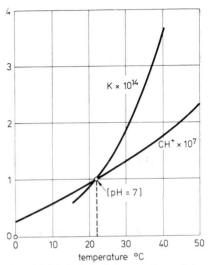

Fig. 35. Variation of the product of hydrogen and hydroxyl ions, and of the pH value, as a function of temperature

lytes as well, since the force of attraction between two ions in vacuum is reduced in water to an 1/80 fraction, this reduction being quite sufficient for the dispersive trend of the kinetic molecular energy to prevail. Around the ions that entered the water, some water molecules will be oriented, because of their dipole structure, with consequent so-called, ion hydration or solvation, where a certain number of the solvent's molecules are connected or bonded to the dissolved ions. The number of molecules thus connected depends on the size, shape and electric properties of the ions, and on the solvent molecules, as well as temperature. Table 8 presents the solvated molecule number for different ions in various liquids.

The fine soil particles and the various forms of water may reach, due to the effect of the structural factors, different states of equilibrium on a contact between dry minerals and soils, and water and vapour, even at an identical water content. The structure and physical properties of the water-soil system depend, furthermore, on how the given water content of the system has been reached. Different structures are obtained if the water had been absorbed by the dry soil from vapour, if a wet soil had been air dried, or if the water had been removed from a we solti by pressure. This means that the colloidal system has a "memory".

The oriented bonding of the water molecules around the ions, and the interference caused by the physical presence of such ions will change the water structure. The internal structure of the water molecules, the interrelation of the H^+ and O^- components is loose enough to allow the latter to oscillate freely in every direction, and utilize the 6 cal/pond atom $\cdot$ °C thermal energy involved. When the water molecules are bonded to ions or surfaces with an electric charge, then the

Table 8

Solvated-molecule number of selected ions
in different solvents

Solvent	Li+	Na+	K+	Cl-	Br-	J-
H_2O	7	4	(2 1/2)	2	—	—
CH_3OH	7 1/2	5 1/2	4	4	2 1/2	1
C_2H_5OH	6	4	3 1/2	4	4	2
Acetone	4	4 1/2	4	2	1/2	0
Acetonitrile	—	5	4	—	2	0
Furfurol	—	5	4	—	—	0
Pyridine	—	4	3	—	—	0

free oscillation will cease, and the thermal energy stored in the system will be released. This heat quantity is the so-called wetting heat, experienced in the course of the dispersion of solids. This strongly bonded water is known as hydration water.

The heat quantity thus released increases until a certain moisture content is reached, but the released heat quantity associated with the same water content increase diminishes with increasing soil moisture. Based on physical considerations, it could be calculated that the first molecule series of the hydration water would be bonded to the solid surface by forces producing a 25 000 kp/cm² pressure. The absorption forces generally encountered in soil mechanics or soil science are much lower. At the shrinkage limit and above, the sorption is transformed into an osmotic phenomenon, and the forces thus produced are easy to calculate on the basis of the water content, the type, number, and activity of the exchangeable ions, and the type as well as concentration of the other ions present in the soil-water system (Ruiz 1961). Under such excessive stresses the water will behave as a solid body, i.e. various types of stable ice form. Away from the surface the pressure rapidly decreases and, at a distance of about 0.5 μ, the water thus bonded will assume normal characteristics (Fig. 36).

If vapour is bonded on the dry soil particles at a low relative humidity, then a monomer solution of H_2O, i.e. a solid solution, is produced over the active surface of the solid grains. In the other extreme case, i.e. in aqueous suspensions, a solution of exchangeable ions is present in the hydrosphere surrounding the surface of the dispersed particles. Between these two extremes, two easily distinguished states can be detected. In the first case, the majority of the exchangeable ions will be outside of the mineral surfaces, so that the surface contains, in addition to the strongly bonded hydration water, groups of fixed water molecules only just contacting each other. In the second case the water content conforms exactly to the water quantity that may be hydrated by the exchangeable ions. In such cases the ion-water system is in a melt type phase which can always be observed when the water content of the system is decreasing and, consequently, the transition up to the boundary of the phase of a coherent water film is more or less continuous.

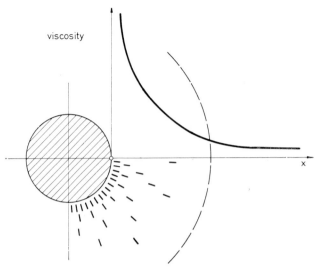

Fig. 36. The effect of molecular forces in a solid-water system;
viscosity decrease with distance from the grain surface

If the soil has achieved the same water content through wetting, then the water film isn ot continuous, nor does it cover individual grains but particle sets. This is rather important when heavy soils are compacted.

In aqueous suspensions, water may be present in the following conditions simultaneously:

(1) In the solid solution of the surface layers of mineral particles. The development of this phenomenon depends on the lattice structure of the mineral in question.

(2) In the form of oriented water molecules over the solid surfaces, bonded partly because of the dipole structure, and partly owing to the interaction between the OH^- and O^{--} ions on these solid surfaces and the adjacent water molecule layer. This effect may be periodically repeated, and in such cases a structure similar to overlapping shells is produced. With Montmorillonite this layer may be rather thick though less dense than that of the normal water.

(3) Oriented water molecules in the field of exchangeable and other ions present in the dispersion, bonded in a form corresponding to their geometrical features. The intensive cation hydration is associated with a wetting heat, while the density of the hydration water is usually greater than that of the normal water.

(4) Relatively free water among the hydrated ions and between them and the hydrated mineral surfaces, slightly bonded to the ion field by electrostatic forces. This type is called osmotic water since it is produced by the osmotic tendency of the cations, whereby they endeavour to fill up the available solvent space.

(5) Free water at a significant distance from the ions, the solid-liquid, and the liquid-gaseous boundary surfaces.

64

(6) Oriented water film over the air-water boundary layer whose thickness at normal temperature may also be of several hundred molecules.

In practice a number of transitional forms of the above water types are also encountered.

2.2.2 Some properties of the solid particles. Interparticle bonds

It might be justified to assume that the mineral composition of the particles forming the soil would critically influence the engineering characteristics of the latter. In the case of coarse-grain sets, however, this is not true: as for their properties most important from technical aspects, the choice of mineral of which the soil particles consist is almost immaterial, since only the surface friction of the individual particles might depend thereon. In granular soils, only gravity and external forces — of those acting between the individual particles — are essential: while the rest may be neglected. On the other hand, the smaller the grains, the more important the surface proportional forces, and in such cases the character of the mineral constituting the grain would also be rather important from the viewpoint of grain-assembly behaviour. In the case of small grains, their interconnection and interactions also become more important since, due to the prevailing force effects, a structure consisting of different phases, force fields, and effects is created and the behaviour of this assembly, that is, of the soil, will be governed by that structure. The following paragraphs discuss the particle properties most important for the subject, then the characteristic features of the structures developed by the interconnections of small particles.

In this context, particles smaller than 2 μ are considered as small. Assemblies consisting of, or mainly of, such grains exhibit clay-type characteristics (plasticity, cohesion). The size of a grain measures indirectly the interparticle gravity forces and surface bond strength. The former are proportional to the mass, and approximately proportional to the volume, so the gravity interactions of identical volume particles are also almost identical. On the other hand, the interparticle bond strength depends on its character and environment in addition to the surface size, so an identical specific surface does not imply identical surface bond strength as well. A coarse-grain assembly has neither plasticity nor cohesion, regardless of the mineral composition of the grains, whereas a fine grain assembly has such characteristics depending on the mineral character and environment of the particles. Since the nature of the atomic bonds within the fine mineral particles govern the behaviour of the minerals, these chemical bond types should be dealt with first.

The surface bonds can be divided in two groups: primary surface bonds which combine the atoms into molecules, and the secondary types connecting the atoms of certain molecules to those of others. The former are rather strong, but the latter very weak. The external electron shell of the nuclear cores of elements able to create chemical bonds is not saturated, so a stable state will develop since each atom combines with another, "borrowing" an electron. The process is usually completed through a minimum electron transfer, and the bond thus created is called an ionic bond. However, the bond is covalent when the external electron shell of each of two atoms is similarly unsaturated, and one or more electron pairs are atom bonded. For example, this is how oxygen atoms are bonded within the oxygen molecules.

The secondary bonds also have two types: the van der Waals forces and the hydrogen bonds referred to above. Due to the orbital movement of the electrons around the atomic nuclei, the molecules have an electric field. The electric fields of nearby molecules interact, thereby producing an intermolecular force of attraction: this is the van der Waals force. Soviet research workers (Abricosova and Deryagin 1956, Deryagin 1960) succeeded in measuring this force experimentally, and their results appeared to support the latest theories on these force fields (Lifschitz 1956). Between two plates the van der Waals force is inversely proportional to the cube of the plates' distance, and for greater distances, to the fourth power. The van der Waals forces are generally considered to result from three different phenomena. If the molecule has a polar structure (like the water molecule, see above), then forces of attraction depending on the orientation of the molecules are produced. Since the water molecules are asymmetric as shown above, many different orientations are possible. Three such cases involving simple dipoles are presented in Fig. 37. The importance of orientation is further emphasized by the fact that, owing to the relation between strength and distance mentioned above, the force between non-parallel mineral lamina depends not only on their average distance, but also on their included angle. The other source of the van der Waals forces is the constant oscillation of the electrons. Consequently, the centre of gravity of the negative charges continuously changes creating temporary dipoles, and these fluctuating dipoles induce forces of attraction called the dispersion effect. The third source is the inductive effect: if a molecule enters an electric field, the electrons are slightly displaced, and so the originally non-polar molecules becomes polarized. The forces originating from the above three sources are distributed approximately as follows:

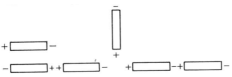

FIG. 37. Three types of dipole orientation

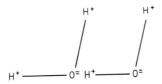

FIG. 38. Hydrogen bond development between oriented water molecules

orientation	77 per cent
dispersion	19
induction	4

Thus the orientation of the water molecules is decisive in determining the value of the van der Waals forces of attraction: if it changes, then the behaviour of the material will be significantly modified.

If a hydrogen atom is exposed to the attraction of two other atoms, the resultant force of attraction is the so-called hydrogen bond. Such bonds are produced between oriented water molecules according to Fig. 38.

The relative strength of the different bond types is approximately as follows:

van der Waals forces	$1-10$
hydrogen bond	$10-20$
ionic and covalent bonds	$40-400$

The fine soil particles consist mainly of crystals. The effect of the small amount of amorphous material present is negligible. Some of the crystalline grains have a low surface activity, so from plasticity and cohesion aspects they are rather insignificant, for example, quartz, calcite, the sulphides, feldspar, muscovite, and biotite. These are the main components of inorganic silts, but can also be found in smaller or larger quantities in clay.

Table 9

Atterberg limits of clay minerals

Clay	Ion	Atterberg limit, %			
		w_f	w_p	w_s	I_p
Kaolinite	Na	53	32	27	21
	K	49	29		20
	Ca	38	27	25	11
	H	53	25		28
	Mg	54	31	29	23
	Fe	59	37	29	22
Montmorillonite	Na	710	54	10	650
	K	660	98	9	560
	Ca	510	81	11	430
	H	440	55	9	380
	Mg	410	60	15	350
	Fe	290	75	10	220
Illite	Na	120	53	15	63
	K	120	60	18	60
	Ca	100	45	17	55
	H	100	51	17	50
	Mg	95	46	15	49
	Fe	110	49	15	60

Clay minerals

The crystalline minerals of a high surface activity are known as clay minerals. These are about 15 of them (Kerr 1959), and many different classifications are known (Grim 1958, Kézdi 1969). From practical aspects the most important are kaolinite, montmorillonite, and illite. The kaolinite mineral is rather stable, with small shrinkage and expansion, and the water molecules are unable to penetrate its strata. Over the individual montmorillonite surface, only cation interactions and weak van der Waals forces provide for a bond, so the water molecules are readily embedded between two elements, and in such cases considerable expansion occurs. Illite is similar to montmorillonite, but in its silicon layer, many silicon atoms are replaced by aluminum atoms. The character of the clay minerals present in a soil greatly affects its physical properties. Járay (1955) demonstrated the effect of cations on the yield point of the soils. Investigations on the shear strength and permeability are also known. Table 9 illustrates the Atterberg limit variations of clay minerals as a function of the ion-type adsorbed (Lambe 1958).

The force fields developed among charged particles, the water surrounding them, and the ions associated have a critical effect on the properties of fine-grain soils. If factors, such as the ion type or concentration, temperature, the liquid involved, etc., are changed, then the soil properties are also greatly changed. This fact has a very important practical significance in soil stabilization.

Other aspects of clay minerals and of the structure of fine-grained soils are treated in the author's Handbook of Soil Mechanics (Vol. 1, Ch. 3).

3. Mechanical soil stabilization

As already mentioned in the introduction, the admixture of the two opposite soil types, sand and clay, renders stable soils. In the list of the various stabilization techniques, the first was the so-called mechanical stabilization which ensures soil stability without the addition of any foreign matter. The present chapter deals with this method in detail. The void-ratio problems of the grain assemblies, the properties of different soil mixtures, the problems of mixing, and the general features of compaction will be discussed.

3.1 Void conditions of particle aggregates

3.1.1 Aggregates consisting of equal spheres

When investigating the properties and behaviour of granular materials, valuable assistance has always been rendered by the theoretical results of research on the characteristics of assemblies of equal spheres. A regular system consisting of equal spheres and built on the basis of mathematical laws is, of course, only abstraction, and the relevant results are not always suitable for direct application. Nevertheless, research on idealized systems will improve our understanding of nature, and explain many important findings. Research on an assembly consisting of equal spheres can be evaluated from an entirely new aspect if, according to the fundamental idea of Winterkorn (1953), the granular aggregates are regarded as liquids consisting of macro-elements.

Slichter (1899) was the first to study systematically aggregates consisting of equal spheres. He determined the build-up of several such systems and their porosities. He was followed by many in the literature, but we will just mention Filep (1937), Sjaastad (1963), Idel (1963), and Scott (1963). The following paragraphs deal with regular sets and their variations (Kézdi 1964).

The minimum volume V_0 required for the arrangement of the units in a regular assembly is obtained in a rhombohedral layout (Fig. 39) where each particle is in contact with 12 adjacent ones. This condition may be called the solid state of the grain assembly. The shear resistance of such an arrangement, filling up infinite space, is infinitely high, since any shear displacement should be associated with a volume increase, but this is impossible under the given conditions. If the volume of the assembly exceeds V_0, then with a gradual increase of the difference $V - V_0$, the "disorder" in the arrangement of the individual particles will similarly increase. The "free" volume $V - V_0$, however, may be assumed to exist in the form of individual voids which, in turn making the existence of a lattice structure most probable. This lattice structure would cease to exist only if the voids made up a certain maximum volume known as the amorphization volume, when the system would behave like a perfect liquid. The associated porosity represents the "melting point" of the system. Thus the porosity is seen to play a role conforming to the given temperature. If the system changes from the most compact state to that corresponding to the melting point, its volume meanwhile increases continuously. At the melting point the system assumes a cube-link arrangement (Fig. 39).

As it is now well known, the porosity of such an assembly amounts to $n = 47.64$ per cent. Let us follow the variation of the porosity when the cubic system of the assembly undergoes a change and becomes an orthorhombic or rhombohedral system. The former is the planar, and the latter the spatial limit state of maximum compactness. The arrangement of the particles is shown in Figs 39a and 39b.

The cubic system transforms to orthorhombic if all the spheres in a given layer slide over the one beneath, so that the direction of the movement always remains parallel to the straight line connecting the centres of a given row of spheres. In order to follow the nature of the changes, it is sufficient to consider only eight spheres whose centres form a "unit cell". Initially, this unit cell is a cube which in the course of the movement described above becomes rhombohedral. The extent of displacement is expressed by the angle of orientation. The porosity, as a function of this

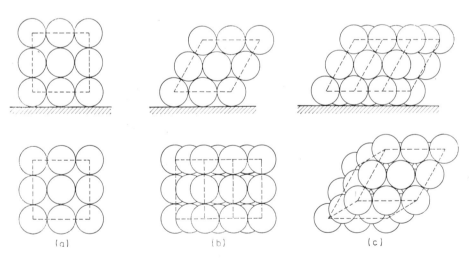

(a)   (b)   (c)

FIG. 39. Regular arrangement of an assembly consisting of equal spheres (a) hexagonal; (b) orthorhombic; (c) rhombohedral system

angle is

$$n = 1 - \frac{\pi}{6 \sin \alpha} \tag{24}$$

The volume of the unit cell varies according to $V = \sin \alpha$, and the same equation also expresses the height variation. The volume of the solid parts, from the equation $n = (V - V_0)$ per V, the constant value written as

$$V_0 = V_t = V(1 - n) = \pi/6$$

This case may be called planar deformation since in a vertical plane, parallel to the direction of the movement, certain changes identical in character and magnitude take place. The unit cell and porosity variations are illustrated in Fig. 40.

In the second basic case the system must perform several movements. In addition to that described above the row of spheres moves normal them, and the row of spheres next to the one underneath will slide forward (Fig. 39c). This movement should be imagined as a deformation of the unit cell taking place uniformly at an identical rate in each of the three directions, i.e. at the sides of the unit cell, the

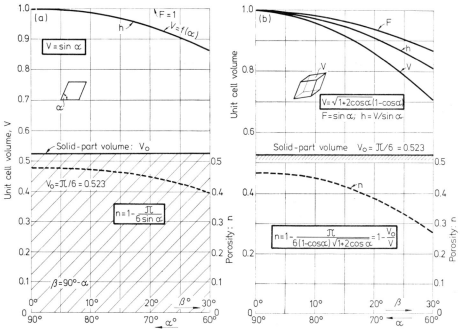

Fig. 40. Variation of the unit cell volume and height, and of the void volume, in the function of the angle of orientation
(a) in the case of planar, and (b) spatial deformations

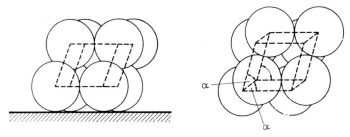

FIG. 41. Intermediate state of the unit cell

angles included by two edges are identical everywhere (see Fig. 41, illustrating an intermediate position).

Under such conditions the entire movement can be described as the variation of the angle of orientation, as a function of which both the cubic capacity and the porosity can then be clearly determined.

The expression defining the porosity is known from Slichter's investigations:

$$n = 1 - \frac{\pi}{6(1 - \cos \alpha) \sqrt{1 + 2 \cos \alpha}} \tag{25}$$

The variation of the unit cell volume is

$$V = f(\alpha) = (1 - \cos \alpha) \sqrt{1 + 2 \cos \alpha} \tag{26}$$

while the solid-part volume is still

$$V_t = (1 - n)V(\alpha) = \pi/6 = \text{constant}$$

The void ratio may be expressed by the following simple equation:

$$e = \frac{n}{1 - n} = \frac{\pi}{6V} - 1 \tag{27}$$

Variation of the V value in this case is also shown in Fig. 40.

The number of spheres in contact with another is called the co-ordination index of the assembly. This index does not change during the above variations of the structure, but assumes the corresponding value only at the moment when the new final position is reached. W. O. Smith (1932), in attempting to apply the results obtained with sphere assemblies to actual granular aggregates, assumed that an actual system could be considered as a set of rhombohedral and cubic unit cells. In these cells the individual configurations would be represented in such a ratio whereby a porosity identical to that of the total set should be the final result. Accordingly, the following equation might express the relation between the "average" co-ordination index and the void volume:

$$N = 26.49 - \frac{10.73}{1 - n} \qquad (28)$$

This correlation is graphically illustrated in Fig. 42a. If the relation between porosity and the angle of orientation as described above is also considered, we get the function $N = f(\alpha)$ expressing the relation between the co-ordination index of the system and the angle of orientation (Fig. 42b). If the co-ordination index thus obtained is then plotted as a function of the relative cubic capacity of the unit

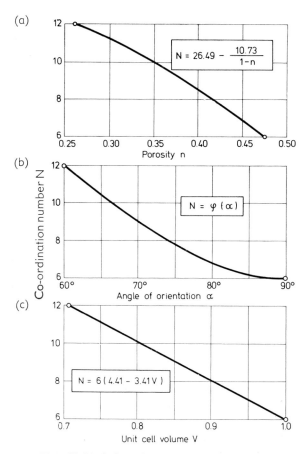

FIG. 42. Variation of the co-ordination index as a function of porosity, angle of orientation, and unit cell volume

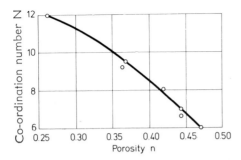

FIG. 43. Experimental results illustrating the relation between co-ordination index and porosity (W. O. Smith, P. Foote, P. S. Busang 1929)

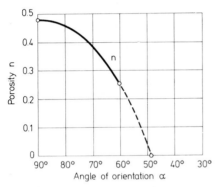

FIG. 44. Extension of the orientation-angle concept

cell, a linear correlation is arrived at:

$$N = 6 + 6(2 + \sqrt{2})(1 - V) =$$
$$= 6(4.41 - 3.41\ V) \qquad (29)$$

This co-ordination index is used to calculate the frictional resistance of particle aggregates. That the results do not have theoretical importance alone is clearly verified by the experimental results presented in Fig. 43, which exhibit good agreement with the curve plotted in Fig. 42a. Thus, through these correlations the state of a sphere assembly and porosity can be readily characterized by either the angle of orientation, or the co-ordination index. In certain cases the assembly consisting of equal spheres and corresponding to an optional aggregate can alsobe determined this way. Since in mixed assemblies the value of n may be less than the minimum $n = 26 - 49$ per cent of an equal sphere assembly, it is best to extend the interpretation of the angle of orientation α below 60°. In such cases, the spheres intersect one another, and n decreases rapidly as the intersecting parts are taken into account twice. When $\alpha = 49°$, this volume is equal to that of the residual voids, so $n = 0$. Using the curve in Fig. 44 the value α can be determined for any porosity.

3.1.2 Two- and three-component grain assemblies

In the previous section we discussed the analogy between temperature and porosity. In the following paragraphs this analogy will be extended to multicomponent systems.

It was understood that the specific state of a material would be a dynamic state of equilibrium between the forces of attraction acting among molecules, atoms, and ions on the one hand, and the kinetic dispersion forces on the other. The latter increase with increasing temperature, associated with a volume increase if the state and structure of the material are constant.

74

The melting point of a mixture consisting of two different materials depends on the mixing ratio. However, since the molecular components generally exert interactions and dissolve each other, the mutual attraction of the molecules of identical character decreases, as do the dispersion forces characterized by temperature. This is why the melting point decreases as a function of concentration, with its lowest value at the point E (Fig. 45) called the eutectic point.

As mentioned above, temperature is only a measure of the free energy of the system and simultaneously, at a given pressure, a measure of the volume of system (or, more precisely, it has a precise correlation with the latter). Accordingly, there is an analogy between the molecular and macromeritic systems, and the importance of the porosity depends on the temperature. However, in such cases the phenomenon illustrated in Fig. 45 must be manifested in the development of the porosity of two-component systems as well, as a function of the mixing ratio. Experience fully verifies this conclusion. A number of inves-

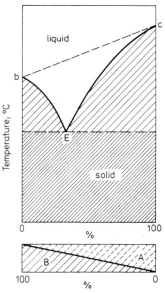

FIG. 45. Phase diagram of the mixture. The melting point as a function of the percentage composition

tigations aiming at the clarification of the compactness conditions of the two-component systems are known. Examination of the porosity of mixtures consisting of two sets of spheres with equal diameters, each, revealed that the void volume in the experimentally loosest condition of the mixtures was always smaller than that of the individual components under identical test conditions. In other words, the situation was exactly as shown by the phase diagram of Fig. 45: such an experimental result is presented in Fig. 46. Okhotin (1929) conducted a number of experiments to determine the optimum grain-size distribution for compaction, and the example illustrated is one of his series. Another experimental result is given in Fig. 47a (Furnas 1931) where the shape of the curves is identical to the same phase diagram. Here the normal porosity value was $n = 50$ per cent, and the different curves pertain to the different diameter ratios of the larger and smaller particles. Minimum porosity was found at any d_1/d_2 diameter ratio, with an intermediate mixing proportion. The ratio $d_1/d_4 = 0$ refers to the case when the voids of a relatively coarse-grain skeleton (sand) are filled up by very small grain clay.

Similar results were obtained in the laboratory of the Department of Geotechnics, Technical University of Budapest, and the resultant curves of Leussink and Kutzner (1962) have the same character: some of them are shown in Fig. 47b, presenting the dry bulk density of identically compacted granular aggregates as a function of composition. In these experiments the mixtures were compacted partly by vibration, and partly by static pressure.

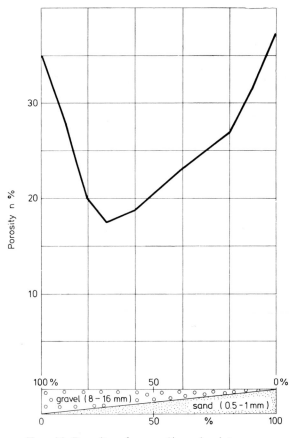

FIG. 46. Porosity of a sand/gravel mixture as a
function of the mixing ratio

Findley et al (1951) ascertained that a three-component system should have two
degrees of freedom its state depending on the relative concentration of the components, and the porosity. If three different grain fractions are selected, and the void
ratio of their different mixtures obtained, however, by an identical energy compaction, then the diagram presented in Fig. 48 is obtained. The character of this diagram is identical to that exhibited by the phase diagram of mixtures consisting of
different liquids: point K is to one side of the three-component system, since the
three components may be admixed in any ratio.

Interesting experimental results are illustrated in Fig. 49 (Domján 1965) where
the maximum and minimum void ratios of different sand mixtures are presented
in triangular-diagram form, as a function of the mixing ratio (Figs 49a and 49b);
Fig. 49c presents the difference between these two values.

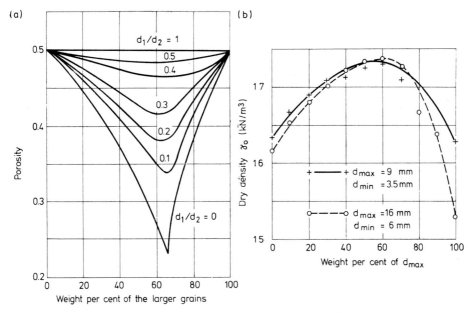

FIG. 47. Experimental results by Furnas (a) and Leussink (b) on the compactness of two-component mixtures

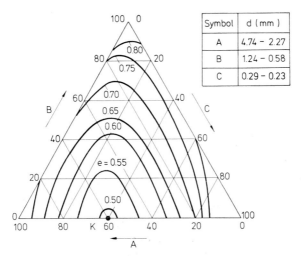

Symbol	d (mm)
A	4.74 – 2.27
B	1.24 – 0.58
C	0.29 – 0.23

FIG. 48. Void ratio of a three-component system as a function of the mixing ratio, in the loosest state of the individual mixtures

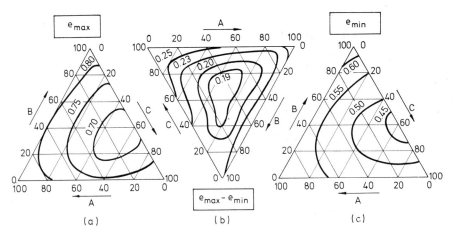

FIG. 49. Maximum and minimum void ratios of a three-component system. The three components are: $A=0.58-0.29$ mm; $B=0.29-0.22$ mm; $C=1.24-0$ 58 mm; (a) void ratio of the loosest state; (b) void ratio of the most compact state; (c) range of void ratio variations as a function of the mixing proportion

From experimental results and theoretical considerations, we may conclude that, if a soil mixture that can be readily and economically compacted with an acceptable quality is to be produced for road-construction purposes, then it is definitely wise to test all the available or economically accessible granular soil types, to determine the optimum mixing ratio. Since the mixing ratio providing the minimum porosity ensures maximum shear strength, this one should be selected.

3.2 Assemblies with continuous grain-size distribution having minimum void ratio

Natural soil roads often exhibit excellent resistance to the effects of moderate traffic, but otherwise they prove to be impassable. If the substance of earth roads convenient for the vehicles is studied, it is found that the grain-size distribution curve of the soil is excessively elongated, the sand and gravel particles provide for a satisfactory skeleton, and the voids are filled with fine-sand, rock flour and silt-clay particles, giving a compact, high load-bearing capacity, water-impermeable mixture.

Soil mechanics research has clarified the nature of such soils, and considers the maintenance of the grain-distribution curve within a certain range as the main criterion of acceptable soil mixtures, although the plasticity index of the "binder" (the $d - 0.1$ mm grain-size fraction) has similar importance. This mixed grain distribution and its flat elongated curve make the efficient compaction of the mixture possible, this being vital since stability depends on the correct selection of

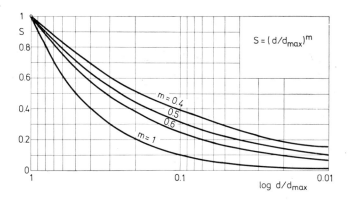

FIG. 50. Curves satisfying the Talbot formula, for various m values

the ratio between the different soil types, their thorough admixture, and their careful compaction at the optimum water content. Compactness is the most essential characteristic of mechanical stabilization. Owing to the significant compression strength of a compact soil, the indentation of wheels and thus the traction resistance will be reduced. Water evaporation from a compact soil is much more difficult, as is adsorption into it, so the water content of such a soil will only experience slight variation during the year. Often a soil mixture meeting the requirements of mechanical stabilization is produced, only to be stabilized by another method, such as bitumen treatment.

Mechanical stabilization is suitable for the development of both the top and base layers of soil roads. Requirements as regards the grain-size distribution of the material involved depend on the layer in which this material is to be used.

We repeatedly attempted to characterize the grain-size distribution curve of a soil mixture providing acceptable compactness, by an empirical formula. Of the suggested equations, the Talbot formula presented below is the best expression:

$$S = \left(\frac{d}{d_{\max}} \right)^m \tag{30}$$

where S is the weight per cent of the particles with diameter less than d, $d_{\max}$ is the diameter of the largest particle in the mixture, and m is an exponent determined empirically whose value, depending on $d_{\max}$, varies between $m = 0.11$ and 0.66; the curves corresponding to this formula are presented in Fig. 50.

The grain-size distribution curve of satisfactory mixtures is usually plotted in a parabola form (Rothfuchs 1935). If the co-ordinates of a point on the curve are d and S, and if the maximum and minimum grain diameters of the mixture are $d_{\max}$ and d_0, then the equation of the grain distribution curve of a favourable

79

mixture is

$$S = \frac{d^m - d_0^m}{d_{max}^m - d_0^m} \qquad (31)$$

The Talbot formula can be obtained from this equation if $d_0 = 0$. As for the value of m, Rothfuchs specified $m = 0.5$ but generally an m value between 0.4 and 0.5 is used today.

Example

The composition of a continuous grain-distribution mixture, easy to compact and satisfying the Rothfuchs equation at $m = 0.5$, is to be determined, when $d_{max} = 25$ mm, and $d_0 = 0.15$ mm (No. 100 mesh).

The curve corresponding to the Rothfuchs equation is plotted using the above data. When plotted in $S = f(\sqrt{d})$ form, it is a straight line. By indicating the mesh sizes of the individual sieves in the series along the horizontal axis, it is possible to read off directly the quantities passing through each sieve, and so the mixture can then be prepared. Presentation and the usual grain-distribution curve of the mixture are shown in Fig. 51.

In order to facilitate the calculations involving Eq. (31), Table 10 presents d^m values for $m = 0.3, 0.4,$ and 0.6, respectively. The table also presents the ASTM

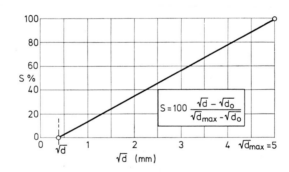

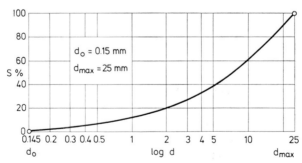

Fig. 51. Example of an equation satisfying the Rothfuchs formula. Grain-size distribution curve in the function of $\sqrt{d}$ and log d, respectively

Table 10
d^m values for calculating the grain-size distribution curve
(after Aichhorn)

ASTM* sieve	Screen sieve	Sieve mesh	d^m			
			$m = 0.3$	$m = 0.4$	$m = 0.5$	$m = 0.6$
200		0.02	0.309	0.209	0.141	0.0956
		0.06	0.43	0.325	0.245	0.185
		0.074	0.458	0.353	0.272	0.209
100		0.09	0.486	0.382	0.3	0.236
		0.149	0.564	0.46	0.386	0.319
		0.2	0.617	0.525	0.447	0.380
60		0.25	0.661	0.574	0.5	0.435
		0.40	0.76	0.693	0.634	0.578
40		0.42	0.771	0.707	0.648	0.594
20		0.6	0.858	0.815	0.775	0.735
		0.85	0.952	0.937	0.922	0.906
	2	1.5	1.129	1.176	1.225	1.273
10		2.0	1.231	1.320	1.414	1.515
8	3	2.3	1.284	1.395	1.517	1.650
	5	3.8	1.494	1.706	1.949	2.230
4		4.0	1.515	1.74	2.000	2.3
		4.76	1.597	1.867	2.18	2.54
	7	5.4	1.659	1.963	2.32	2.75
	8	6.0	1.71	2.045	2.45	2.93
	10	6.2	1.729	2.08	2.49	2.98
		7.8	1.892	2.27	2.79	3.42
3/8″	12	8.0	1.865	2.295	2.825	3.48
	15	9.5	1.965	2.46	3.08	3.86
		12.0	2.11	2.70	2.46	4.45
	18	14.6	2.24	2.92	3.82	5.0
		15.0	2.27	2.96	3.88	5.08
	20	16.4	2.31	3.06	4.05	5.35
		18.0	2.38	3.17	4.24	5.66
3/4″		19.05	2.42	3.25	4.37	5.86
	25	20.8	2.49	3.37	4.56	6.16
1″	30	25.2	2.63	3.64	5.02	6.95

* ASTM = American Society for Testing Materials

6 Kézdi: Stabilized

Table 10 (continued)

ASTM* sieve	Screen sieve	Sieve mesh	d^m			
			$m = 0.3$	$m = 0.4$	$m = 0.5$	$m = 0.6$
.	35	29.6	2.76	3.88	5.44	7.64
	40	34.0	2.88	4.1	5.83	8.31
		35.0	2.90	4.15	5.91	8.44
1 1/2″		38.1	2.98	4.29	6.17	8.89
	50	43	3.09	4.50	6.56	9.54
		45	3.13	4.58	6.71	9.82
2″		50.8	3.25	4.81	7.13	10.53
		55	3.32	4.96	7.40	11.08
	70	61	3.43	5.18	7.81	11.80
		65	3.50	5.32	8.05	12.21
3″		76.2	3.67	5.66	8.73	13.45

* ASTM = American Society for Testing Materials

sieve denotations and the corresponding mesh sizes in mm (which can be used advantageously elsewhere).

Requirements as regards the grain-size distribution of the material depend on which layer of the pavement construction the mixture will be used in. In the base layer coarse particles are used, in the load-bearing layer they are somewhat finer, while in the upper one a soil mixture consisting of still smaller particles is used. Figure 52 illustrates the curves of advantageous mixtures. As a general rule, the

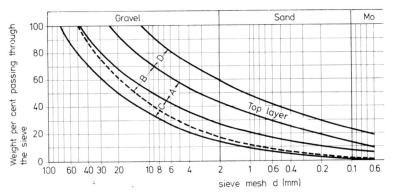

FIG. 52. Grain-size distribution curves of favourable soil mixtures. A = Grain-size distribution most favourable in a load-bearing layer; B and C = range of the still useful mixtures; D = range of the mixtures suitable in upper layers

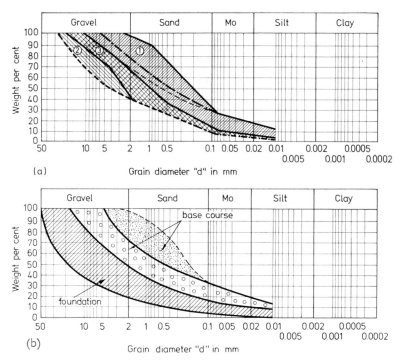

(a)

(b)

FIG. 53. Limiting grain-size distribution curves of mechanical stabilization according to Hungarian findings (a) for a load-bearing top layer; (b) for base and subbase (1) under dry, (2) wet, (3) normal climatic conditions

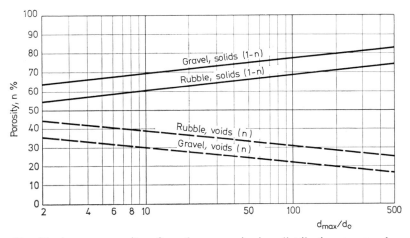

FIG. 54. Average porosity of continuous grain-size distribution curve substances as a function of the maximum and minimum grain diameter ratio

Table 11

Grain-size distribution of the base layer, according to the 1958 AASHO*
specifications

Screen denomination and mesh		Weight per cent			
		A	B	C	D
Class I (coarse grain)					
	76.2 mm	100			
	50.8 mm	—	100		
	37.6 mm	—	—	100	
	25.4 mm	35–65	50–80	—	100
4	4.76 mm	10–30	15–35	20–40	25–45
200	0.076 mm	—	—	<10	<10
Class II (medium)					
	76.2 mm	100			
	50.8 mm	—	100		
	37.6 mm	—	—	100	
	25.4 mm	45–75	50–80	—	100
4	4.26 mm	15–45	20–50	25–55	30–60
10	2.00 mm	—	—	—	20–50
200	0.076 mm	<10	<12	<12	<12
Class III (stabilized)					
	76.2 mm	100			
	50.8 mm	65–100	100		
	37.6 mm	—	70–100	100	
	25.4 mm	45–75	55–85	70–100	100
	18.8 mm	—	50–80	60–90	70–100
	9.4 mm	30–60	40–70	45–75	50–80
4	4.76 mm	25–50	40–60	30–60	35–65
10	2.00 mm	20–40	20–50	20–50	25–50
40	0.42 mm	10–25	10–30	10–30	15–30
200	0.076 mm	3–10	5–15	5–15	5–15

* AASHO = American Association of State Highway Officials

maximum grain diameter in the base must not exceed 50 mm, while with respect
to the fine particles, it is rather important that the weight per cent of the fraction
passing through the $d = 0.074$ mm mesh size (No. 200) screen should not exceed
two-thirds of the weight per cent of the quantity passing through the $d = 0.4$ mm
mesh.

According to results from Hungary, the grain-size distribution-limit curves may
be plotted as shown in Figs 53a and 53b. The former applies to the top layer of
earth roads, while the latter applies to the fundamental and base layers.

If the material also contains a considerable amount of crushed rubble, then its
grain-size distribution curve may deviate from the range of the medium class

Table 12

Grain-size distribution of the wear-off layer according to AASHO (1958)

Screen denomination and mesh			Weight per cent			
			A	B	C	D
Classes I and II						
	37.6	mm	100			
	25.4	mm	—	100		
	18.8	mm	—	—	100	
	12.7	mm	45–75	—	—	100
4	4.76	mm	30–60	40–75	45–80	
10	2.00	mm		25–60	25–60	25–60
200	0.076	mm	12	12	12	12
Clas III						
	25.4	mm	100			
	18.8	mm	85–100			
	9.4	mm	65–100			
4	4.76	mm	55–85			
10	2.00	mm	40–70			
40	0.42	mm	25–45			
200	0.076	mm	10–25			

Atterberg limit specifications

Class	Layer	I_p	w_l
Class II	base	<6	<25
	wear-off	<6	<25
Class III	base	<6	<25
	wear-off	4–9	<35

limit curves. Partial crushing of the largest gravel fraction might greatly increase stability.

Accordingly, the normal average porosity of continuous grain distribution curve (well graded) materials can be readily expressed as a function of the ratio d_{max}/d_0, as shown in Fig. 54.

Other specifications supply the desired mixture compositions in tabulated form. Tables 11 and 12 present American specifications reflecting today's practice there, and Table 12 also contains specifications on the Atterberg limits.

In order to meet the grain-size distribution requirements, often fines must also be added to the local soil. Although in general this method really provides a much more stable material, we must remember that by adding fines a material easy to drain and not susceptible to frost might be transformed into a soil of impeded water discharge and endangered by frost. This technique should be employed, therefore, with utmost care only, and generally the thicker the layer built, the more important the careful study of drainage problems.

Another Aichhorn composition (1963) is presented in Table 13 where the limit weight percentages of layers having different purposes and the Atterberg limits can be found.

Table 14 was prepared on the basis of Hungarian findings, to show sand-clay and gravel-sand-clay soil-mix data, and to supply the required plasticity index as well as liquid limit values. For dry weather use, a top layer increasingly exposed to dry-out, and rectangular particles, mixtures approximating the top limit of the plasticity index should be used, while for wet weather or more precipitation and with spherical particles, those near the lower limit of this index should be used.

Table 13

Favourable soil-mixture data according to Aichhorn

Screen mm dia	Sieve (mesh) mm dia	Embedment		Foundation			Wear-off layer D
				Excellent	Good	Adaptable	
				A	B	C	
d_{max} (mm)		Weight S (per cent)					
		76.2	18	50.8	50.8	76.2	25.4
	76.2	—	—	—	—	100	—
	65	100	—	—	—	82–100	—
	55	94–100	—	100	100	85–100	—
50		85–100	—	84–100	92–100	75–94	—
	35	80–100	—	86–100	83–100	67–86	—
30		70–100	—	76–100	70–100	56–76	100
	18	62–100	100	66–88	58–88	47–66	88–100
15		55–85	85–100	56–77	47–77	37–56	77–100
	8	46–75	68–100	48–67	38–67	30–48	67–88
7		40–66	62–100	40–59	30–59	25–40	59–78
	4	35–60	55–100	36–54	26–54	20–36	54–72
	2	25–50	40–75	28–42	17–42	14–28	42–58
	1	18–40	27–56	21–33	10–33	9–21	33–48
	0.4	10–28	12–35	15–24	5–24	5–15	24–36
	0.2	5–20	6–23	10–18	3–18	2–10	18–20
	0.074	0–10	0–10	7–10	0.5–10	0.3–7	10–21
	0.06	0–8	0–8	6–8	0–8	0–6	8–19
Liquid limit w_L non-plastic				<25			<35
Plasticity index I_p non-plastic				0–6			4–9

Table 14

Mixtures suitable for mechanical stabilization

Screen diameter mm	Sand-clay mixture		Coarse grain mixture				
	Wear-off layer	Load distribution layer	Wear-off layer		Load distribution layer		
			d_{max} (mm)				
			25.4	19.1	76.2	50.8	25.4
		Fallen through fraction, weight per cent					
76.2	100% of the mixture will pass through the 25.4 mm screen					100	
50.8						65–100	100
38.1							70–100
25.4	65–100% through the 2.00 mm unit		100		45–75	55–85	100
19.1			85–100	100		50–80	75–100
9.5	the fallen through fraction should have the following grain composition		65–100	100	30–60	40–70	50–80
4.8							
			55–85	70–100	25–50	30–60	35–65
2.0	100		40–70	35–80	20–40	20–50	25–50
0.84	55–90						
0.42	35–70		35–70	25–50	10–25	10–30	15–30
0.074	8–25		10–25	8–25	3–10	5–15	5–15
Wet climate I_p	3	6	3		3		
Normal climate I_p	4–8	6	4–3		3		
Dry climate I_p	9–15	6	9–15		3		
w_L less than	35	25	25		25		

Fine fraction quantity: the material fallen through the 0.074 mm mesh should be less than 2/3 of that passing through the 0.42 mm screen
The maximum grain size should be less than 1/3 of the cover thickness

3.3 Determination of the mixing ratio

If a natural soil meets the requirements specified, then it is directly suitable for stabilization. This category includes silty or slightly clayey gravels, coarse silty sands, mixed grain-size distribution limestone or dolomite ratchel, and also certain demolition products, industrial by-products, silty pit dirt, and brickyard scrap. Prior to use, these materials and their particle distribution and plastic properties should be examined. These are always determined by their particle content smaller than $d = 0.42$ mm. Finally, their wear and disintegration aspects must be considered. Inclination to the former is determined by cooking: contaminants and the adherent, heavy soil particles are removed from the sample by intensive wash-off, then the sample is cooked in water for about 10 min. If the water assumes turbidity, the sample is inclined to weathering. If at the beginning of the work-in process the coarse grains disintegrate under the compactor roll, then the extent of disintegration should be assessed through test runs, and the result ought to be taken into account when specifying the grain distribution.

In many cases no soil directly adaptable without modification can be found, so the stabilization material must be produced by admixing two or three different soils. To determine the admixture ratio, several methods, described below, are known.

(1) If two soils of given grain-size distribution curve (Fig. 55) are mixed in a weight ratio of $1 : n$, then the weight per cent of the resultant soil at an optional grain size d is given by the following equation:

$$S = \frac{S_1 + n S_2}{1 + n} \tag{32}$$

If, for example, the admixture ratio is $1 : 1$, then $S = (S_1 + S_2)/2$, i.e., the resultant curve in section No. 2 is obtained is by halving the ordinate difference between curves 1 and 2. In stage No. I only the grains of soil No. 1 are found, in No. II both, while in No. III there are only particles of soil No. 2. Thus in stages I and III the ordinates $1 - S_1$ and S_2, respectively, will be directly halved.

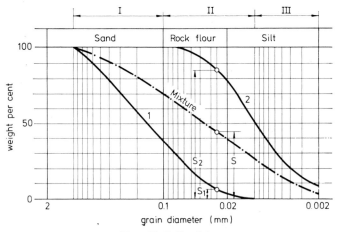

Fig. 55. Soil mixing

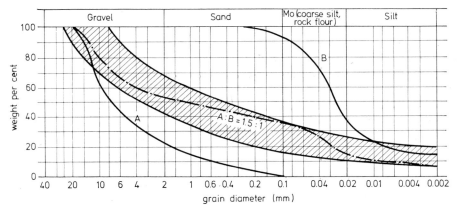

FIG. 56. Mixing with given limiting curves

(2) If, using two different soils, a resultant having a weight per cent S specified for a given grain diameter d is to be produced, i.e. where the grain distribution curve intersects a given point, then the mixing ratio may be calculated on the basis of Eq. (32):

$$n = \frac{S - S_1}{S_2 - S} \tag{33}$$

(3) In practice, the mixing problems usually occur in the need for admixing soils for a given grain-size distribution curve in such a ratio that the curve of the resultant soil would lie between two prespecified limit curves. Since the solution of this problem is rather lengthy, by trial-and-error or calculation, the following simple graphical process is suggested (Barabás 1951).

The hatched area in Fig. 56 indicates the required range of the grain-size distribution curves. Soils A and B are available for mixture.

Plotting is done according to Fig. 57. Two vertical axes, A and B, are plotted with optional spacing and graduated to 100 per cent. At a given grain diameter d, first

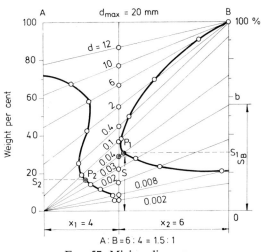

FIG. 57. Mixing diagram

89

the S_A and S_B weight percentages of soils A and B are read off, and indicated along axes A and B, and then the points thus obtained are connected. The inclined straight line, $a-b$ is next intersected by the horizontal lines corresponding to the weight percentages S_1 and S_2 read off the limit curves at diameter d, whereby points P_1 and P_2 are obtained. This plotting is repeated for several diameters d, and the points obtained are connected by curves. If a vertical straight line that will not intersect any of the curves can be drawn then the desired mixing ratio at which the resultant grain-size distribution curve will still remain between the limit curves specified, can be obtained from the following equation:

$$n = A : B = x_2 : x_1 \tag{34}$$

If no such straight line can be plotted, then the problem cannot be solved: the resultant curve will leave the range referred to at the section between those grain diameters where the vertical straight line corresponding to the mixing ratio specified would intersect the curves.

The validity of this plotting method is quite obvious if Fig. 58 is considered. We get, based on similar triangles,

$$\frac{S - S_A}{x_1} = \frac{S - S_B}{x_2}$$

thus

$$\frac{S_B - S}{S - S_A} = \frac{x_2}{x_1} = \frac{1}{n}$$

and

$$S = \frac{S_A + n S_B}{1 + n}$$

is obtained, i.e. the formula under (1).

(4) With respect to compactibility and the dry strength of the mixture, the best result is obtained at the maximum inequality coefficient of the mix. The mixing ratio yielding for this situation can be determined as shown in Fig. 59, via the determination of the U values of the different ratio mixtures.

(5) Figure 60 presents lucid method for the admixture of the two different soils.

Along the two vertical scales, the grain-distribution data of the two substances given are indicated, and the points of the associated grain sizes are connected. A master is now plotted on

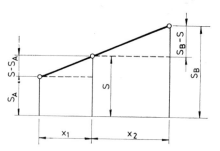

FIG. 58. Verification of the plotting method presented

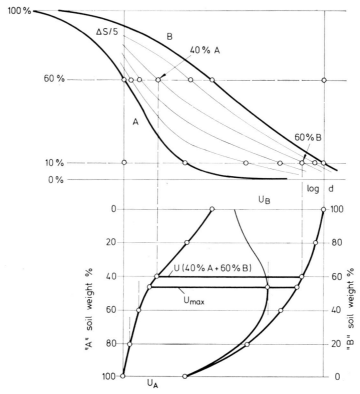

FIG. 59. Determination of the optimum mixing ratio to ensure the maximum U value

a piece of transparent paper, and the weight per cent limits specified are illustrated on the same scale. The master is then moved in its vertical position from left to right until it is intersected by the oblique lines of all the different grain sizes within the range specified. At this stage the admixture ratio of the two soil types can be read off the horizontal axis (Aichhorn 1963).

(6) The mixtures can be fairly well evaluated from grain-size

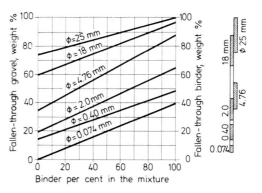

FIG. 60. Aichhorn plotting technique for the determination of the optimum mixture

distribution aspects by means of the triangle diagrams. From this viewpoint, the grains may be categorized into the following groups:

Gravel-sand-clay

Gravel   35 and 20−2 mm resp.
Sand   2−0.1 mm
Binder $d < 0.1$ mm

Sand-clay

Coarse sand   2−0.5 mm
Fine sand   0.5−0.1 mm
Binder $d < 0.1$ mm

The triangle diagrams are illustrated in Fig. 61. The point inside the diagram corresponds to the admixture ratio of the three components predetermined, on the basis of the well-known characteristics of the diagrams. In both diagrams hatching indicates the ranges in which the points represent mixtures of advantageous stable composition. Using these diagrams one can simply and rapidly determine whether two or more soils are suitable for the preparation of favourable mixtures, and it is possible to find the ratio in which the individual soil types should be admixed for this purpose. The method is illustrated by the example below.

The following materials are available:

— sand (a), consisting of   50 per cent coarse and
                             45 per cent fine sand,
             and   5 per cent binder,
and — silt (b), consisting of 10 per cent fine sand,
             and   90 per cent binder.

In Fig. 62 these soils are indicated by points a and b. If these two points are connected, each point on the line thus obtained indicates a feasible mixture of the two soils. This line intersects the square of the optimum mixtures at points c_1 and c_2, so mixing within the $c_1 - c_2$ range is actually feasible. The more point c approximates to point c_2, the greater the amount of material b used. The mixing weight ratio can be calculated from the formula

$$a : b = 1 : n = \frac{\overline{bc}}{\overline{ac}}$$

After determining of the mixing ratio the mixture must be checked with regard to the plastic index. If this is lower than the specified value then more binder must be added, if it is higher then less binder is needed, but the point indicating the mixture in the triangle diagram must remain within the hatched area, otherwise the mixture is not suitable for earth-road construction.

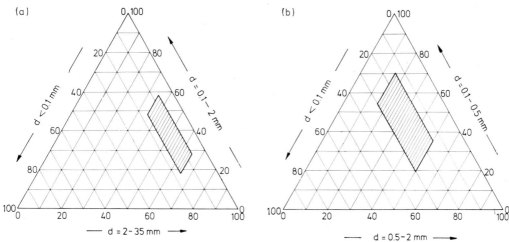

Fig. 61. Determination of (a) gravel-sand-clay, (b) sand-clay mixtures by means of the triangle diagrams

In the case of three components, construction is as follows. A coarse sand (a), a fine sand (b), and a silt (c) are mixed into a soil mortar, with the following component weight percentages:

Soil	Coarse	Fine	Binder
	sand		
	weight per cent		
a	78	12	10
b	10	75	15
c	5	10	85

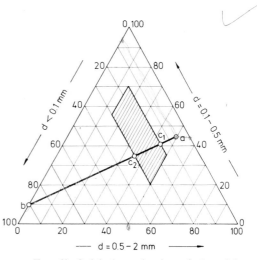

Fig. 62. Quick determination of the mixing ratio

The points indicating the three components are plotted and connected into a triangle (Fig. 63), whose sides do not intersect the hatched range, thus the problem cannot be solved by the admixture of two components. However, along the line (*ab*) indicating the mixture of components *a* and *b* there is a point whose connecting line to *c* intersects the

93

rectangle. If, for example, the $\overline{cf}$ straight line is taken, then the required mixing ratio can be readily calculated on the basis of the points of intersection obtained. The same ratio is of course obtained, if mixing is performed according to the lines $\overline{ad}$ or $\overline{be}$. In the given case, first the mixing ratioassociated with the soil, characterized by point f obtained through the admixture of components a and b, is first determined:

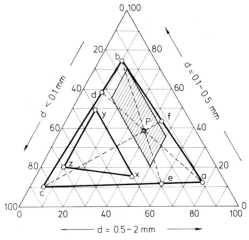

$$a : b = 1 : n_1 = \frac{\overline{af}}{\overline{bf}} = 1 : 1$$

Admixture of the soils characterized by points c and f is:

$$(a, b) : c = 1 : n_2 = \frac{\overline{fP}}{\overline{cP}} = 1 : 6.2$$

Thus the three components should be admixed in the ratio

$$a : b : c =$$

$$= 1 : 1 : 0.32 \ (43\% \, a, 43\% \, b, 14\% \, c)$$

FIG. 63. Mixtures of three components

If the triangle made up of characteristic points of the component soils is completely outside the hatched range (e.g. soils x, y, and z), then the problem cannot be solved.

3.4 Atterberg limits of soil mixtures

As mentioned earlier, in addition to the grain-size distribution specifications, stable soil mixtures must also satisfy the Atterberg limit requirements. This is because only the clay particles are expected to produce a bond between coarse grains uniting the loose aggregate. The fine grains are connected to the coarse particles by hydrogen bonds whose strength is greater, the lower the number of water-molecule layers, through which their effect must penetrate. The cation shell of the clay particles thus bonded bonds further clay grains until these forms, between the coarse grains, in their smallest voids, an actual bridge is formed whereby the skeleton develops sufficient cohesion. According to Bernatzik (1947), the powerful manifestation of this effect is promoted by the collection of the fine particles of the binder precisely in the small voids during the dry-out of the soil. In the pore water filling the coarse grain voids, the clay particles first float freely, but during the course of drying their area gradually reduces (Fig. 64). However, no further shrinkage of the water films is permitted by the clay particles, so the stress increase during dry-out is distributed over an ap-

94

proximately identical surface. The force of attraction therefore increases considerably and to a similar extent, increases the strength of the structure.

However, the strength of the bonds described is always smaller than the natural strength of the coarse grains. This will govern the fracture type, since the fracture always occurs over the surface of the coarse grains or along the surfaces through the voids, meaning that although the bonds create adhesion on the grain surface, they do not induce cohesion between the grains. The adhesive force of attraction determines the strength of the stabilized soil which depends on the compactness and water content of the mixture, in addition to the binder characteristics and the strength of the bonds referred to. Figure 65 illustrates the results of a relevant experimental series and the variation of the unconfined compression strength as a function of water content and compactness. Unfortunately, too few such comprehensive investigations have been conducted, so we do not yet understand sufficiently, for example, the correlation between the quality and quantity of the clay, i.e. the binder, and the actual strength.

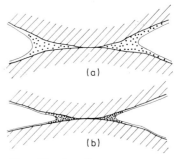

FIG. 64. The effect exerted by the minute solids suspended in the pore water on cohesion. (a) The fine grains float freely in the water (b) after dry-out they increase the surface over which a force of attraction due to surface tension is produced

The Atterberg limit specifications have already been presented in tabulated form. Accordingly, if the mixture is used as a wear-off layer, then under wet climatic conditions the plasticity index must not exceed 3, while under average conditions it may be $I_p = 4$–8 per cent. As a base-course layer only soils with $I_p < 6$ per cent plastic index, and $w_L < 25$ per cent may be used.

Every Atterberg limit figure referred to here and in the tables should be determined using the $d < 0.4$ mm soil fraction.

If the production of a mixture requires the use of different cohesive soils, then it is important to know the correlation between the components' and the resultant Atterberg limit. According to Dos Santos (1955), these values can be estimated without experimentation if the relevant data of the components are known. He claims that if the grain distribution curves and Atterberg limits of soils Nos 1 and 2 are known, then the Atterberg limits of the mixture can be obtained by means of the following formula:

$$x = \frac{A_1 a_1 w_{x1} + A_2 a_2 w_{x2}}{A_1 a_1 + A_2 a_2} \tag{35}$$

Here w_x means the Atterberg limit tested (w_L, w_p, or w_s), a is a quantity that can be calculated from the grain-distribution curve, while A indicates the percentage ratio of the individual components in the mixture.

95

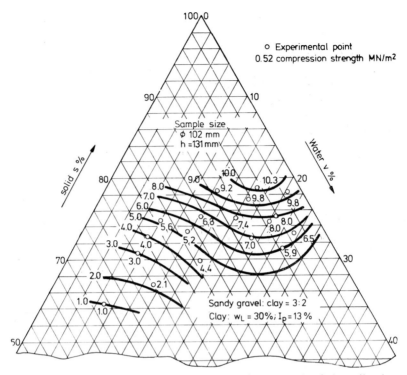

FIG. 65. Variation of the unconfined compression strength of the soil mixture as a function of the phase volume percentages

$$a = \frac{\sum\limits_1^n S_i\%}{100\,n} \tag{36}$$

where $S_i\%$ is the ordinate of the grain-size distribution curve, while n is the number of sections along one curve (see grain-size coefficient, Fig. 7).

The validity of the procedure described above has been verified by a number of experiments although it was found that a simple rating would supply similarly good approximate results if geologically and chemically common-origin soil types are mixed. For example, testing a mixture of the soils characterized by the data of Fig. 66, our calculation rendered the results indicated by the small squares. On the other hand, an experiment with that mixture gave the results indicated by circles. Both are very close to the straight line of simple rating:

$$w_x = \frac{A_1\,w_{x1} + A_2\,w_{x2}}{A_1 + A_2}$$

For the production of a soil of predetermined plastic index by mixing, Aichhorn (1957) has suggested the following method. First the plasticity indices I_{pa} and I_{pb} of the available components a and b, and the weight per cent of the particles smaller than $d = 0.4$ mm are determined. Let the latter be $S_a^{0.4}$ and $S_b^{0.4}$, respectively. Then the ratio

$$K = \frac{I_p - I_{pa}}{I_{pb} - I_p} = \frac{a\,S_b}{b\,S_a} \qquad (37)$$

is calculated, where I_p is the predetermined plasticity index of the mixture. Now soils a and b must be admixed according to the following weight percentages:

$$a\% = \frac{100\,S_b^{0.4}}{S_b^{0.4} + S_a^{0.4}\,K},$$

$$b\% = \frac{100\,S_a^{0.4}\,K}{S_b^{0.4} + S_a^{0.4}\,K} \qquad (38)$$

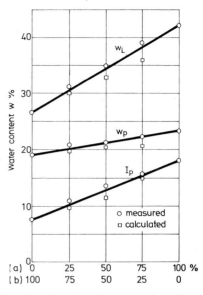

FIG. 66. Variation of the Atterberg limits of soil mixtures; comparison of the measured and calculated values

If, however, the mixing ratio and the plasticity indices of the components are known, then the plasticity index of the mixture can be determined by means of the following equation:

$$I_p = I_{pa} + \frac{S_b\,b}{S_a\,a + S_b\,b}\left(I_{pb} - I_{pa}\right) \qquad (39)$$

It can be seen that the method assumes (Eq. (37)) a simple rating between the plasticity index and the weight per cent of grains with diameter less than $d = 0.4$ mm diameter. This obviously only applies to soils having identical geological origin, so this method is limited. Aichhorn himself commented that when, for example, a lime-content type and a quartz sand were admixed, the plasticity index calculated from Eq. (39) could deviate to some extent from the actual figure.

It is interesting to note here that the mixtures of cohesive soils, too, reveal a physico-chemical analogy. In the course of phase-diagram studies, physics proved that if the structure and chemical characteristics of the molecules of two different components were almost identical, then the molecules could substitute each other, in both liquid and solid state. As a result, there is no eutectic point, and the melting point of the mixture varies continuously. This phenomenon is called isomorphism, and is exampled in Fig. 67. The above phenomenon observed with the Atterberg limits of cohesive soil mixtures is the soil physics equivalent of isomorphism. The liquid limit and plasticity limit of the mixture or, in other words, its porosity associated with a certain prespecified condition (which, according to earlier considerations, is a concept analogous to temperature !) can be calculated from the respective data of the two

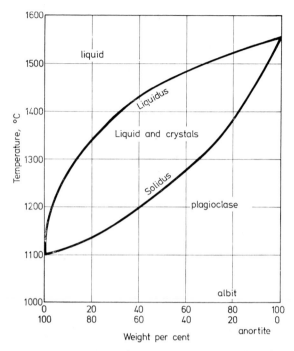

FIG. 67. Example on isomorphism; no eutectic point

components by a simple rating (Fig. 66), if the components are chemically similar, have a geologically common origin and, particularly, they do not exhibit significant differences in grain size.

However, if these conditions are not satisfied, then for the Atterberg limits only correlations which will give less reliable results are obtained, as in Fig. 47. The same was confirmed through experimentation by Seed et al. (1964), (see Kézdi: Handbook of Soil Mechanics).

On the basis of the results obtained by Seed, it can be shown that plotting on the sides of a triangle (see Fig. 68) the volume percentages of the relatively coarse fraction ($d > 0.002$ mm) of clay and water, and constructing the point (v_{fa}, $1 - v_{fa}$, 0) representing the liquid limit of the pure clay fraction, the liquid-limit values of the mixtures are represented by points on the streight line $\overline{OP}$. This straight line is given by the points (v_{fa}, $1 - v_{fa}$, 0) and (0, 100, 0).

This straight line only holds true up to the point where the liquid limit is governed by the clay fraction, i.e., the coarse grains swim in the clay-water matrix ($d \leq d_0$). Hence the liquid limit is constant, independent of the clay content, with a value corresponding to the triangle co-ordinates of point P'.

To illustrate the scope of the Atterberg limits in dealing with problems, Fig. 69 shows its variation in a sand-clay mixture, as a function of the mixing ratio. It is

98

remarkable that above a certain mixing ratio, the shrinkage limit exceeds the plastic limit. This means here that the sand particles have already formed a skeleton which can withstand the capillary compression forces.

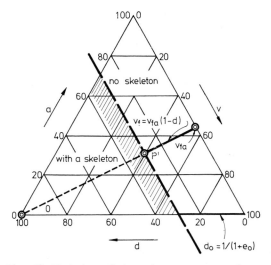

Fig. 68. Variation of the volume per cent values pertaining to the liquid limit point in the triangle diagram

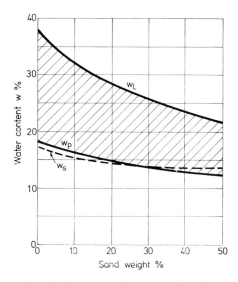

Fig. 69. Variation of the Atterberg limit of a sand-clay mixture as a function of the mixing ratio

3.5 Soil mixture behaviour with water effects

In connection with Fig. 65 it has already been mentioned that the water content and, of course, bulk density would greatly influence the strength of soil mixtures. We ourselves determine the water content during construction and by drying or wetting the soil may be made to have the specified water content for compaction. On subsequent effects, however, such as the penetration of precipitation from the surface, capillary absorption upwards or laterally from the ground water level, the water content may change significantly, in turn radically reducing soil strength.

Soaking effects are clearly illustrated by the experiences obtained when testing mechanically stabilized soil mixtures with the run-around machine (see Fig. 70). A mixture having favourable properties, meeting all relevant specifications, whose physical characteristics are presented in Fig. 71, remained load bearing even after 100 000 cycles and suffered insignificant indentations when worked into the test trough with an optimum water content of compaction ($w_{opt} = 7.7$ per cent, $\gamma_d^{max} = 2.18$ Mp/m^3, $w = 8$ per cent, $D_\gamma = 0.98$) (see the profilometer plotted section in Fig. 72a).

When the machine was started immediately after surface irrigation simulating a 15 mm precipitation, the previous traces were levelled out, and the water penetrated into the soil to a depth of only 2–3 mm, i.e. from water infiltration aspects the

Fig. 70. Soil mixture behaviour in a run-around machine test

100

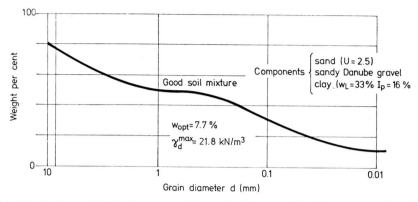

FIG. 71. Grain-size distribution curve of the soil mixture tested in the run-around machine

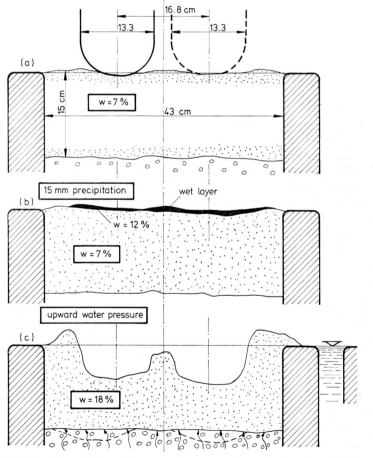

FIG. 72. Behaviour of the soil mixture in the test through (a) after 100 000 cycles
(b) surface precipitation effect; (c) upward water pressure effect from below

FIG. 73. The effect of moistening on the soil surface

soil behaviour was very favourable (Fig. 72b). However, the top layer was completely destroyed and large potholes were produced even after 25 or 30 cycles, when
the stabilized soil mixture was exposed to a water pressure from below by filling
the trough illustrated in Fig. 25 with water. This condition is shown in Fig. 72c,
while Fig. 73 presents the top layer in a good condition after the test with surface
irrigation, and Fig. 74 explains the effect of water pressure.

Thus water reduces stabilized soil strength through the following effects:

(a) Fill-up of the voids with water eliminates cohesion due to the capillary
stress;

(b) Owing to the hydration of the particles, the strength of the hydrogen bonds
connecting the particles decreases;

(c) With water molecules embedded into the lattice structure, the clay minerals
inclined to expansion and present in the binder break the coarse grains by expansion and so destroy the skeleton; this expansion reduces bulk density;

(d) Compression and expansion caused by wheels, loading and load release lead
to water movement; thus a pumping effect is exerted which, together with the
simultaneous shear stresses, destroys the various interparticle bonds and disintegrates the soil;

(e) In the case of frost, if water repletion should exist in the stabilized soil
mixtures generally considered as being frost susceptible; ice lenses will be produced,
and the consequent strain may further reduce the total mass cohesion;

(f) Under thaw conditions the water from the ice lenses is absorbed, the wet soil
is kneaded by the dynamic affect of traffic, thus decreasing its strength to zero.

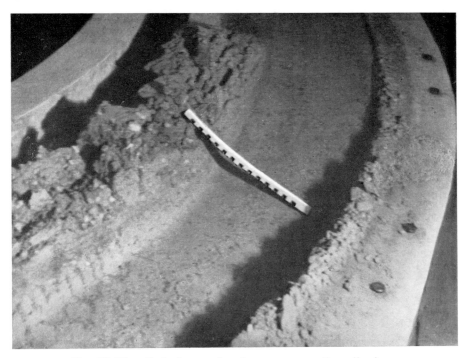

FIG. 74. The effect of upward water pressure on the soil mix

The above findings reveal that the simultaneous effects of water and traffic are of critical importance, as they destroy the soil mixture, i.e., the road. Above all, the extent of strength reduction due to capillary water absorption depends on the intensity of effects (a)–(c). As systematic experiments still have not been conducted in this field, Fig. 75 presents only one example on the strength decrease of a given soil mixture for various states of compaction, due to capillary saturation. Strength is here characterized by the CBR value of the mixture because, in a saturated condition, the uncon-

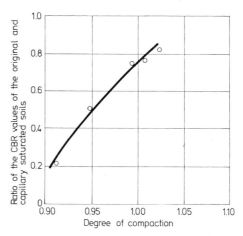

FIG. 75. Strength reduction of soil mixtures upon the effect of capillary absorption

fined compression strength may not have been determined in each case. The samples were always moulded in the CBR cylinder at maximum density using various compaction loads. The CBR values after capillary wetting were determined

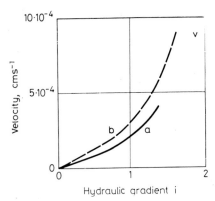

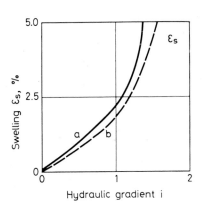

FIG. 76. Influence of the hydraulic gradient on the specific swelling of a silt.
a — dense, b — loose

FIG. 77. Change of phase composition during infiltration of water as function of time and depth

using special cylinders. This figure supports, in its numerical data, the qualitatively obvious statement that the strength reduction due to capillary saturation is greater, the lesser the initial density of the soil.

With cohesive soils, infiltration causes swelling; its amount depending on the initial phase composition and on the value of the hydraulic gradient (Fig. 76).

The process of infiltration in time is represented in Fig. 77.

Moisture infiltrating the soil depends on the capillary conductivity of the latter. Unfortunately, experiments aimed at determining capillary rise in soils are not suitable for describing the wetting process using the physical characteristics thus determined, so another method must be selected (Winterkorn 1963).

In a horizontal capillary tube, the movement is described by the Poiseuille equation:

$$\frac{\mathrm{d}x}{\mathrm{d}t} = \frac{r^2}{8\eta} \frac{\mathrm{d}p}{\mathrm{d}l} \tag{40}$$

where r is the capillary radius, η indicates the viscosity of the liquid, and $\mathrm{d}p/\mathrm{d}l$ represents the pressure gradient. If $r^2/4$ is substituted by

$$\frac{r^2}{4} = \left(\frac{r^2 \pi}{2r \pi}\right)^2 = \left(\frac{F}{K}\right)^2$$

where F is the capillary cross section and K its periphery, then the above equation will assume the following form:

$$\frac{\mathrm{d}x}{\mathrm{d}t} = \frac{1}{2\eta} \left(\frac{F}{K}\right)^2 \frac{\mathrm{d}p}{\mathrm{d}l} \tag{40a}$$

104

Here F/K may be regarded as the ratio of the void porosity and the internal moistened surface, if the numerator and the denominator are both multiplied by the
tube length h. If the pressure gradient is zero, then the liquid infiltration to the
soil is due to the capillary suction force, whose magnitude is $2r\pi\sigma \cos\alpha$. Assuming
$\cos\alpha = 1$, and that this force is uniformly distributed over the whole $r^2\pi$ cross
section, we get

$$\frac{2\pi\sigma r}{\pi r^2} = \frac{F}{K\sigma}$$

and for the pressure gradient

$$\frac{dp}{dl} = \frac{F}{K}\frac{\sigma}{x}$$

where x is the capillary length filled by the liquid. Thus Eq. (40a) may be written

$$\frac{dx}{dt} = \frac{1}{2\pi}\left(\frac{F}{K}\right)^2\frac{K}{F}\frac{\sigma}{x},$$

that is,

$$\frac{dx}{dt} = \frac{1}{2\eta}\frac{F}{K}\frac{\sigma}{x} \qquad (40b)$$

When the porous soil mass, i.e., the stabilized soil mix, contacts water which only
infiltrates the soil through the capillary-suction effect, one of three different situa-
tions can develop:

(a) the system remains integral, no disintegration takes place, and the value of
x will increase from zero to h, i.e., the full length of the capillary system;
(b) the wet particles peel off as scales, lamellae, or clods, and although wetting
progresses, the x value calculated from the temporary surface will remain approximately constant;
(c) water infiltration is followed by a slow decrease of the bond forces, and the
soil disintegrates.

In case (a), the differential equation can be solved directly: for the penetration
after a period t the equation

$$x = \sqrt{\frac{1}{\eta}\frac{F}{K}\sigma t} \qquad (41)$$

is obtained.
In case (b), the thickness of the layer peeled off by wetting depends on the size
of the secondary stable aggregates. If this value is d, we then get

$$\frac{dx}{dt} = \frac{1}{2\eta}\frac{F}{K}\frac{\sigma}{d}$$

105

and

$$x = \frac{1}{2\eta} \frac{F}{K} \frac{\sigma}{d} t \qquad (42)$$

To examine case (c), we introduce the following symbols:

τ = the time required for bond destruction,
x = linear water movement progress,
ξ = linear progress of the scale peel-off.

During the period τ, the water travels from the destroyed part a distance of $(x - \xi)$. Now x is the function of t, and ξ depends on $(t - \tau)$ and thus we may write

$$\frac{dx}{dt} = \frac{1}{2\eta} \frac{F}{K} \frac{\sigma}{\phi(t) - \phi(t - \tau)}$$

where $\phi(t) - \phi(t - \tau)$ is the length of the moistened soil section. Expanding the second term as a series we get

$$\phi(t - \tau) = \phi(t) - \phi'(t)\,\tau + \phi''(t)\,\frac{\tau^2}{2!} - + \cdots$$

while to a first approximation for a rapid-rate decomposition of the bonds,

$$\frac{dx}{dt} = \frac{1}{2\eta} \frac{F}{K\tau} \frac{\sigma}{\phi'(t)} = \frac{1}{2\eta} \frac{F}{K} \frac{\sigma}{\tau \dfrac{dx}{dt}}$$

giving

$$\left(\frac{dx}{dt}\right)^2 = \frac{1}{2\eta} \frac{F}{K} \frac{\sigma}{\tau}$$

and

$$x = \sqrt{\frac{1}{2\eta} \frac{F}{K} \frac{\sigma}{\tau}}\, t \qquad (43)$$

The equations thus obtained ((41), (42), and (43)) offer an interesting opportunity to compare the three cases. First it is found that the water infiltration rate depends on the porosity, the internal surface of the soil (F/K), viscosity and surface tension of the water, i.e., on its surface energy. (In porous media the energy of interaction between the internal soil surface and water should be considered with instead of the surface energy.) For some assumed values, the standard relation $x = f(t)$ for the three instances is shown in Fig. 78.

One more comment should be added to the above. When discussing the water infiltration to a dry or generally unsaturated soil, it must be taken into consideration that the pore space available for water movement is less than that calculated on the basis of the dry unit weight and the specific gravity, since at the initiation of water movement, part of the void space is occupied by internal water adsorption or internal expansion. If the latter exceeds the available pore space, then the entire soil mass will expand while disintegrating in water. If, on the other hand, the internal expansion exactly fills up the pore space, then the water infiltration will be rather slow. Experience shows that in dry soils the energy leading to water movement is closely correlated to the wetting heat, that is, the contact energy of the liquid medium and the internal soil surface. Accordingly, Eqs (41) and (42) may be written as

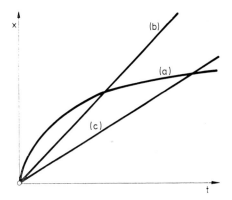

FIG. 78. Water-adsorption progress in soils (a) no disintegration; (b) the wet particles peel off; (c) soil disintegration resulting from the reduction of bond strength

$$x = \sqrt{\frac{1}{\eta} \frac{n_0}{f} Et} \qquad (41a)$$

and

$$x = \frac{1}{2\eta} \frac{n_0}{f} \frac{E}{d} t \qquad (42a)$$

where n_0 is the free pore space per unit volume,
f indicates the internal surface of the unit volume, and
E means the free energy variation per internal unit surface.

4. Stabilization with cement

4.1 Introduction

(Stabilization of soils with cement means the mixture of pulverized soil, cement, and water, and the compaction of this mix, producing a new building material, soil cement which, due to its strength, favourable deformation characteristics, resistance to water, thermal, and frost effects, etc., is well adaptable as a road pavement, road and building foundation, canal lining, etc.)

Although, on the basis of the above definition, concrete and cement mortar should also be considered as soil cements, there is a distinction. In these materials, there are barely any fine soil particles, the additive has a coarse-grain character, and the cement particles are usually assumed to surround the granular additive and bridge its particles, giving the considerable strength to the concrete. In the cement-stabilized soil, on the other hand, the individual cement particles are surrounded by fine soil grains, giving rise to much weaker bonds and, consequently, strength. In other words, in soil cement there are always certain fine-grain-soil varieties.

Stabilization by cement belongs to the stabilization category using foreign matter, where the effect of the chemical added is based partly on its interaction with the soil particles, and partly on its own properties.

Cement is the most generally and successfully used stabilizer. The very first cement-stabilized road was constructed in Johnsonville, (South Carolina, USA) in 1935, and is still in use. Cement stabilization has been applied since then to many million m² of road, airport, and other surfaces.

Cement-stabilized soils have five main types:

(1) *Soil cement*. This is the most general category, and the mixtures used for the construction of stabilized soil roads are usually in this class. They have to meet predetermined strength, durability, and frost resistance requirements, and can be used for the construction of the load-bearing layers of roads, bank reinforcement, parking lots and storage area cover, etc.

(2) *Cement-improved granular-soil mix*. This has less cement addition than the previous type, with the intention of altering certain soil characteristics, such as the reduction of expansion or contraction, plasticity, etc., and thereby the increase of load-bearing capacity. It can be used as a base layer under the flexible or rigid

108

pavement of higher-order roads. The measure of cement addition starts at 1 weight per cent.

(3) *Cement improved silt-clay mix.* Cement addition again has the intention of reducing expansion and contraction, whereby, under favourable water content conditions, the existing natural strength can be readily maintained. Cement addition is lesser than in the case of soil cement. It is often used for foundation-layer improvement.

(4) *Plastic soil cement.* This is a higher water content, plastic-state, mortar-consistency soil cement; it can be used for lining, ditches, and irrigation channels, and for their protection against erosion. This mixture which is easy to work in must satisfy strict strength and durability requirements and is therefore usually made of light sandy soils.

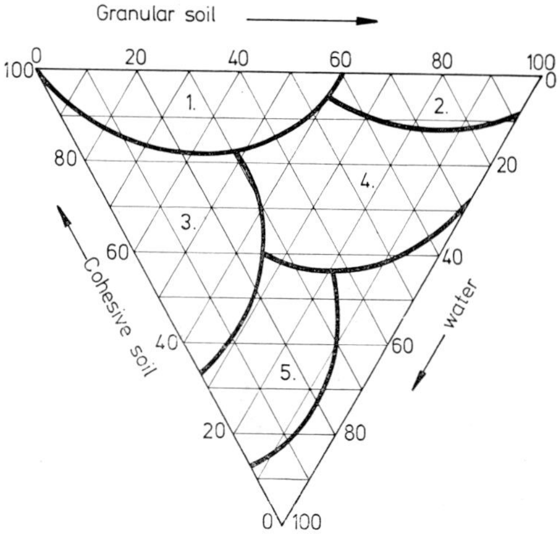

Fig. 79. Approximate percentage composition of the mixtures prepared by stabilization with cement. (1) soil cement; (2) cement-improved granular soil mix; (3) cement-improved silt-clay soil mix; (4) plastic soil cement; (5) cement-treated soil pastes and mortars

(5) *Cement-treated soil pastes and mortars.* These are high water-content, thick liquid mixtures usually containing other chemicals. They are used mainly for the injection of railways and road pavements.

The composition by volume of the substances categorized above, and their approximate grain-size distribution ranges are illustrated in Fig. 79.

Utilization of the various types is listed below:

Soil cement
— bases and base layer under rigid and flexible pavements; road pavements; bank reinforcement; parking and storage area, reservoir lining; slope (e.g. against surf effects) and trench protection; earth dam core; building foundations; frost protection;

Cement-improved granular mixtures
— foundations and basic layers under the rigid and flexible pavements of roads and runways, and for the repair thereof; erosion and frost protection;

Cement-improved cohesive soil mix
— strength increase by decreasing shrinkage and volume change; reduction of frost susceptibility;

Plastic soil cement
— trench, ditch, and irrigation canal linings, erosion protection.

The following sections deal mainly with the soil cement, since this is often used in the construction of stabilized soil roads.

4.2 Interaction between cement and soil

The interaction between cement and soil is usually described as follows, with particular respect to the fact that the role played by cement is different in mostly granular or cohesive soils.

In fine-grain silts and clays, the hydration of cement creates rather strong bonds between the various mineral substances, and forms a matrix which efficiently encloses the non-bonded soil particles. This matrix develops a cellular structure on whose strength that of the entire construction depends, since the strength of the clay particles within the matrix is rather low. Since this matrix pins the particles, the cement reduces plasticity on one hand, and increases shear strength on the other. The chemical surface effect of the cement reduces the water affinity of the clay and, thereby, the clay's water-retention capacity. Together with a strength increase, this results in the enclosure of the larger unstabilized grain aggregates which, therefore, cannot expand and will have improved frost resistance.

In granular soils the cementation effect is similar to that in concrete, the only difference being that the cement paste does not fill the voids of the additive, so that the latter is only cemented at the contact points (e.g. "spot welding", see Fig. 80). Thus no continuous matrix is formed, and the fracture type depends on whether the interparticle bond or the natural strength of the particles themselves is stronger. The better graded the grain distribution of a soil, the smaller the voids, and the greater the number and the larger the interparticle contact surfaces, the stronger the effect of cementation

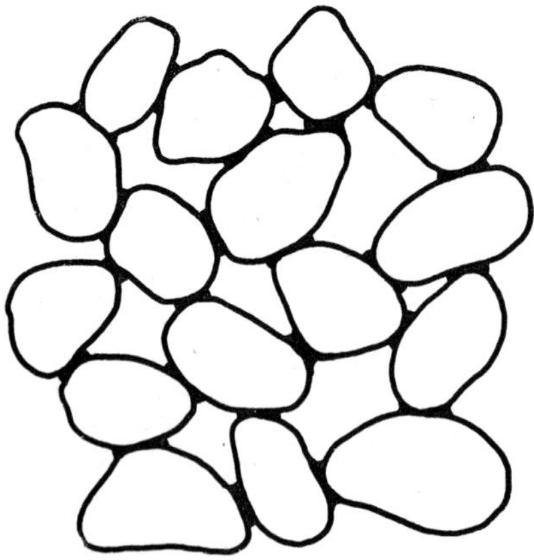

The latter explanation, although rather superficial, explains the relevant conditions seasonably correctly. The previous statements on cohesive soils, on the other hand, explain only one side of the question. In order to approximate the essentials of the problem, let us deal first with the bonding of a pure cement paste alone (Herzog and Mitchell 1963).

A dry Portland cement particle is a heterogeneous substance, containing minute

Fig. 80. Cementation effect around the contact points of the coarse grains

C_3S^*, C_4S, and C_3A crystals and a solid solution described as C_4AF. During the hydration of the cement the components react with water, so producing hydrated silicates, aluminates, and calcium hydroxide. According to Taylor (1961) and Brunauer (1964), the silicate and aluminate phases are internally mixed, so it is most likely that none is completely crystalline. Part of the $Ca(OH)_2$ may also be mixed with other hydrated phases, therefore being only partially crystalline.

The composition of hydrated cements is still not clearly defined by a chemical formula, so considerable variations are feasible. In the calcium silicate hydrate (CSH), for example, which is produced from C_3S and is the most important compound as regards strength production, the Ca : Si ratio varies between 0.8 and 1.33, while the CSH compounds resemble the natural tobermorite mineral. Taylor (1961) in his investigations treated the CSH compounds with water and lime solutions. In the presence of solutions rich in lime, the lime content of the CSH increased, while in the case of a low lime content of the solution it decreased. The pore water is, therefore, able to extract lime from the cement under hydration, if the lime content of the latter is rather small owing to the reaction with the clay.

According to Brunauer and Copeland (1964), the compounds in the Portland cement are transformed on the addition of water as follows:

$2(3CaO \cdot SiO_2)$ $+ 6H_2O$ $= 3CaO \cdot 2SiO_2 \cdot 3H_2O + 3Ca(OH)_2$
(tricalcium silicate)   (water)   (tobermorite gel)   (calcium hydroxide)

$2(2CaO \cdot SiO_2)$ $+ 4H_2O$ $= 3CaO \cdot 2SiO_2 \cdot 3H_2O + Ca(OH)_2$
(bicalcium silicate)   (water)   (tobermorite gel)   (calcium hyroxide)

$4CaO \cdot Al_2O_3 \cdot Fe_2O_3$ $+ 10H_2O + 2Ca(OH)_2$ $= 6CaO \cdot Al_2O_3 \cdot Fe_2O_3 \cdot 12H_2O$
(tetracalciumalumino-   (water)   (calcium   (calcium aluminoferrite hydrate)
ferrite)   hydroxide)

$3CaO \cdot Al_2O_3$ $+ 12H_2O + Ca(OH)_2$ $= 3CaO \cdot Al_2O_3 \cdot Ca(OH)_2 \cdot 12H_2O$
(tricalcium aluminate)   (water)   (calcium   (tetracalcium aluminate hydrate)
                             hydroxide)

$(3CaO \cdot Al_2O_3$ $+ 10H_2O + CaSO_4 \cdot$ $= 3CaO \cdot Al_2O_3 \cdot CaSO_4 \cdot 12H_2O$
(tricalcium aluminate) $\cdot 2H_2O$ (calcium monosulfoaluminate)
            (water)   (gypsum)

---

* According to the expressions of the cement chemistry: $C = CaO$, $S = SiO_2$, $A = Al_2O_3$, $F = Fe_2O_3$, and $H = H_2O$.

The first two equations whose materials constitute 75 per cent of the Portland cements, show that the hydration of the two calcium silicate types produces new compounds: lime and tobermorite gel, with the latter playing the leading role as regards strength, since bondage, strength, and volume variations are mainly governed by them.

Changes in the composition of the hydrated calcium silicates are not necessarily associated with those in their X-ray pattern. Regardless of the Ca : Si ratio of CSH, the X-ray pattern is similar to that of the tobermorite.

In order to have additional bonding forces produced in the cement-clay mixture, the silicates and aluminates in the material must be soluble. The solubility of the clay minerals is not such a well-defined process as is any other known phenomenon in connection with other chemical compounds. Solubility is equally affected by the impurities present, the crystallization degree of the materials involved, the grain size, etc. Acids generally separate aluminum and other metal oxides from the minerals, while the bases mainly dissolve the silicates, although the aluminates are also attacked by the high pH environment. Correns (1961) observed that small quantities of Al_2O_3 and SiO_2 of a montmorillonite or kaolinite origin dissolved, even in distilled water. Hashimoto and Jackson (1960) found that 3 per cent SiO_2 was dissolved from kaolinite, and 8 per cent from montmorillonite, both oven-dried, after boiling in 0.5 N NaOH. Thus, for clay minerals we may expect to increased dissolving with smaller grain size and degree of crystallization. The three-layer minerals, such as montmorillonite, dissolve much more readily than the duplex ones, such as kaolinite, since their specific surface is larger, and their resistance to cation penetration between the layers is lower. In the case of a high base-exchange capacity, certain cations which would have produced a cementation substance are bonded to the surface of the mineral. The other soil components present in addition to the clay minerals, particularly the amorphous silicates and aluminates of fine distribution, are much less resistant to the chemical effects, and will supply cementation substances playing, therefore, a significant role in cement stabilization.

During the hydration of the Portland cement lime is produced, so the interaction between the lime and the clay minerals may be expected to have a rather significant importance in the process of cement-clay interaction. Clay mineral and lime reactions may be classified into two groups: rapid rate (ion exchange and flocculation) and slow processes (carbonatization, puzzolanic reaction, and the production of new substances). These reactions are dealt with in detail when discussing lime stabilization, and so it will suffice to note here that after a rapid-rate flocculation or ion exchange, the lime left over after supplying the exchangeability of the clay is able to react with the clay minerals. These reaction products are amorphous but assume a crystalline form. (Incidentally, it should be noted that lime attacks montmorrillonite much more intensively than kaolinite.)

Based on the research results referred to, it is possible to elaborate the hypothesis on clay-cement interaction. First of all, a primary and a secondary process must be distinguished in the consolidation of the clay-cement mixture. The primary process includes hydrolysis and the hydration of the cement, in the course of which the usual hydration products appear, and the pH value of the water increases. The calcium hydroxide produced in this period ("in statu nascendi") can react much more strongly than ordinary lime.

Clay is important in the secondary processes. The calcium ions produced during cement hydration transform the clay first into calcium clay, and increase the intensity of the flocculation that had been initiated by the increased total electrolyte content due to cement addition. Calcium hydroxide then attacks, thereafter, the clay particles and the amorphous compound parts. Then the silicates and aluminates dissolved in the pore water will mix with the calcium ions, and additional cementing material is precipitated. The calcium hydroxide consumed during the course of the secondary processes is partly replaced by the lime produced by cement hydration. Thus the primary reaction products supply material for the continuation of the secondary processes.

During the secondary processes, the cementation substance are formed over the surface of the clay particles or in their immediate vicinity, causing the flocculated clay grains to be bonded at the contact points. Still stronger bonds may be created between the hydrating cement paste and the clay particles coating the cement grains. It is possible, furthermore, that the particles may be "integrated" (epitaxy) due to the identical structure of the clay minerals and certain cement-hydration products.

All this means that in the soil cement containing fine clay particles, "primary" and "secondary" cementing substances are formed. The primary products harden into high-strength additives and differ from the normal cement hydrated in concrete or mortar only by their lower lime content. The secondary processes increase the strength and durability of the soil cement by producting of an additional cementing substance to further enhance the bond strength between the particles.

Herzog and Mitchell conducted detailed experiments to verify this hypothesis, and the following paragraphs present some of their results.

Figure 81 illustrates the variation of the pH value during consolidation. The high pH value of samples containing hydrating cement may be attributed to the dissociation of OH^- ions from the $Ca(OH)_2$ produced during hydration. The pH value of the pure Portland cement, C_3S, and pure clay did not change with time in the given case, but that of the soil cement decreased, implying a process consuming OH^- ions during hardening.

The dependence of the pH value on the cement content is illustrated by our own experiments (Fig. 82). These experiments involved the following technique:

First, the required cement quantity was admixed to the air-dry pulverized soil, then 50 cm³ distilled water was added to 20 p thereof. The suspension thus obtained was left to settle for 24 hours in a hermetically sealed container, with only a few shake-up interruptions. After the last shake-up the suspension was sedimented, and the glass container of the pH electrometer was then filled up with the pure water by means of a pipette. The changes in two soil types (silt and sand) are shown in Fig. 82.

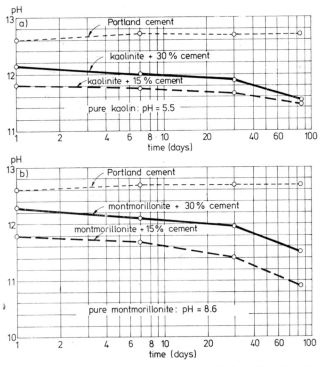

FIG. 81. The pH value of the mixture of clay minerals and Portland cement as a function of the treatment time. (a) Kaolinite experiments; (b) Montmorillonite experiments

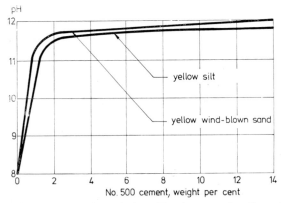

FIG. 82. Variation of the pH value as a function of the cement content

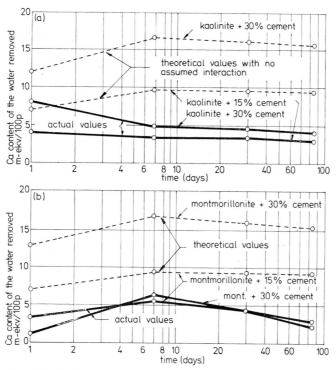

FIG. 83. Calcium content in the mixture of clay minerals and Portland cement, as a function of treatment time. (a) Kaolinite experiments; (b) Montmorillonite experiments

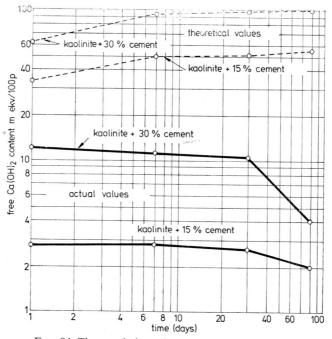

FIG. 84. Time variation of the free calcium content

Following the determination of the free calcium hydroxide content of the mixtures, the results presented in Fig. 83 were obtained. This figure illustrates, on the one hand, the theoretical values arrived at by measurement involving cement mortars under hydration, calculated with no assumption of interaction between cement and clay. On the other hand, the actual measurements revealed much lower values, justifying the assumption that the calcium produced during hydration but absent from the cement soil underwent a puzzolanic reaction with the clay, and certain interactions between the calcium and the clay minerals also took place. The same is confirmed by Fig. 84, illustrating the time variation of the free $Ca(OH)_2$ content. Again, a significant difference can be observed between the actual values and those calculated by neglecting the clay-cement interaction.

Based on the various experimental results, the structure of cement soils may be imagined as follows.

Since the cement particles compared to the clay grains are very large, a clay-cement skeleton and a clay matrix is most likely to form. The skeleton units contain a core each consisting of hydrated cement gel, to which layers made up of modified clay particles are added. Modification of the clay particles is brought about by the dissolution of the silicates and aluminates originating from the clay particles themselves and the amorphous components, in the high pH environment, caused by the highly reactive $Ca(OH)_2$. The material thus dissolved associates with calcium ions, producing additional cementation matter which, in turn, connect with the adjacent clay particles. The material around the cement grains create aggregates, packing some slightly modified clay in the space between the individual particles. In the case of montmorillonites the modified clay particles lose their volume-change characteristics.

Having understood the processes taking place in the cement soils, the conclusion that the larger the specific surface of a soil, the more cement is needed to reach the predetermined strength may be inferred.

4.3 Properties of cement-treated soils

4.3.1 Introduction]

The properties of cement-treated soil mixtures are developed by a number of factors, the most important being

(1) the quality and percentage of
– soil,
– cement, and
– water
per unit volume;
(2) the conditions following the hydration of the cement (temperature, moisture content, etc.);
(3) the age of the mixture.

116

Owing to the large number of alternatives and combinations, it is impossible to tabulate the various mechanical properties as functions of these factors, so the experimental determination is occasionally indispensable. There are, nevertheless, several tables and diagrams presented below on the various properties, but they only provide information outlining order-of-magnitude value, description of the various types, and illustrating the effect of cement-content variation on the other characteristics. These data are, therefore, of quite economical importance.

From road-construction aspects, the behaviour of cement-treated soils can be evaluated if the following characteristics are known:

- plasticity,
- compactibility,
- strength,
- volume change,
- deformation properties,
- water permeability,
- water adsorption,
- thermal properties,
- endurance, and
- frost resistance.

The factors resulting in these characteristics are, in addition to those under (1)–(3) above,

- mixing method and extent,
- compaction technique and degree,
- the time lag between mixing and compaction,
- the method and duration of post-treatment.

These are the characteristics and factors to be studied, but the correlations between them and the influence on the various characteristics of further additives will also be examined. The factors exerting an influence on the properties of cement soils are illustrated in Fig. 85.

We should make it clear here in the Introduction that the cement content of mixtures is usually expressed as a percentage of the soil's dry weight, although it is sometimes indicated, as under 2.11, as the percentage of the compacted mixture's total volume. These two data appear in the following relation (see Fig. 86):

$$c_v\% = 100 \frac{c_s\%}{100 + c_s\%} \frac{\gamma_d}{\gamma_c} \tag{44}$$

where

$c_v\%$ is the volume per cent of the cement related to the total volume of the soil cement;

$c_s\%$ is the weight per cent of the cement related to the dry weight of the soil,

γ_0 is the dry density of the soil cement in relation to the total volume (p/cm^3),

γ_c indicates the bulk density of the cement bulk (1.5 p/cm^3).

117

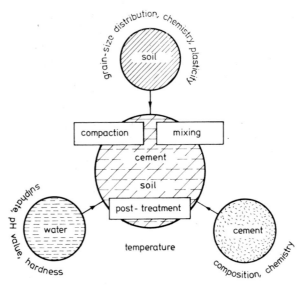

FIG. 85. Factors affecting the properties of cement soils

In practice, an easily adaptable figure is the required cement quantity expressed in kp/m², i.e. per m² of the road surface. If a surface layer of 15 cm thickness is assumed, this value is calculated as

$$q(\text{kp/m}^2) = 2.25 \, c_v\% = 150 \, \frac{c_s}{1 + c_s} \qquad (45)$$

and, if calculated for a thickness of 1 cm, we get a cement requirement of

$$q_1 = 0.15 \, c_v = 10 \, \gamma_0 \, \frac{c_s}{1 + c_s} \qquad (45a)$$

In Eqs (45) and (45a) the γ_d value should be substituted as a Mp³ dimension, with c_s as a ratio.

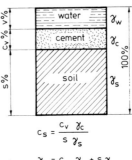

$$c_s = \frac{c_v \, \gamma_c}{s \, \gamma_s}$$

$$\gamma_d = c_v \, \gamma_c + s \, \gamma_s$$

FIG. 86. Correlation between the weight per cent and volume per cent values of cement

4.3.2 Strength characteristics

Cement soils are most frequently characterized by the unconfined compression strength, determined in Hungary by the fracture of either 4 cm ∅ and 6 cm height, or 10 cm ∅ and 15 cm height cylinders. In the United States 15 cm ∅ and 30 cm height cylinders, while in FRG cubes of a 7.07 cm edge length are usually used.

The compression-strength value can characterize the degree of soil-cement-water reaction and the progress of hardening; it is usually the empirical compression-strength value, on which basis the necessary cement quantity is determined. If the quantity of cement addition is determined according to behaviour during the frost-thaw experiment (see 2.13), then the unconfined compressive strength of the various soils will be within the range of Table 15. These data render satisfactory information in 90 per cent of the cases.

Table 15

Compressive strength of cement soils

Soil class	Soil type	Compressive strength kp/cm²	
		7 days	28 days
A-1 A-2 A-3	Sand + gravel	20 − 40	30 − 70
A-4 A-5	Silt	18 − 35	20 − 64
A-6 A-7	Clay	15 − 30	18 − 42

Table 16

Physical characteristics of the soils used in strength experiments

Soil	1	2	3	4
Liquid limit	16	17	28	26
Plasticity index	non-plastic	non-plastic	15	7
Optimum water content	9	10	12	15
Maximum bulk density, γ Mp/m³	2.10	2.07	1.96	1.80
AASHO soil class	1-b	2−4	6	4

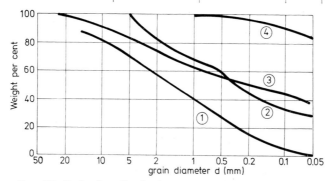

FIG. 87. Grain-size distribution curves of the soils used in strength and other experiments

119

Some examples on strength variation now follow, to illustrate the effect of the various factors.

Figure 87 presents the grain-size distribution curves of four different soils. Some other important characteristics of soil physics are presented in Table 16. The unconfined compression-strength values measured after 7, 28, and 90 days are illustrated as a function of the cement content by Fig. 88. With an increasing quantity of the fine particles the strength value would generally decrease, except in the case of soil No. 4, where certain chemical effects are most likely to be present.

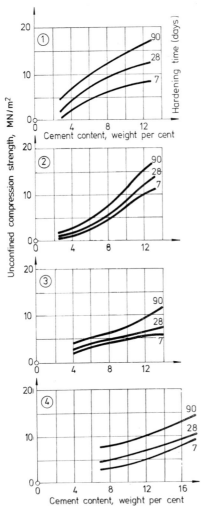

FIG. 88. Variation of the compression strength as a function of the cement content and the hardening time, in the case of 4 typical soils

The soil samples prepared for examination have been compacted to maximum density, at the optimum water content, so that they do not reflect sufficiently the effect of compaction, since their void ratio would be associated with a certain predetermined compaction effort. This is why Fig. 89 supplies a better review, giving a triangle diagram, for a given cement content (8 weight per cent, No. 500 Portland cement), in which the compression strength values measurable at 7 days can be seen. The sides of the triangle indicate the sand content ($d > 0.1$ mm), the Mo + silt content, and the volume percentage occupied by air and water. On the basis of this figure it is possible to readily determine the range in which a cement soil can be produced at all, and studied from strength aspects, and also a clear picture can be obtained on both the strength variations and the role played by compactness and water content. Similar information is offered by Fig. 90 where, again for a given cement content, strength has been plotted as a function of the soil-water-air volume percentages corresponding to Fig. 14. Further, this method of illustration informs on the optimum composition. The importance of compactness is stressed by Fig. 91. Here, a 10 per cent increase in the dry density has enhanced compression strength by 30 to 40 per cent. Figure 91 presents, in addition to our own experimental results, some findings reported in the literature. Density is correlated.

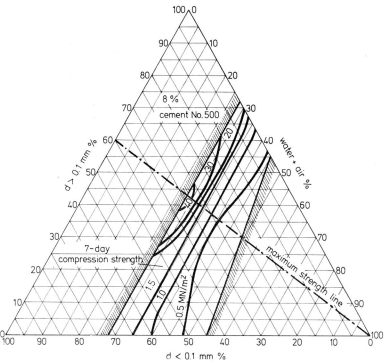

FIG. 89. Variation of the compressive strength
of soil cement as a functive of percentage composition, at an 8 per cent cement addition

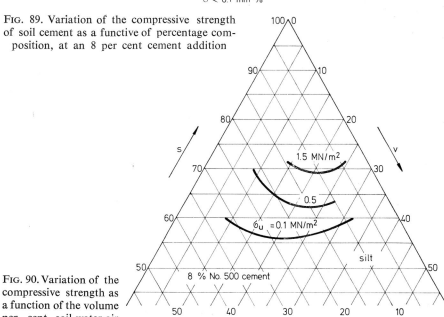

FIG. 90. Variation of the
compressive strength as
a function of the volume
per cent soil-water-air
distribution

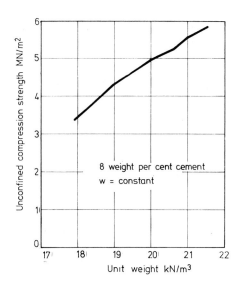

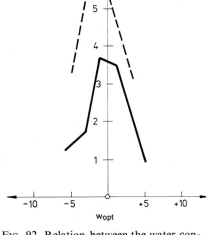

FIG. 91. Compression strength as a function of the unit weight

FIG. 92. Relation between the water content during moulding and the compression strength at identical compaction efforts

among others, to the effect caused by changing the water content during preparation. If throughout the production of the soil cement identical compaction energy is employed, then density depends on the water content according to the regularities of compaction. The compression strength values will exhibit a variation similar to the Proctor curve, with the single exception (Fig. 92) that the maximum compression strength is obtained at a w value somewhat lower than the optimum favourable compaction water content.

Interesting results are shown in Fig. 93, illustrating the strength, dry unit weight, and uniformity coefficient of two typical Hungarian soil mixtures as a function of the mixing ratio, for identical cement content. With respect to each of the three values, the optimum mixing ratio is the same as the highest strength, and unit weight figures are obtained where the U value is also the highest. There is also a clear correlation between the unconfined compressive strength and the uniformity coefficient, as shown in Fig. 93b, namely, the compression strength is identical at various mixing ratios if the U value is identical.

Information on the dependence of the strength of soil cement on the hardening time was given by Fig. 88, but Fig. 94 illustrates it in detail. Here the compression-strength variation of two soil types is shown as a function of the consolidation time, and it can be clearly seen that the log function of hardening is again valid or, in other words, strength can be illustrated by a straight line as a log function of the hardening time.

Since we are dealing with roads, we should remember that as far as the behaviour in the surface layer is concerned, the unconfined compression strength is not the only, nor even the primary, essential feature. Wheel load generates tensile and bending stresses in the cover layer (Chapter 8), and the load-bearing capacity of this type depends largely on whether it is capable to withstand them or not. With this idea in mind, detailed investigations have been conducted to determine the compression, tensile, and bending-tensile strength. These strength experiments and the Mohr circle of their stress states are shown in Fig. 95. In addition to the unconfined compression, the same samples were subjected to Brasilien tensile tests.

It is well known (Nagyváti 1958) that, accordingly, the values of cohesion, friction angle, and unconfined tensile strength may be calculated by using the following formulae:

$$c = \frac{\sigma_u}{2} \sqrt{\frac{\sigma_2}{\sigma_u - 3\sigma_2}}$$

$$\tan(45° - \Phi/2) = \sqrt{\frac{\sigma_2}{\sigma_u - 3\sigma_2}}$$

$$\sigma_t = \frac{\sigma_2}{\sigma_4 - 3\sigma_2} \sigma_4 \qquad (51)$$

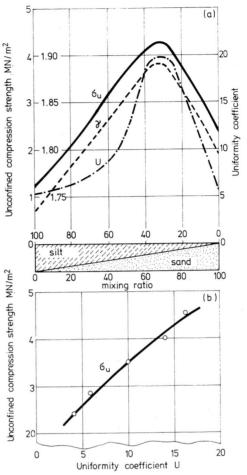

Fig. 93. (a) Compression strength, unit weight, and uniformity coefficient of soil cement vs. mixing ratio; (b) Compression strength vs. uniformity coefficient

In our work, the bending-tensile strength was determined by the bending test known from the practice of concrete testing using $5 \times 5 \times 30$ cm beams. The test results obtained with four different soil types are presented here. The grain-distribution curves of these soils are illustrated in Fig. 96, while the variations of the three strength values (σ_u, σ_{bt}, σ_t) as a function of the cement content can be surveyed in Fig. 97. These strength figures were determined after 7 days.

It may be stated that the strength values change, in most cases, in accordance with the cement content, and the ratios as a function of the cement content are almost constant. This in turn confirms that, within the cement-addition range test-

123

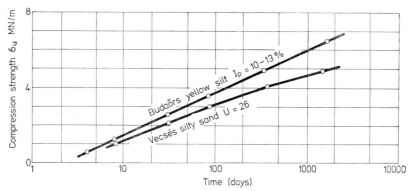

FIG. 94. Compression strength vs. of the hardening time

ed, the angle of the envelope of the Mohr circles (the "angle of friction") similarly has an almost constant value. The friction angle values, which can be readily calculated from the relation $\sigma_u/\sigma_t = \tan^2(45° + \Phi/2)$, are presented in Table 17, at a 10 per cent cement addition.

The finer the soil being stabilized, the larger the angle of friction and the relation of compression to tensile strength and, consequently, the lower the suitability of the soil thus stabilized for paving.

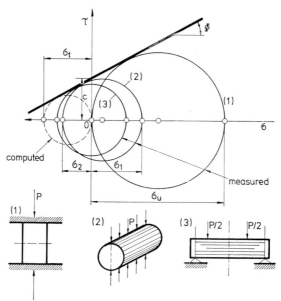

FIG. 95. Strength tests of the experimental series and the Mohr circles of their stress states

124

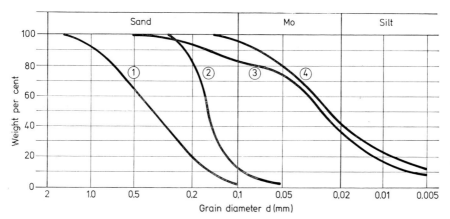

FIG. 96. Grain-size distribution curves of the soils used in the experiments

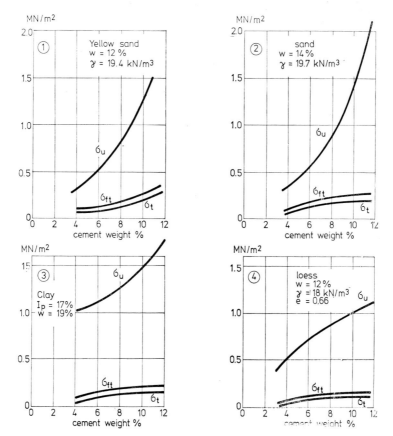

FIG. 97. Variation of the compression strength (σ_u), bending-tensile strength (σ_{ft}), and tensile strength (σ_t) as a function of the cement content

Table 17

Friction angle of cement-stabilized lean clay. Soil type: Budaőrs lean clay, $w_L = 33$ per cent, $I_p = 15$ per cent, $w = w_{opt} = 14$ to 16 per cent

Cement content weight %	Compression strength, kp/cm²	Tensile strength, kp/cm²	Friction angle, deg	NOTE
1.7	3.7	0.24	48.5	uncertain figure
3.3	6.1	0.45	37.0	uncertain figure
5,0	11.0	0.96	47.0	
6.7	14.7	1.45	47.4	
8.3	20.0	2.02	52.0	
10.0	24.3	2.60	54.0	

Figure 98 presents data slightly different from the above. Here the variations of the friction angle and cohesion are illustrated, on the basis of triaxial compression tests, as a function of the cement content. Accordingly, the greater amount of cement in the mixture, the greater the angle of friction, but cohesion will reach a maximum at a certain cement content. In the given case the soil was a well-graded gravel silt ($I_p = 7$ per cent).

The strength of the soil cement is influenced by the conditions prevailing during hardening. According to the experimental results obtained by Gáspár (1964a), the compressive strength figures exhibited by samples kept in a humid atmosphere during hardening and underwater revealed a difference of 20 to 30 per cent in the favour of the former. Figure 99 presents such an experimental result, while Fig. 100 illustrates the result of an experiment conducted in India (Chadda 1956): the compression strength values of two soils measured under dry and wet conditions display significant differences.

Frost effects, too, generally reduce strength. Thus after repeated freezing test cycles strength values 20 to 40 per cent lower are usually obtained. This reduction, however, decreases with increased cement content. Several experiments revealed that the strength of the specimen did not decrease even after 12 freezing cycles, if the cement addition exceeded 11 to 12 weight per cent.

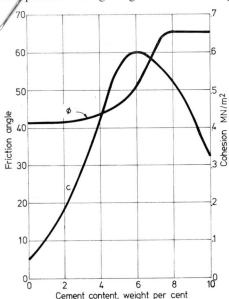

FIG. 98. Variation of the friction angle and cohesion of soil cement vs. cement content

126

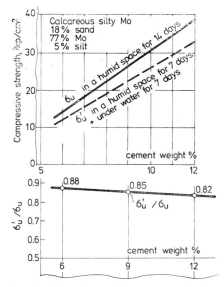

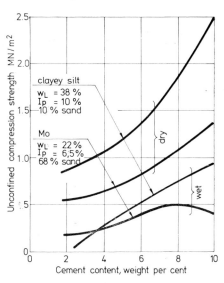

FIG. 99. The effect of the storage technique on the compression strength of the samples

FIG. 100. Unconfined compression strength figures under dry and wet conditions, respectively, vs. function of the cement content

4.3.3 Deformation characteristics

The deformation characteristics of soil cement also depend largely on the cement content. In Table 16 and Fig. 87 the Young modulus was determined for the four soil types described by their physical characteristics. Further, static elasticity modulus determination is shown in Fig. 101, while Fig. 101b illustrates the variation of the E value thus obtained with the cement content, for two of the four soil types mentioned.

The value of the dynamic elasticity modulus can be calculated if the rate of elastic wave propagation is known, and these data may be regarded as standard for high-speed vehicle traffic. Since, however, the speed of vehicles travelling along stabilized earth roads is slow, the static state should really be considered as standard. However, if we take into account the fact that the Young modulus is needed for pavement dimensioning, but the permanent load-bearing capacity depends on the behaviour of the pavement under repeated loading conditions, then we approximate best by determining the Young modulus by means of a consolidometer, that is, on the basis of repeated loading tests performed without lateral deformations. This technique is illustrated in Fig. 102. After the preselected hardening time, the soil sample is subjected to a load corresponding to its own weight, then stress due to the vehicle weight is applied for 1 sec. Thereafter the load is removed, the sample stress released for 1 sec, and the loading cycle repeated several times. The

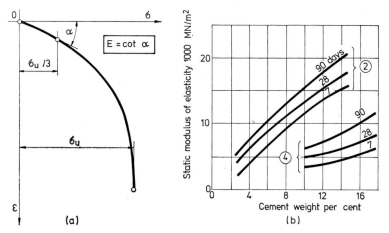

FIG. 101. (a) Determination of the static elasticity modulus, (b) values of the Young modulus for the soils described in Fig. 95 and Table 16

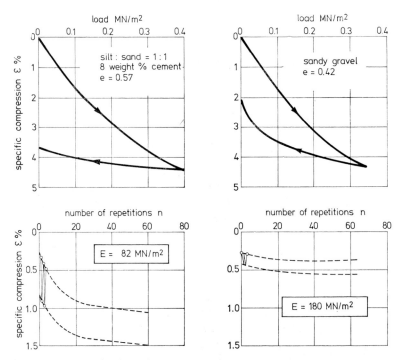

FIG. 102. Determination of the Young modulus on the basis of repeated loadings

deformations are measured precisely in each case. Figure 102 illustrates the results obtained with a sandy gravel and a soil cement produced with an equal-weight ratio mixture of silt and sand (8 per cent cement). This figure also indicates the loadings applied, but it should be noted here that if the total specific compression is plotted as a function of the log of the number of loading repetitions, then a straight line is obtained for both natural and stabilized soils (see Fig. 29).

Thus we may state that generally the Young modulus depends on the cement content, the age of the stabilized soil, and the nature of the test, and it should be emphasized that it is rather sensitive to the stresses applied. Informatory figures on cement-treated soils are given in Table 18.

Table 18

Young modulus of soil cement
Soil type: 3 to 1 sand and silt mixture

Cement content weight %	Compressive strength (kp/cm²)	Proportionality limit	E (kp/cm²) based on the first loading cycle
5.0	12.3	6.4	1790
6.7	19.6	10.0	2150
8.3	22.8	12.2	2630
10.0	30.2	17.2	3500

Another deformation characteristic is the Poisson ratio, which is indispensable if the stresses produced in soil cement are to be calculated on the basis of elasticity. Unfortunately, however, very few measurement data are available. Dynamic experiments involving the soils of Table 16 and Fig. 87 rendered the following results:

Granular soils Nos 1 and 2	$\mu = 0.22$–0.27
Clay soils No. 3	$\mu = 0.30$–0.36
Silty soils No. 4	$\mu = 0.24$–0.31.

4.3.4 Plasticity and volume change

(If a plastic soil is treated with cement, its plasticity index decreases. This effect is reflected by the different type of failure encountered in such cases, and by the increased Young modulus. Reduction of the plasticity index as a function of the cement content is illustrated in Fig. 103\ Here the data on the cement soil are the results of a test series completed with pulverized stabilized soil. This method usually consists of mixing the soil cement, compacting it in the standard way, then storing the specimen for 7 days, drying, and performing the Atterberg limit

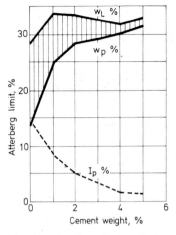

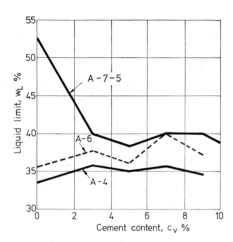

FIG. 103. Atterberg limit variations vs. cement content

FIG. 104. The effect of cement addition on the liquid limit of three different soils

test with the repulverized material. It is interesting to note that in the given soil the reduction of the I_p value was due mainly to the increased plastic limit. It may be, however, that the liquid limit would change to a similar, excessive extent. According to general findings, if the liquid limit of the natural soil exceeds 40 per cent, then the cement addition exerts decreasing effect, while if it is less than 40 per cent, then an increasing effect is observed, as verified by Fig. 104.

Figure 105 illustrates a rather interesting correlation, by presenting the plasticity index as a function of the hardening time.

The volume change of soil cement is of particular importance with respect to pavement cracking. Crack formation is a natural characteristic of cement soils, whose tendency to crack is definitely related to strength, although this relation is not yet fully understood. Small cracks occur rather densely, and wider ones further aspect to an equal extent. Hair-cracks, too, may appear and though they do not affect durability, they greatly reduce the tensile strength. Because of this inclination to cracking, and owing particularly to the development of hair-cracks, there is an opinion in the literature that a cement soil surface must not be regarded as a rigid pavement, e.g. concrete, since the cracks cause this layer to be almost as flexible as a Macadam road.

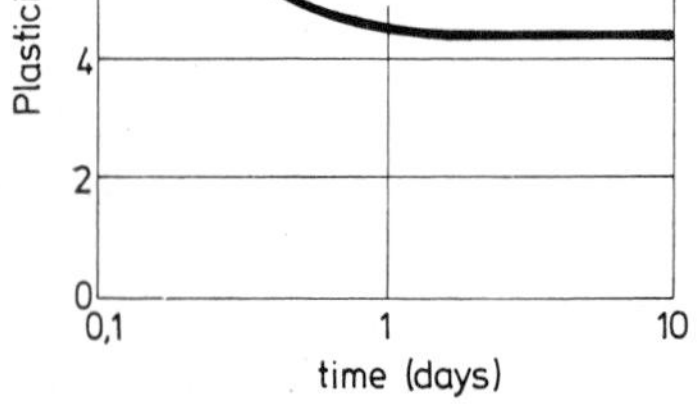

Apart from fractures due to loading, cracks are caused by volume changes which may be

FIG. 105. Plasticity index of soil cement vs. time

130

caused by three effects: water content or temperature changes, and freezing. If a cohesive soil is treated with cement, then the shrinkage due to water-content variation of the soil cement thus obtained will certainly be less than that of the original soil, as shrinkage decreases with increased cement content, owing to the development of a solid-cement matrix. If, on the other hand, cement is added to a soil which is not liable to volume change, the volume change of the product will be greater, because of the shrinkage during the cement hydration.

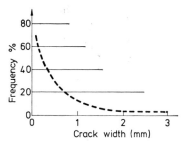

FIG. 106. Relation between the opening and frequency of cracks

Such cracks were formed in a cement soil road made of 8 per cent Mo content wind-blown sand ($U = 1.7$): the cracks formed perpendicularly to the axis of the road, at regular 8–10 m intervals.

As mentioned already, the extent of plastic soil shrinkage decreases with an increasing cement content. A higher cement content, however, also increases the tensile strength, whereby less frequent but wider cracks are produced in the surface layer. The same applies to the granular soils. The crack character depends, in addition, on the soil type. The volume change of clay is greater, but the cracks therein are smaller but more frequent. Crack opening and frequency measurements reveal an interesting correlation (see Fig. 106).

The volume change of soil cement is determined by the usual shrinkage test method through direct volume measurements. The relevant informative data on

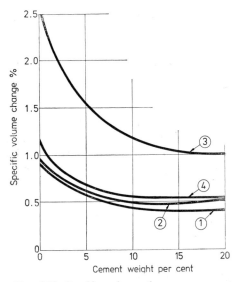

FIG. 107. Specific volume change vs. cement content

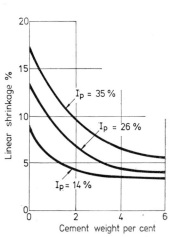

FIG. 108. Reduction of linear shrinkage upon the effect of cement addition

9*

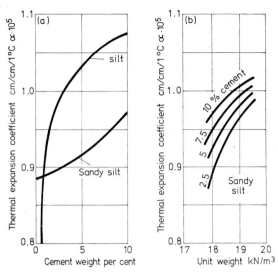

FIG. 109. The thermal expansion coefficient of cement soils as a function of cement addition and compactness

the soils discussed at length earlier (Table 16) are presented in Fig. 107, where cement addition is seen to reduce the specific volume variation to 50 or even 33 per cent. Figure 108 illustrates the reduction of linear shrinkage in three different cohesive soils.

Another reason for the volume change of cement soils is temperature variation, which has here the same effect as in any other material. According to measurements performed in India, the thermal expansion coefficient depends on the cement content and density. The character of the variation is illustrated in Fig. 109 for an ordinary and a sandy silt. The effect of density is shown in Fig. 109b.

The volume change due to frost effect also depends on the cement content. Here, however, the type of freezing is critical. Freezing may take place in a closed system, when there is no water addition during the course of the freezing process (the soil is tested in such a closed system by the freezing experiment under 2.13), or in an open system, when water may reach the sample while exposed to freezing. The quality specifications of cement soils do not permit a volume change of more than 2 per cent during 12 cycles of the freezing test. Experience shows that the soil cement usually meets the strength requirements satisfactorily from volume change aspects.

4.3.5 Behaviour due to water effects

Behaviour in connection with water is particularly important since, if the cement soil has an excessive water permeability, then water movement is caused by the effect of traffic, i.e. the wheels rolling along, the high-speed loadings and load-release instances, thus the traffic brings about a pumping action. This water movement breaks down the intergranular cement bonds, and strength rapidly decreases. The extent of water uptake is similarly important, partly because of the effect above, and partly with respect to the frost effect.

Table 19

Compression strength of cement soils
as a function of the post-treatment temperature

Temperature	Unconfined compressive strength, kp/cm²		
	3 days	7 days	28 days
Humid, 10 °C	10.6	20.2	29.8
Humid, 22 °C	15.6	22.5	35.0
Humid, 40 °C	20.5	29.8	42.4

The permeability coefficients of two soil types compacted as normal are shown in Fig. 110, illustrating that the k value can be readily decreased by several orders of magnitude.

Few data on the water adsorption of cement soils are available, and Fig. 111 only presents information on the water uptake of a yellow silt as a function of the cement content and time.

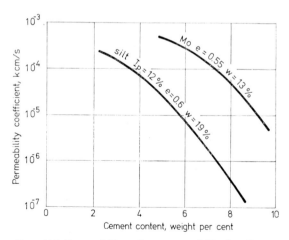

FIG. 110. Permeability of cement stabilized soils as a
function of the cement content

133

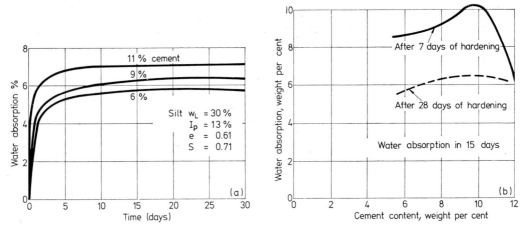

FIG. 111. Water adsorption as a function of cement content and time

4.3.6 Optimum water content of compaction and maximum dry density

With respect to the compaction of soil cement, the most important factors are the optimum moisture content and the maximum dry unit weight. Generally these two data can be said to vary only slightly from the w_{opt} and γ_0^{max} figures obtained with the untreated basic soils. With a cement addition, the γ_0^{max} value would be

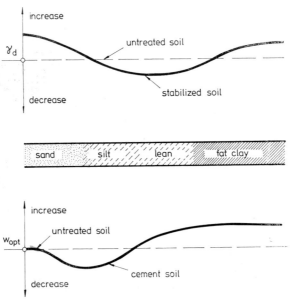

FIG. 112. The effect of cement addition on the compaction characteristics

somewhat higher for sands, it does not change if light or medium clays are involved, it increases slightly with fat clays, and there is a slight decrease in silts. Small changes can also be observed in the optimum water content of compaction (Fig. 112).

As another consequence of cement addition, the soil is much more sensitive to water effects, i.e. the two branches of the Proctor curve run much closer to each other than in the case of untreated soils and, therefore, certain specified dry densities are attainable over a much narrower water-content range (Fig. 113).

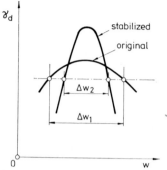

FIG. 113. Difference between the Proctor curves of untreated soil and soil cement

4.4 Effects of construction process and additives on the properties of cement-treated soils

For the production of a soil cement, first the in-situ available soil must be pull verized, then mixed with cement and, perhaps, with other additives (soils) as wel as water, and the mixture compacted. After the construction of the road profile the surface needs further treatment. Since all these operations affect the quality of the cement soils, they will be dealt with here.

Pulverization is particularly important in the case of cohesive soils, where the extent of this process determines the feasible degree of mixing.

So far we have been examined how far pulverization would influence the frost resistance and compression strength of the soil cement. In a test, three soil samples (silt $I_p = 9$ per cent, lean clay $I_p = 17$ per cent, and clay $I_p = 23$ per cent) were supplemented after complete pulverization ($p = 100$ per cent according to Eq. (22), that is, the samples did not contain greater than 5 mm particles) with 5 to 10 mm clods in an increasing weight per cent, and only then were cement and water added. Mixing was identical in each case, and most of the clods added remained intact. In one experimental series the clods were dry, while in the other the water content of the soil used for the production of the clods was the same as that of the stabilized mixture.

The amount of water added was identical in relation to the total dry weight of the mix, but its distribution varied: in the first case dry clods were embedded in a wet material, whereas in the second instance the water content was quite uniform. The mixtures were then used for the preparation of 10 cm diameter and 15 cm height cylindrical samples, always with the same compactive effort. Some of the samples were subject to freezing, the others to compression test. Cement addition was constant in each case. Accordingly, only the percentage quantity of the coarse clods varied between the sample types.

The test results are illustrated in Figs 114 and 115.

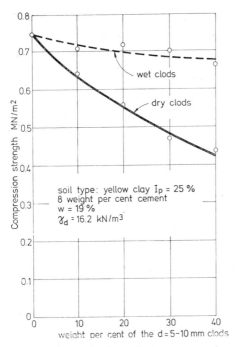

FIG. 114. Reduction of the compression strength as a function of weight percentage of clods

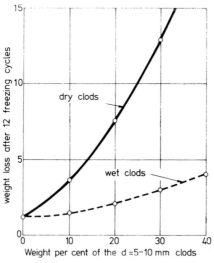

FIG. 115. Weight losses suffered in 12 freezing cycles, as a function of the weight percentage of coarse clods

Figure 114 illustrates the reduction of the compression strength: here particularly the presence of dry clods seems to have a detrimental effect, although whenever the water content of the soil in the in-situ condition is less than the optimum water content of compaction or, in other words, if water must be added to the mixture before compaction, then this situation prevails since the surface of the non-disintegrated clods are only soaked slightly but they remain dry internally.

Figure 115 reveals the weight loss of the cylinders after 12 freezing cycles. Insufficient pulverization has again led to serious consequences.

These results lead to the conclusion that it is a mistake to carry out under laboratory conditions exaggerated pulverization which cannot be performe on the site and to perform the strength, freezing, etc., experiments with the material thus obtained, because the results will deviate from the feasible safety figures. In-situ pulverization and mixing, on the other hand, should endeavour to prevent the clods left in the soil from remaining dry, otherwise the quality of the soil cement will be extremely poor.

After pulverization, the soil should be mixed with the cement in dry condition. The usual criterion for assessing whether mixing has been satisfactory or not is an entirely uniform mix colour. The success of mixing depends on efficiency and length. Instead of the subjective evaluation of mix-colour uniformity, in Great Britain experiences prefer to express the efficiency of mixing is preferably expressed by means of the following equation:

$$K_h^{\%} = \frac{\sigma_u^{\text{field}}}{\sigma_u^{\text{labor}}} \cdot 100 \qquad (52)$$

where σ_u^{field} is the in-situ compression strength on the 7-day old soil compacted by the available building machinery after a mixture conforming to the construction requirements;

σ_u^{labor} 7-day unconfined compression strength of a sample from the in-situ mix, in compact condition after continued laboratory mixing.

Experience shows that under average conditions a $K_h = 60$ per cent value can be readily obtained. For a predetermined strength value at a low K_h a larger cement quantity is required.

An unpleasant type of unequal mixing results when the cement is not distributed evenly in the vertical direction. This may be due an unsuitable mixer or soil, and the situation may only be remedied by replacing the machine or, perhaps, by changing the technology. Such an uneven mixing is exampled in Fig. 116. The great drawback here is the increased shrinkage of the top cement-rich layer, while the low strength of the under layer, very poor in cement, will result in an insufficient load-bearing capacity of the cover layer.

In addition to the soil type and water content, the efficiency of mixing depends on the mixing time. An increased wet-mixing time usually increases the optimum water content of compaction, reduces the compression strength, and increase the weight losses measured during freezing and endurance tests: thus its effect is undesirable in every way. The actual effect depends on many factors. Variation in the optimum water-content value seldom exceeds 1 or 2 per cent, whereas the difference observed in the freezing experiments may be much greater. A relevant example involving three different soil types is presented in Fig. 117, also indicating the soil type symbols.

Studies on cement hardening and certain in-situ experiences gave rise to the idea that the compression strength of the mix could be increased by waiting between wet mixing and compaction. In such cases consolidation can even start during this rest period, while in the course of compaction the clinker covers under

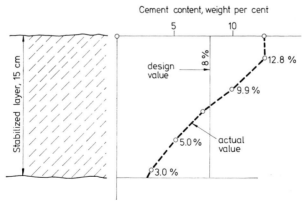

FIG. 116. Distribution of the cement within the thickness of a stabilized soil layer

development would be torn off and prepared for further hydration. This is all be reflected by an increased strength. Although Hungarian experiments (Quirico 1953) support this assumption (see Fig. 118, where the compression strength is plotted vs. the time lag between the completion of wet mixing and the beginning of compaction), it still does not seem to be generally valid: Marshall (1954) claims that this waiting period would lead to strength reduction in the case of several soil types (Fig. 119). Similarly, Marshall demonstrated that uninterrupted mixing

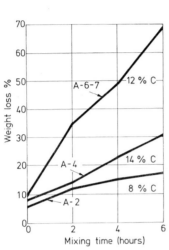

FIG. 117. The effect of mixing time on the weight loss measured in the freezing test

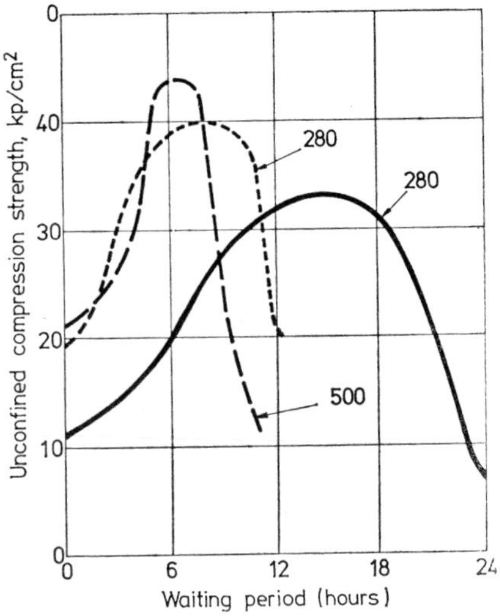

FIG. 118. The effect of the rest period on the strength of cement soil mixtures

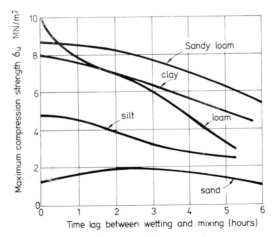

FIG. 119. Effect of the waiting period on compression strength, according to Marshall (1954)

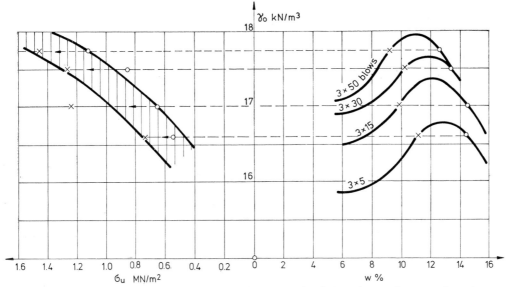

FIG. 120. For granular soils, the compression strength of the mixture does not depend on the degree of compaction alone

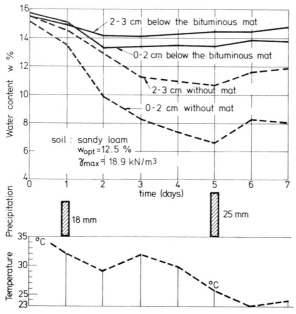

FIG. 121. Variation of the water content in the soil cement during the post-treatment period

was far less detrimental than with an intermediate wait. This detrimental effect, however, can be readily eliminated if compactness is increased to the level of the nowait process, by increasing the compaction energy.

The method and extent of compaction is rather important as regards the resultant compactness or dry density. In the case of heavy soils the water content during production has a similar importance, particularly as the layout and location of the particles is also quite significant, and under identical compactness but different water content conditions and different compression strength values may result from this structural difference. The strength of coarse sands is determined exclusively by the dry density achieved. All what the water content during production does is to influence, among others, the dry density. The two points of the Proctor curve where $\gamma_d = $ const. have identical strength values associated with them, but in fine sands certain differences occur (Fig. 120).

When compaction is completed, the cement soil is subject to further treatment to provide a wet environment, as in the case of concrete. This treatment period is a minimum of seven days. When the various characteristics of the cement soils are referred to, it is always assumed that during this period there is sufficient water content for the completion of the hardening process. For this purpose the fresh surface must be covered, after consolidation has begun, by a loose material such as straw, foliage, reed, earth, etc., kept in a wet condition throughout. Another way is to cover the surface with a water-proof protective coating, usually bituminous, which then keeps the water in the pavement. The efficiency of these coatings is illustrated numerically in Fig. 121.

Finally, let us sum up how much temperature affects the soil cement. According to British research results, at a temperature of about 25 °C the 7-day strength value would increase with 2 or 2.5 per cent for every further 1 °C during the post-treatment period. Thus if the quality specification of the cement soil requires a certain predetermined strength level, under high temperature conditions less cement is needed. Hardening, however, also takes place under cold climatic conditions, provided that the temperature remains above 0 °C. In such cases, the strength eventually reaches the level arrived at more rapidly in hot weather.

In order to improve the strength and other properties of the cement soils, small quantities of various chemicals have always been used. Very favourable effects were observed upon the addition of certain compounds of the alkali metals (sodium, potassium, lithium), but experimention also involved other substances. With many of them it is a distinct advantage that the desired effect can be secured even by the addition of very small specific quantities. Lambe et al. (1960) conducted detailed examinations with alkali metals and found that

(1) the addition of 1 to 4 weight per cent of the hydroxides and various salts of the alkali metals would greatly increase the compression strength (Fig. 122);
(2) each of the sodium compounds of a favourable effect produced with potassium certain rather insoluble salts; particularly the sodium hydroxide, carbonate, sulphite, sulphate, metasilicate, and aluminate proved to be highly efficient;

140

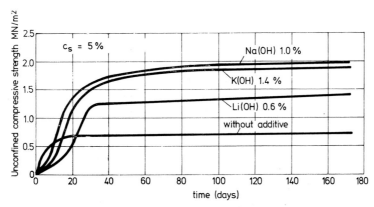

FIG. 122. The effect of alkali metal hydroxides on the compression strength
of cement-stabilized silt

(3) the efficiency of the sodium compounds depended on the soil type involved;
the higher the plastic index or the organic matter content, the lower the efficiency;

(4) the effect of the individual sodium compounds exhibited the following
features:

— sodium hydroxide was always efficient in soils having a low organic matter
content;

— sodium metasilicate was most efficient in pure sands;

— sodium sulphate had particular advantage in sandy soils of appreciable
organic matter content;

— the sodium salts of weak acids were inefficient in rich clays;

— in silts, the effect of the different sodium compounds decreased in the following order: sulphate — aluminate — metasilicate — carbonate — hydroxide —
sulphite;

(5) Optimum concentration would be the 1.0 normal value of the alkali in the
water admixed; higher concentrations led to the same final strength but retarded
consolidation;

(6) the efficiency of the additives depended on the amount of reactive silicate
in the soil (Fig. 123);

(7) the best results could be achieved by the simultaneous addition of the compound and the cement to the soil;

(8) compound addition increased the strength particularly at the beginning of
the hardening period.

The same authors explain these favourable effects in the following way:

When cement is mixed with soil and water, and then during the hydration of
the cement, calcium, calcium silicate, and calcium aluminate are produced in that
order. Reaction of the calcium with the reactive silicates and aluminates of the
soil results in the production of additional calcium silicate and aluminate, with

141

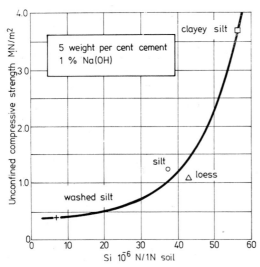

FIG. 123. The effect of extractable silicate content on the compressive strength of a soil cement- [treated with 1 per cent sodium hydroxide

decreasing pH. The end products of the reaction between soil and cement are hydrated aluminates and a calcium-silicate gel of a low Ca : Si ratio.

If an alkali metal compound such as caustic soda, sodium sulphite, etc., is present during the consolidation process, then the calcium-ion concentration in the solution decreases considerably, due partly to an ordinary ion exchange, and partly by the caustic reaction $Na_2X + Ca(OH)_2 \rightarrow \rightarrow CaX + 2Na(OH)$.

At the same time the hydroxyl-ion concentration, i.e., the pH value increases greatly. The reduced calcium concentration may delay the precipitation of the insoluble calcium silicate gel, while the pH increase certainly accelerate the formation of soluble alkali silicates and aluminates. The alkali silicates are present in the entire soil mass in a uniform distribution via the pore water. Thus the reaction between the free alkali and the soil again decreases the pH value and the calcium ion, too, enters into the solution. Reaction between the calcium and the alkali silicates and aluminates uniformly distributed in the pore water then leads to the production of a mixed calcium–sodium–silicate matter, and to gel formation, the quantity of which exceeds that produced when only cement is added, and this explains the favourable effect of the alkali metal compounds.

In Fig. 124 some of our own experimental results illustrate the strength-increasing effect of sodium sulphite.

Other cement soil additives include calcium chloride, bitumen, and bitumen emulsions.

Calcium chloride addition, too, can increase the compression strength to a certain degree, as shown in Fig. 125. The optimum additive quantity is about 0.6 per cent of both the immediate and long-term effects are considered. In many soil types, on the other hand, calcium chloride does not exert such an effect, but accelerates hardening.

The strength-increasing effect of the various additives is also quite significant from economic aspects, since the same specified strength can be achieved when using such additives with a much lower cement consumption. Numerical data of the economics are presented in Table 20.

The addition of bitumen emulsion was experimented with in Great Britain (Lawrance 1948). The emulsion formulated specially for this purpose remained

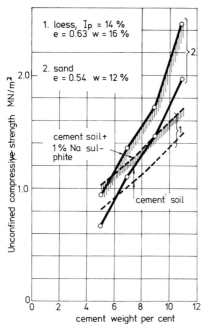

FIG. 124. The effect of sodium sulphite on the strength of cement soils

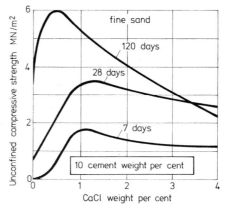

FIG. 125. The effect of calcium chloride on the compression strength of cement-stabilized organic sand

stable for a short while when admixed to a fine grain soil type, all owing the bitumen to be evenly distributed in the soil. The cement added thereafter had three duties: to break up the emulsion, to absorb certain part of the moisture released by hydration, and to increase

Table 20

Data on the cost reducing effect of strength-increasing additives

Soil	Cement weight %	Additive	Additive quantity weight %	Relative cement-additive cost	Savings per cent
Silt	11.0	—	—	1.00	—
	7.5	NaOH	0.9	0.98	2
	6.5	Na_2CO_3	1.0	0.81	19
	5.0	Na_2SO_4	0.8	0.54	42
Silty sand	13.0	—	—	1.0	—
	7.0	Na_2SiO_3	1.0	0.96	4
	10.5	$CaCl_2$	0.6	0.89	11
	9.0	NaOH	0.5	0.86	14
	9.5	Na_2SO_4	0.5	0.81	19
Silty clay	18.5	—	—	1.0	—
	13.0	NaOH	1.0	0.81	19

the strength of the soil thus treated and compacted. According to the results collected, about 5 to 7.5 per cent emulsion and 3 to 5 per cent cement had to be added in order to achieve a favourable effect. The "end product" was something between the cement and bitumen soils: slightly rigid and rather water impermeable.

143

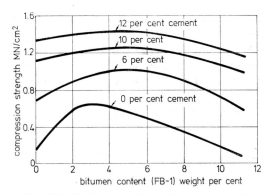

FIG. 126. Variation of the confined compression strength of loess as a function of the bitumen and cement contents ($w = w_{\text{opt}} = 9$ per cent)

Experiments involving bitumen addition were conducted in the Soviet Union (Bezruk-Knazyuk 1951) and in Hungary (Quirico 1953). The latter revealed a favourable effect upon liquid-bitumen addition up to a maximum of 6 per cent, while the compression strength as a function of the cement and bitumen contents developed according to Fig. 126. This confirms that cement hardening was not prevented by the bitumen addition.

4.5 Design and testing of soil-cement mixtures

Following the correct selection of the stabilizer, the process of stabilized earth-road design is made up of three steps, in addition to the usual road-construction design work. First the required thickness of the stabilized layer must be determined. As it will be seen in Chapter 8, this depends partly on the mechanical equipment employed, and partly on the traffic and load-bearing requirements of the complete pavement containing the stabilized layer. Next the composition of the mixture must be specified, and finally the construction, compaction, and post-treatment specifications have to be elaborated. The present Chapter deals with the second step, that is, how to design soil cement mixtures, whereas the first and third problems are discussed in Chapter 8. However, before dealing with the mixtures themselves, the problems of how to determine the various properties of the individual components (soil, cement and water), most critical from a stabilization viewpoint, must be settled.

4.5.1 Examination of the soil-cement components

The design of cement stabilization must be preceded by the exploration and sampling of the soil concerned (see Chapter 8). Generally the following physical characteristics of the samples must be determined under laboratory conditions:

— grain-size distribution curve,
— liquid and plastic limits, and perhaps the shrinkage limit,
— the optimum water content of compaction and the associated dry density,
— the water content and void ratio of the undisturbed sample.

If there is any as to doubt whether the soil is suitable for the purpose from chemical aspects, the following properties must also be determined:

— sulphate content (SO_3),
— magnesium salt content,
— calcium and organic matter content,
— hydrogen ion concentration (pH),
— eventually, the examination of the clay mineral involved.

These are the material properties from which it is possible to decide whether or not the soil is suitable for stabilization by cement. Hungarian experience shows

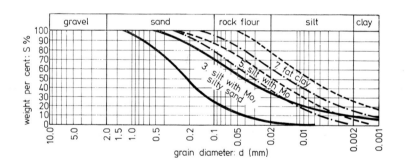

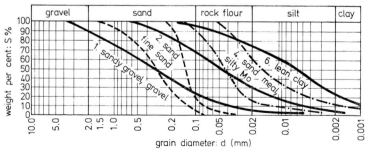

Fig. 127. The grain-size distribution curve range of soils suitable for cement stabilization according to Hungarian experiments

sand, silty sand, Mo, silty Mo, silt, and lean clay to be suitable. The grain distribution curve range of these standard soils is presented in Fig. 127, while the same is shown in triangle diagram form in Fig. 128, also presenting the position of the cohesive soils involved (types Nos 3–5) in the Casagrande diagram (see Table 21). If the characteristics of the soil under test are in the given range, then the next step is to determine the amount of cement to be added. Of the soil types illustrated, those marked by Nos 2–6 can be cement stabilized.

Table 21

Physical characteristics of soils
suitable for soil cement road-construction purposes

Type	Soil	Weight %		I_p %	Permissible maximum volume change %	NOTE
		d-0.1	d-0.005			
		(mm)				
1	Sand, fine sand	0	0	–	2	Excessive cement demand
2	Mo-sand, silty sand	20–70	0	–	2	Favourable
3	Mo, silty Mo	60–90	5–20	7	2	Favourable
4	Silt with Mo and ordinary silts	90–100	30	7–15	2	Intensive pulverization required
5	Lean clay	100	35	15–20	2	Sensitive to frost

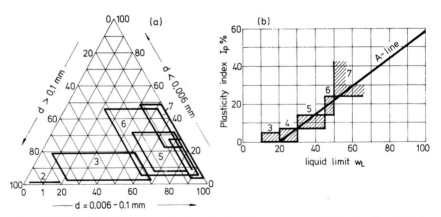

FIG. 128. Typical soil ranges (a) in triangle-diagram form; (b) in the Casagrande plasticity diagram

The required cement content depends, among others, on the quality of the cement. For cement stabilization only but Portland cement is used, in general. Based on their strength, the Hungarian Portland cements are classified into four categories, indicated by the compression-strength limit values of a 28-day old specimen made of standardized moist mortar (MNOSZ-523), and are Nos 600, 500, 400 and 300 (MNOSZ 4702-56). The strength of the Portland cement standard mortar samples must not be below that shown in the data presented in Table 22.

Among the various cement types, those of a low strength contain more filler. This has given rise to the idea (Gáspár 1959) that they can be best used for the stabilization of uniform grain size fine sands since, in such cases, a few per cent of a fine-grain must also be in the mixture to reach the required sttength. However, it is another question whether it is worthwhile to purchase, transport, and work-in the missing fine fraction in the form of cement knowing the local conditions. Often it is much more economical to admix a local material for the replacement of the fine grain fraction, though extra mixing work may be needed.

An argument in the favour of using lower strength cement is that the larger quantity required can be admixed much more readily. This argument, however, is not fully supported by experience: the difference between the two cement quantities is usually not great enough to represent a significant difference in mixing.

For the preparation of the stabilization schedule, the hardening time of the cement must also be known since the mixture would have to be worked in before the completion of the hardening period.

As for the water quality, experience proves that sweet, drinking water is always suitable for cement stabilization purposes, while mineral waters and the water grades containing more than 300 mg/litre SO_3 can never be used for cement soil production. If there is any doubt, some of the laboratory examinations should be repeated using the water available at the construction site. If the results of the second test performed under identical conditions do not equal at least 90 per cent of the values obtained previously, that water should be avoided.

Table 22

Strength figures of samples made of standard cements

Cement	Compression strength			Tensile strength		
	after					
	2	7	28	2	7	28
	(kp/cm²)			(kp/cm²)		
	days					
No. 400	—	280	400	—	20	26
No. 500	200	350	500	20	27	30
No. 600	250	450	600	25	32	35

4.5.2 Determination of the required cement content

There are a number of methods and criteria known in connection with the determination of the amount of cement required. The simplest solution is the empirical method giving the cement quantity figure as a function of the soil type. Other criteria may be the compression strength, resistance to frost effects or wetting/drying, and finally this cement quantity may also be determined on the basis of the stress state in the pavement, with known loading.

Thus the first and the simplest method is based exclusively on the soil type. The cement requirements of the soil types listed in Table 21 are presented in Table 23.

These data apply to cement No. 500. If cement No. 400 is used, they should be multiplied by 1.3; the ASTM proposal on cement content determination is based on Table 24, where the weight losses in the freezing and durability tests, and the maximum volume change are criteria. In addition, these specifications claim that the stabilization is only satisfactory, if the compression strength of the soil cement increases with time and/or with an increasing amount of cement addition, even although the above criteria are satisfied.

Finally, the two tables prepared by the Portland Cement Association (USA) are presented here* (Table 25), which, for granular and cohesive soils, specify as a function of grain distribution and degree of compaction the cement contents which may be used as a basis for selecting the correct amount of cement in samples to be used for detailed examinations.

On the basis of extensive laboratory investigations, Gáspár (1964) suggests for stabilization the Nos 400 and 500 cement contents shown in Fig. 129. He describes the soils concerned by several physical characteristics and, in addition to the cement requirement, he recommends that the optimum water content during construction and/or the dry density figures achieved are specified. Although these

Table 23

Cement quantities required for the construction of a 15 cm soil-cement layer

No.	Soil	Water content during constr. w %	Void ratio e	Bulk density γ Mp/m^3	Cement quantity kp/m^2
1	Sand, fine sand	5–10	0.40–0.50	1.90–2.00	25–35
2	Mo-sand, silty sand	10–12	0.40–0.50	2.04–2.10	25–28
3	Mo, silty Mo	10–14	0.55–0.65	1.85–1.95	30
4	Silt, with Mo silt	10–14	0.60–0.70	1.80–1.93	25–30
5	Lean clay	12–16	0.50–0.60	2.02–2.08	25–35

* Soil-Cement Laboratory Handbook — Portland Cement Association; 33 West Grand Avenue, Chicago 10 Illinois 1959.

Table 24

Cement content determination by soil class

Soil class	1	2	3	4
Soil type	Very sandy	Silty	Clay type	Heavy clay with peat
Yield point	w_L — 50 per cent			
Plastic index Weight per cent of the $d = 0.005$ mm grains	I_p — 25 per cent S — 35 per cent			No stabilization possible
Compression strength after 7-day hardening	foundation: min 15 kp/cm² wear-off layer: min 17.5 kp/cm²			
Cement required, weight per cent	6–10	8–12	10–14	
After the cement treatment	Very considerable hardening	Considerable hardening	Hardening	No treatment possible
Permissible weight loss in the freezing and durability tests	14%	10%	7%	—
Maximum permissible volume change	2%	2%	2%	2%

experimental data undoubtedly exhibit considerable scatter (the points represent-ing these data are indicated for easy), they are quite satisfactory as preliminary information, and may be accepted even as final figures if there is no time or oppor-tunity for a detailed examination. It should be added that the values in the figure were calculated on the basis of the unconfined compressive strength figures ob-tained with 40 mm diameter and 60 mm height cylinders.

The following paragraphs describe the "short-cut" technique elaborated by the American Portland Cement Association for the determination of the cement content by graphs, based on the statistical evaluation processing of the mass experi-mental results involving almost 2500 different soil types. The method cannot be used if the weight per cent of particles less than $d = 0.05$ mm diameter, exceeds 50 per cent and/or than of particles smaller than 0.005 mm is less than 20 per cent. Nor it can be used with organic soils.

149

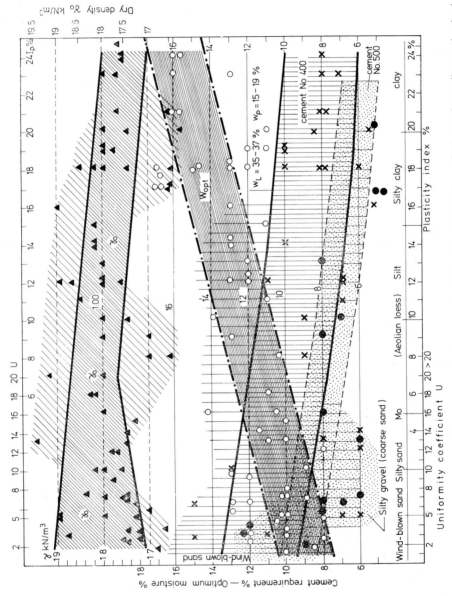

FIG. 129. Determination of the cement contents required for the stabilization of Hungarian soils on the basis of results collected by the Hungarian Road Research Institute

Table 25

(a) Granular soils

Weight per cent of d-4.76 mm particles	Weight per cent of particles smaller than 0.05 mm	Cement requirement weight per cent					
		Maximum density, Mp/m²					
		1.68–1.75	1.76–1.83	1.84–1.91	1.92–1.99	2.00–2.07	$\geq$ 2.08
0–14	0–19	10	9	8	7	6	5
	20–39	9	8	7	7	5	5
	40–50	11	10	9	8	6	5
15–29	0–19	10	9	8	6	5	5
	20–39	9	8	7	6	6	5
	40–50	12	10	9	8	7	6
30–45	0–19	10	8	7	6	5	5
	20–39	11	9	8	7	6	5
	40–50	12	11	10	9	8	6

(b) Cohesive soils

Soil index No.	Weight per cent of the fraction between 0.05 and 0.005 mm	Cement requirement, weight per cent						
		Maximum density, Mp/m²						
		1.44–1.51	1.52–1.59	1.60–1.67	1.68–1.75	1.76–1.83	1.84–1.91	$\geq$ 1.92
0–3	0–19	12	11	10	8	8	7	7
	20–39	12	11	10	9	8	8	7
	40–59	13	12	11	9	9	8	8
	$\geqq$60	–	–	–	–	–	–	–
4–7	0–19	13	12	11	9	8	7	7
	20–39	13	12	11	10	9	8	8
	40–59	14	13	12	10	10	9	8
	$\geqq$60	15	14	12	11	10	9	9
8–11	0–19	14	13	11	10	9	8	8
	20–39	15	14	11	10	9	9	9
	40–59	16	14	12	11	10	10	9
	$\geqq$60	17	15	13	11	10	10	10
12–15	0–19	15	14	13	12	11	9	9
	20–39	16	15	13	12	11	10	10
	40–59	17	15	14	12	12	11	10
	$\geqq$60	18	16	14	13	12	11	11
16–20	0–19	17	16	14	13	12	11	10
	20–39	18	17	15	14	13	11	11
	40–59	19	18	15	14	14	12	12
	$\geqq$60	20	19	16	15	14	13	11

Table 25 (cont.)

(c) In the soil classes of Tables 4 and 5

Soil class	Cement requirement		In the compaction test samples, weight per cent	In the freezing and durability test samples, weight per cent
	Volume per cent	Weight per cent		
A-1-a	5– 7	3– 5	5	3– 5– 7
A-1-b	7– 9	5– 8	6	4– 6– 8
A-2	7–10	5– 9	7	5– 7– 9
A-3	8–12	7–11	9	7– 9–11
A-4	8–12	7–12	10	8–10–12
A-5	8–12	8–13	10	8–10–12
A-6	10–14	9–15	12	10–12–14
A-7	10–14	10–16	13	11–13–15

Again, the grain-distribution curve is plotted first but, in addition, the bulk density of the assembly retained by the 4.76 mm mesh (No. 4) is also determined. If all the particles are smaller than 4.76 mm then process *A* is followed, if not, then process *B*.

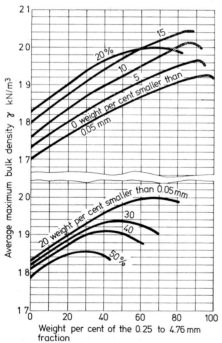

FIG. 130. Approximate determination of the maximum bulk density

Process A

1. A soil-cement mixture is prepared with the soil type under test, and used for a standard compaction experiment, to determine the optimum water content and the maximum dry density. Informative data thereon can be obtained using Fig. 130.

2. By means of the experimentally determined maximum density data, the required amount of cement is read off (Fig. 131).

3. With this cement content, three cylindrical specimens are produced to determine the compression strength (diameter 100 mm, height 115 mm; prior to fracture the cylinders are submerged in water for a period of 4 hours), having the optimum water content and maximum degree of compaction.

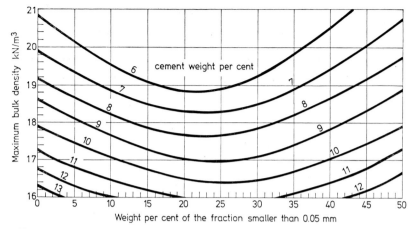

FIG. 131. Graph for the approximate determination of the cement quantity

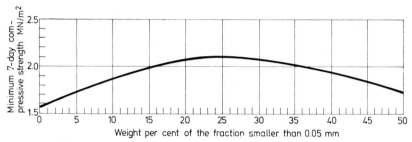

FIG. 132. Minimum required value of the 7-day strength in soils containing particles no larger than 4.74 mm

4. After a 7-day period in wet conditions, the average compression strength is determined.

5. This average value is then indicated on the graph of Fig. 132. If this point is above the curve, then the cement content determined under 2) is satisfactory, but if not, then a specimen of slightly increased cement content is produced and subject to the freezing test.

Process B

1. A soil-cement mixture is prepared with the soil type under test, and subjected to the standard compaction experiment, and the optimum water content and the maximum dry density are determined.

The maximum degree of compaction of the soil-cement mixture to be tested can be estimated using Fig. 133. Thus, with the grain-size distribution already known, the cement content to be used in the test can be determined by making use of Fig. 134.

153

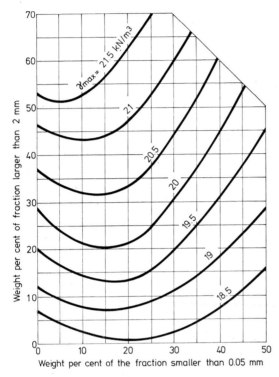

FIG. 133. Graph for the approximate determination of the maximum compactness of the soil-cement mix under test, if the mixture also contains particles larger than 4.74 mm

2. Based on the compaction curve data obtained experimentally, the required cement content can then be determined again by means of Fig. 134.

3. By using the material described under 1) three specimens are produced for the determination of the compression strength at the optimum water content and maximum dry density.

4. After a 7-day period under wet conditions, the average of the unconfined compression-strength values exhibited by the three specimens is determined.

5. The permissible minimum compression-strength of the mix is now determined using Fig. 135. If the compression strength as determined under (4) is equal to or exceeds this figure, then the cement addition is correct.

Example

The following example is intended to illustrate the practical application of the method:

Let us assume the following test results, that is, weight per cent values passing through the different meshes:

No.	4	4.76	mm	82 weight per cent
No.	10	2.00		77
No.	60	0.25		58
No.	200	0.074		37

The grain-size distribution curve is shown in Fig. 136, where the weight per cent of particles smaller than 0.05 mm is seen to be 32%, and that of particles less than 0.005 mm 13%. The bulk density of the material retained by the No. 4 mesh is 2.50.

Accordingly, in this case process B should be pursued. From Fig. 133, with the grain-size distribution known, the estimated maximum bulk density of the mixture can be read off: $\gamma = 1.94$ Mp/m³. The cement content is given by Fig. 134: according to the relevant data, 6 per cent is required.

Now the compaction test is performed with this amount added. The result will be: $w_{opt} = 10.2$ per cent, $\gamma_{max} = 1.965$ Mp/m³. Figure 134 again renders a cement content of 6 per

154

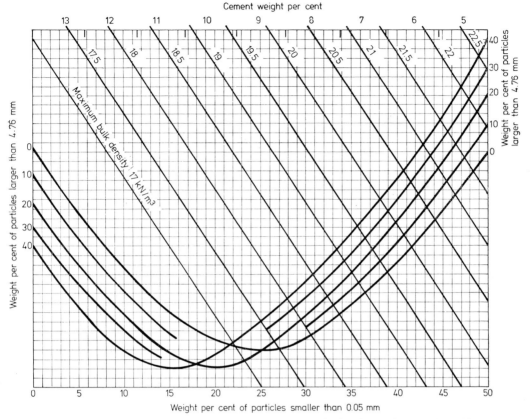

FIG. 134. Determination of the cement content on the basis of experimental data, if the mixture contains particles larger than 4.74 mm

cent for this figure. The next step is to produce specimens of 1.965 volume weight by using the 10.2 per cent water content material, maintain them under wet conditions for seven days, and determine the average of their compression strength values. In the given case this was 24.2 kp/cm², that is, higher than the 19.6 kp/cm² minimum specified by Fig. 135. Consequently, the 6 per cent cement addition is correct.

The last method presented for the determination of the necessary cement content takes into account the stress state of the pavement.

The test described below requires about 10 days and laboratory equipment suitable for unconfined compression and tensile tests, or for a Brasilien test.

A 15 kp test soil is dried or moistened to give it the optimum water content of compaction. This soil quantity is divided into five equal weight parts which are then mixed with 190, 250, 320, 380 and 440 p of No. 500, and 240, 320, 410, 480 and 560 p of No. 400 cement, respectively (in the case of the No. 500 cement, these values correspond to 5, 6.8, 8.5, 10, and 11.7 weight per cents). In the one litre

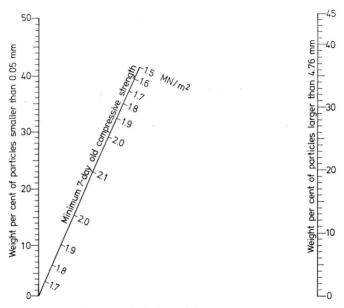

FIG. 135. Nomogram for the determination of the minimum permissible compression strength of soil-cement mixtures also containing particles larger than 4.76 mm

cylinder of the compaction equipment, the soil is compacted in three layers, with 25 blows on each, and then both ends of the cylinder are levelled. After removal from the metal cylinder the cylinders are stored in a wet atmosphere for seven days, then fractured in a compression-test machine. At a load corresponding to about one-third of the estimated fracture-load, the whole load was removed, followed by reloading, in order to determine the Young modulus of the mixture. The compression strength values thus obtained are plotted as a function of the cement content (Fig. 137).

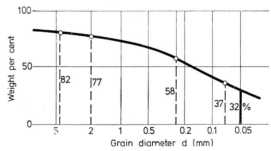

FIG. 136. Grain-size distribution curve of the soil in the example

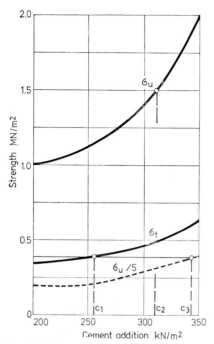

FIG. 137. Strength values as a function of cement addition

In addition to the compression test, each mixture must also supply samples for tensile test purposes, fractured after a 7-day hardening period, with results as indicated also in Fig. 137. Assuming its specified compaction, the Young modulus of the substrate may be determined according to Table 26. After determining the Young modulus of the pavement material according to Fig. 138, the average of the five experiments is calculated and the ratio E_1/E_2 determined. (E_2 is the Young modulus of the substrate, and E_1 is that of the pavement). Hence, using Fig. 139, the required tensile strength of the soil cement is determined. Next, by means of the experimental curve (Fig. 137), the necessary cement addition (c_1) can be readily obtained. Thereafter the $\sigma_u = 15$ kg/cm^2 horizontal is plotted in Fig. 137 and using its intersection with the experimental curve, the associated cement addition (c_2) is determined. Fi-

Table 26

Young moduli of soils upon repeated loadings

Soil type	Soil condition	Young modulus E (kp/cm²)
Sand, fine sand	medium compact	700
	compact	800
Mo with sand and silty sand	medium compact	600
	compact	800
Sand meal, silty sand meal	dry, medium compact	500
	dry, compact	700
	wet, medium compact	400
	wet, compact	500
Silt, sand meal type silt	dry	400
	medium wet	200
Lean clay	dry	300
	medium wet	100

NOTE: For soils or soil conditions omitted from this table, the construction of cement-soil roads is neither advisable nor economical.

157

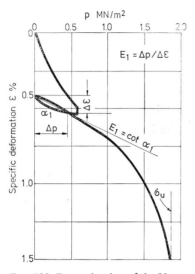

Fig. 138. Determination of the Young modulus of the pavement

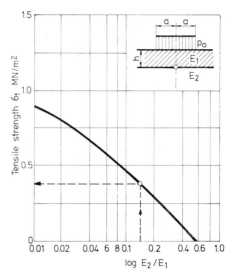

Fig. 139. Determination of the required strength

nally, the intersection of the horizontal indicating the required tensile strength with the $\sigma_u/5$ curve, and the pertinent cement content (c_3) are defined. The highest value of c_1, c_2 and c_3 is considered standard. As regards loading, this method considers with the vehicle of Fig. 140.

Another method deserving mention determines the cement content on the basis of the specific surface. This method may be used if the weight per cent of the 0.074 to 0.005 mm fraction has a maximum of 45 per cent. In this case the cement quantity providing for a maximum 10 per cent weight loss during the standard freezing test (see 2.13) can be calculated from the following equation:

$$c_s = 0.087 f + 3.79 \qquad (48)$$

where f is the specific surface of the soil used and can be determined by the glycerole test (see Diamond–Kinter 1956). c_s is the cement content related to the weight per cent of the dry soil. According to results, Eq. (48) offers an excellent statistical average as shown in Fig. 141. The dash lines representing the scattering range reveal a correlation coefficient of $r = 0.93$, but if on the basis the permissible weight loss is only 7 per cent for the soil type involved, then 2 per cent must be added to the cement quantity obtained from this formula, whereas if as much as 14 per cent weight loss is permissible, then 0.7 per cent may be deducted.

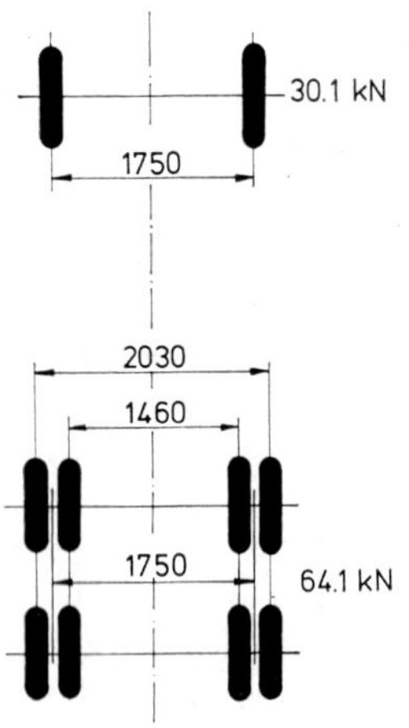

Fig. 140. Vehicle data for dimensioning

158

If this method is employed, it is expedient to perform confined compression tests as well as supplemently experiments in order to decide whether or not hardening is satisfactory. Small samples can be used (4 cm diameter, 6 cm height). One series is subject to the unconfined compression test after seven days of wet storage, another after 14 days of the same, and a third after seven days of wet storage and a further seven days of submersion in water. A comparison of the strength values will clearly characterize the behaviour of the soil cement.

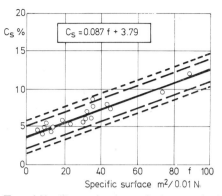

FIG. 141. Determination of the required cement content as a function of the specific soil surface

Let us now review briefly the criteria whereby the other soil cement types (see Section 4.1) can be assessed. So far we have discussed the soil cement. In the case of a "cement-improved granular soil mix" the cement addition will depend on the destination of the mixture. This material, making use of the soil types of the A-1, A-2, and A-3 categories, is used for the following purposes, if the weight per cent of the particles passing through the No. 200 mesh does not exceed 35 per cent, and the plastic index is less than 15:

1. to prevent erosion and the "pumping effect" below the rigid pavement;
2. to prevent later compaction of the basic layers;
3. to reduce the volume variation of sand and gravel content, but plastic soils; and
4. to increase the load-bearing capacity of the basic layers.

Since no definite criteria have yet been developed, the designer must select the experiment most essential with respect to the desired behaviour of the mix (strength, shrinkage, expansion, etc.). However, we mention certain relevant experiments below.

If considerable traffic is expected (5 million per year, 2 tons load equivalent wheel weight), then the 7-day compression strength of the cement-improved foundation layer should be at least 5 kp/cm², which can be achieved by the addition of 3.5 to 6 weight per cent cement. In the case of less traffic, a strength of 2 kp/cm² will suffice (2.5 to 3.5 weight per cent cement addition).

In order to reduce shrinkage a cement addition of 2–5 weight per cent will be needed, depending on the soil type. This would reduce the original $I_p = 10$ to 15 per cent plasticity index to at least $I_p = 5$ per cent, and restrict the volume change to a permissible limit. The same amount of cement is usually added to increase load-bearing capacity. The behaviour of the mixture is best controlled by the CBR test techniques.

159

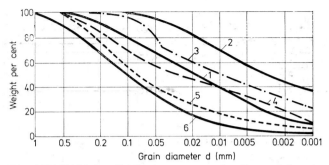

FIG. 142. Grain-size distribution curves of soils used for the production of cement-treated soil masses. 1 and 4: acceptable results; 2 and 3: excessive clay fraction, mixing with water is rather difficult; 5 and 6: with only cement a rather rigid or brittle paste, but the addition of calcium has made it smooth and easy to work

Again, there is no well-established rule for the cement addition to the "cement improved silty clay soil mix" referred to under (3) and the experiments of the designer will be decisive. The problem may often be solved by simple volume-change tests through the observation of compacted and post-treated samples. If the cement is added to increase the load-bearing capacity, then strength tests can facilitate decision, and the CBR tests can be particularly recommended for the purpose. The desired CBR value of the cement-improved soil is chosen in the course of dimensioning the pavement and, on this basis, the cement addition can be readily determined.

For the production of a "plastic soil cement" as under (4) the slightly plastic Mo soils, silts, sandy silts, etc., are most suitable. The weight per cent of particles smaller than 0.05 mm should not exceed 30 per cent. The water content of such a soil is much higher than that of the soil cement usually produced and compacted under optimum water-content conditions, since its consistency almost corresponds to that of a cement mortar. This increased water content, of course, demands increased cement addition, generally an extra 4 weight per cent above the case of normal soil cement.

For the production of cement-treated soil pastes mentioned under (5) the soil types of a grain-size distribution curve as shown in Fig. 142 are usually employed. Several alternatives are known, but since we do not intend to offer descriptions in minute details in this volume, only two mixtures which have given favourable results will be quoted:

Symbol	Soil	Cement	Liquid bitumen
	volume per cent, water excl.		
1	60–84	16–40	—
2	77	16	7

These data apply to volume per cent figures. The required amount of water equals to about 50 per cent of the loose volume of the other materials involved. First the soil and the water are admixed, then the bituminous substance, and finally the cement is added.

The tests of the different cement-treated soil mixtures are summed up in Table 27.

Table 27

Tests for designing cement-treated soil mixtures

Class	Observations and tests	Cement soils		Cement-modified granular soils		Cement-modified heavy soils	Plastic cement soils
		major	minor	major	minor		
		operations		operations			
I	In-situ exploration	.	.	.	.	.	.
	In situ identification	—	.	—	—	.	—
II	Soil examination						
	grain-size distribution	.	.	o	o	o	.
	liquid limit	o	o	o	o	o	o
	plastic limit	o	o	o	o	o	o
	specific gravity and absorption	.	o	.	o	o	.
	volume change	—	—	—	—	.	—
III	Examination of the cement-treated soil						
	compaction test	.	.	.	.	.	.
	compression strength	.	o	.	o	o	.
	durability test	.	o	—	—	o	.
	freezing	.	o	—	—	o	.
	volume change	—	—	—	—	o	.
	adsorption (water content after expansion)	o	—	—	—	o	—
	Atterberg limit of the pulverized soil cement	—	—	o	—	o	—

Key: . determination indispensable
     o determination recommended
     — determination unnecessary

4.5.3 Determination of the cement content of the stabilized mixture

The previous paragraphs have dealt with the determination of the cement content which could ensure the designed behaviour of the soil cement. During construction, in order to control the work performed, it might be necessary to determine the cement content of the ready-made mixture or even of the hardened pavement. From such measurements, for example, the phenomenon presented in Fig. 126 was discovered, i.e. the cement added is very unevenly distributed within the thickness of the cover. Unfortunately, the relevant test methods are not at all simple, and this prevents frequent check-up during construction, and eventually the repair of some defects in due course.

Two methods are described below, and neither requires special knowledge in chemistry or any analytical practice and experiment. In addition, they are suitable for testing almost every soil type, except those of excessive or variable calcium and/or magnesium content. Both determine the cement content with a 0.2 per cent accuracy. Since, however, the second method is faster, it is strongly preferred.

The first method known as EDTA was elaborated by Gilliland and Hunter (1952)[*]. Essentially, it consists of extracting calcium and magnesium from the stabilized soil by six normal hydrochloric acid, which implies the simultaneous extraction of iron and aluminum and these must therefore be precipitated by ammonia as hydroxides. Thereafter the calcium and aluminum are titrated at a pH of 10.0 by means of the "EDTA indicator" (disodium, dihydrogen ethylenediomine tetra-acetate, or sometimes known as complexon). Some calcium may also be precipitated during this process, either because soluble calcium ions are adsorbed over the surface of the insoluble precipitate, or since soluble materials are enclosed during the crystallization. The quantity of the calcium thus precipitated depends mainly on the iron and aluminum concentrations.

The cement content can be calculated from the following equation:

$$c \% = 100 \frac{Y - X}{Z - X} \qquad (49)$$

where X, Y and Z represent the calcium content of the natural soil, stabilized soil, and cement, respectively. If the above phenomenon, that is, a simultaneous precipitation actually takes place, then a correction may be introduced. This is particularly necessary if the soil does not contain calcium ($X = 0$), its iron and aluminium contents are rather excessive, while the amount of cement is small. All this is only encountered in the case of tropical soils.

In the second method, first the calcium is extracted from the soil cement, as in the previous case. After the removal of the sesquioxides, the solution is examined in the gas flame of a flame photometer. The calcium in the solution will give the flame a red color, whose intensity is proportional to the calcium content. Strength is measured by a photo-electric cell connected to a galvanometer. Numerical values can be obtained by calibrating the apparatus with a soil of known cement content. Here the phenomenon of simultaneous precipitation cannot lead to any error since the calibration curve will contain the same.

*Road Note, No 28; Road Research Laboratory, 1960. Harmondsworth, Middlesex.

5. Stabilization with lime

5.1 Introduction

Soil stabilization by lime means the admixture of this material in the form of calcium oxide or calcium hydroxide (slaked or quick lime, limewash, etc.) to the soil, and the compaction of the mixture at the optimum water content. Calcium addition will reduce soil plasticity, increase strength and durability, decrease water absorption and swelling. Here the stabilization effect is due to certain chemical processes, so it is not a mechanical reinforcement. These chemical processes modify the soil structure whereby larger grain aggregates are formed, leading to several advantages in the suitability of the soil for road construction.

From a lime stabilization viewpoint, the soils can be classified by their grain-size distribution curves into the groups shown in Fig. 143. In range A no stabilization is possible since these coarse materials simply cannot be worked by the available equipment. In range B the grain-distribution curves of the additives used in the concrete and asphalt pavements are found; here the soil behaviour is governed mainly by the grain distribution itself. In mechanical stabilization a similarly good grain-size distribution is aimed at, so the relevant grain-size distribution curves are in the same range. Improvement of the strength and other properties of these soils is readily feasible by cement or bitumen stabilization, that is, by hydraulic binders or bituminous adhesives. In road construction lime cannot be used for sand stabilization since, contrary to the mortar employed in building engineering, the calcium hydroxide cannot be carbonatized in this case as the stabilized layers are often hermetically sealed.

In range C the grain-size distribution is insignificant since here the mineral-chemical action of the fine grains ($d < 0.01$ mm) is essential. Mechanical stabilization cannot even be considered, since the achievement of a favourable grain distribution would require an excessive amount of foreign material. Stabilization by hydraulic binders, cement, etc. would only be economical in the case of soils of maximum $w_f = 40$ per cent liquid limit and $I_p = 15$ per cent plastic index, as demonstrated above, since no intensive mixing is even expected beyond these limits. Treatment of these soils with quicklime or calcium hydrate, on the other hand, can favourably modify both grain structure and plasticity. Thus range C is the main area of lime stabilization. CaO is transformed into calcium hydrate in the soil, binding part of the water content chemically, while another part thereof will

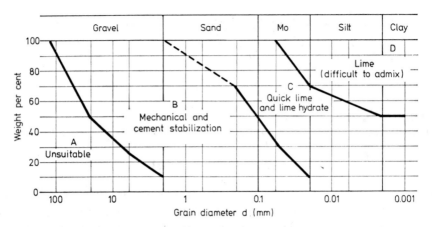

Fɪɢ. 143. Lime stabilization ranges of grain distribution

evaporate because of the heat produced during slaking. The optimum water content will increase, as does the load-bearing capacity.

The favourable effects exerted by lime on soil have long been known. Silt and clay mixed with lime were used for the construction of the Shensi Pyramid in Tibet and some of the Roman roads. At several points along the Great Wall in China, a calcium-hydrate reinforced earth wall in sandwiched between the two 1 m brick walls. Lime-stabilized soil had also been used for other construction purposes in China. Its re-introduction started around 1930 after the development of soil-mechanics tests, and high-level mechanization has given further resurgence to this technique. Its dissemination and general acceptance was promoted by the efforts of the lime-kiln enterprises to seek new fields of application and thus new market areas for their products.

In Hungary, no in-situ technology of lime stabilization has yet been developed nor has this technique passed much beyond the phase of experimentation, although quite a number of laboratory test results are already available and a few in-situ experiments have been completed. Nevertheless, its still more extensive introduction would be desirable as it often could lead economically to favourable results as shown below.

5.2 Physical and chemical effects of lime

As it is well known, "lime kilning" involves the following reversible chemical process:

$$CaCO_3 + 4300 \text{ cal} \leftrightarrows CaO + CO_2$$

Thus the process is endothermic in nature since, theoretically, 4300 calories of heat are required for the dissolution of 1 mole of $CaCO_3$. The oxide of Ca, with bivalent calcium, is the burnt or quick lime. Oxides can be produced from dolomite or calcium magnesium carbonate: $CaO + MgO$, but while quick lime can be readily hydrated according to the equation

$$CaO + H_2O = Ca(OH)_2 + 15.3 \text{ kcal}$$

which is actually the lime kilning process, this process is very difficult with magnesium oxide, and usually takes place only under pressure. Under normal conditions

$$CaO + MgO + H_2O \rightarrow Ca(OH)_2 + MgO$$

monohydrated dolomite lime is produced, and the $Ca(OH)_2 + Mg(OH)_2$ compound is formed under pressure. Lime hydration, as shown by the above equation, is an exothermic process where 16 000 calories of heat are released on the production of each mole (56 p) of calcium hydroxide. Thereafter the calcium hydroxide (quick lime) is transformed again and the hardening reaction is:

$$Ca(OH)_2 + H_2CO_3 + 2H_2O$$

Carbonic acid is produced from the carbon dioxide content of the air in the soil, and free water. The opinion of the processes taking place after the admixture of calcium hydrate to the soil has been developed.

√Immediately after mixing the soil structure starts to undergo a transformation: flocculation and coagulation begin, then the clay particles form much larger grains in the silt-Mo fraction. This, in turn, will modify the Atterberg limits and the compaction properties, and so in practice the soil becomes much easier to handle in the course of earthwork.

√Flocculation is usually attributed to ion exchange: the dissociating calcium ions occupy the place of others, generally sodium ions in the adsorption complex of the clay minerals. Ion exchange, however, must not be regarded as the only reason for the changes referred to, since they also occur in soils saturated with calcium ions before the calcium-hydrate addition. Nor are the processes taking place during slow reactions are not explained satisfactorily. During the carbonatization as reflected by the above equation, some calcium carbonate should be produced which would exert a slight cementation effect. Another effect in such cases is the "puzzolanic reaction", resulting again in slow cementation of the compacted soil–calcium mixture. As mentioned earlier, it is still not clear how this is brought about, except that it is caused by an interaction between quick lime, and the silicate and aluminate minerals of the soil on the other, in the presence of moisture. In the puzzolanic reaction it is most likely that the separation of silicate and aluminate elements from the clay minerals is equally important, and their solubility depends on the pH value. Lime addition will increase the pH of the water content in the soil, and give rise to increased solubility according to Fig. 144. Due to the dissolution these compounds may then be rearranged.

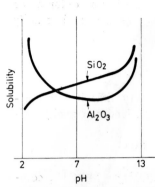

FIG. 144. The solubility of silicate and aluminate as a function of the environmental pH

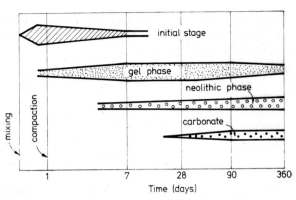

FIG. 145. Development of the individual reaction stages and their participation in changing the soil characteristics

These phenomena have so far been studied in the most minute details by Brand (1962) so far who, by microscopic, electron microscopic, radiographic, and chemical examinations, demonstrated that certain reactions will take place between calcium hydroxide and the elementary soil particles, whereby new minerals develop. Firstly the clay minerals participate in these reactions, and it is most likely that their abundant crystal lattice defects in represent the starting points. The rate and intensity of the reactions are greatly promoted by the high pH developed through calcium addition. In the given case, certain reaction products could be readily identified via the thin microsections obtained, and thus the reaction mechanism could be understood precisely. As shown in Fig. 145, the individual stages follow in the sequence explained below.

The initial stage is started by the dissociation of the admixed $Ca(OH)_2$ into Ca^{2+}- and OH^- ions, which modifies the electrical surface forces of the clay minerals. The $Ca(OH)_2$ thus added loses most of its crystalline form and can no longer be detected by an X-ray examination. Assuming an amorphous form, it creates a transition to the gel phase. The finest soil particles coagulate and, thereby, the entire structure and consistency of the soil undergoes a significant change.

The gel phase is the most important stage from the aspect of strength, as the gel substance will connect and cement the mineral grains, thus changing the entire pore structure. It is most likely that the reduced water uptake and increased resistance to water of the calcium-hydrate stabilized soils should be attributed to the gel phase. This gel phase could be clearly discerned through the microscope although its chemical and crystalline composition could not be determined in the experiments. It is assumed to consist of tobermorite type calcium silicate hydrates.

From the gel the "neoliths" will then slowly develop, some crystals being clearly seen through the microscope, creating the "neolithic" phase which is the most important part of the consolidation process. In this stage, however, the soil is somewhat less resistant to the water effects than in the gel phase.

In practice, development of the carbonate phase could only be observed for samples stored in air. On the atmospheric effects, spherulitic calcium carbonates will develop over the surface, these mineral particles creating a compact "crystalline mortar". From practical aspects this has no importance at all, since the surface of lime-stabilized earth roads is usually sealed hermetically.

During the process described above, the CaO distribution in the

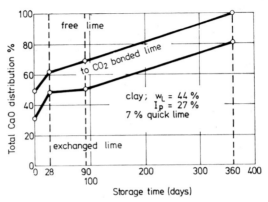

FIG. 146. Variation of the CaO bond type in the soil, as a function of time

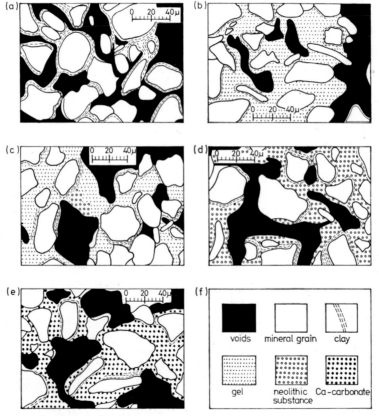

FIG. 147. Schematic diagrams drawn on the basis of the microscopic image of thin sections taken from hardening lime soil to characterize strengthening process. (a) the original soil; (b) gel phase; (c) beginning of the neolithic phase formation; (d) well-developed neolithic phase; (e) carbonate phase; (f) key of symbols

soil will undergo a characteristic change as shown in Fig. 146, where the reactions between calcium hydrate and soil can be clearly seen.

Brand prepared thin microsections of the hardening soil and examined them with a polarizing microscope. He illustrated schematically his observations through these exposures wich explain lucidly the process described. One series of these schematic illustrations, these taken during hardening of a coarse silt is shown in Fig. 141, with the symbols explained in the right-hand-side bottom corner.

Part (a) illustrates the fine skeleton of the original soil, including the clay particles bonded around the coarse silt grains. In part (b) the development of the gel phase is shown: the skeleton particles displayed in (a) are cemented by a gel-type substance. Lime addition amounted to 7 per cent. Part (c) reveals a neolithic-phase formation under progress: some particles are already by neolithic bridges. In part (d) the neolithic phase is well developed, forming a coherent mass like the gel phase. Finally, in part (e) the carbonate phase can be seen: the fine skeleton is held by a well-developed fine crystalline carbonate cover with round pores.

5.3 Effect of lime on the physical properties of the soil

Considering the processes described in the previous section, one can conclude that lime addition affects all physical properties of the soil. Owing to the coagulation, the grain-size distribution curve will obviously change and, a number of other characteristics will undergo similar changes due mainly to this cause. Changes in the grain-size distribution curve, however, are rather difficult to determine as the usual hydrometric method does not render a true picture, so these changes should be expressed numerically on the basis of another characteristic property.

Figure 148 illustrates some results obtained in the Hungarian Road Research Institute: a significant decrease of the I_p value is shown, due mainly to the rapid increase of the plastic limit. These experiments involved quick lime powder, limewash, and calcium hydrate, and the differences did not exceed the usual standard deviation figures.

Figure 149 illustrates the time-dependent process of plasticity index reduction, which incidentally is also characteristic of the development rate exhibited by the processes described in 5.2. Generally, quick lime will bring about a faster reaction.

The effect of calcium treatment on the volume change of the various soils is similarly significant, as swelling will be almost completely eliminated, and the volume change greatly reduced (see Fig. 150). This effect clearly follows from the explanation of the hardening process.

The effect on the compaction characteristics is also quite interesting. A typical example is shown in Fig. 151 where the optimum water content is increasing while the maximum dry density is being reduced — this phenomenon is mainly due to

168

flocculation. The water in the soil is consumed for calcium hydration, so it cannot reduce the intergranular friction. The non-coagulated particles can be readily relocated by compaction, which is not the case for larger clods. In connection with compaction, we should note here that a waiting period will always have a disadvantageous effect in the case of stabilization with lime (Mitchell and Hooper, 1961).

The most important calcium effect in road construction is the increased strength, though extent depends on a number of factors. Firstly, the calcium content is most important, as shown in Fig. 152, where the strength is illustrated as a function of the lime weight per cent added, for three different heavy-soil types.

Figure 153 demonstrates that the time involved has only a slight effect at small calcium contents, but if the latter are increased, the time becomes important. Since consolidation is rather slow, a final conclusion often cannot be reached at in the case of 7- or even 28-day stored specimens. Besides, it may be that an increased calcium content would reduce strength.

From strength aspects the lime-addition technique is also important. Quick

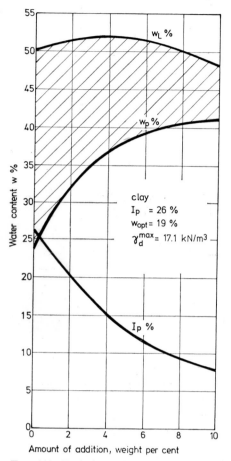

FIG. 148. Variation of the Atterberg limit figures of a fat clay upon the effect of lime addition

lime is generally much more efficient than slaked lime. However, the method of admixture cannot be selected arbitrarily: if the soil to be stabilized has a greater moisture content during construction than the optimum water content of compaction, then quick lime should be added in powder form, since the water required for slaking will be absorbed from the soil. However, when using quick lime, increased care should be used to avoid danger. To a soil of a water content approximately w_{opt} admixture of calcium hydrate is preferred, whereas a dry soil can best be stabilized with limewash, in a dilution where the soil might then assume the optimum condition for compaction. Unfortunately, certain chemical properties of the admixed lime play an essential role, particularly from the viewpoint of the puzzolanic reactions. Such a lime type qualification, on the other hand, is still not feasible because of the absence of the relevant data.

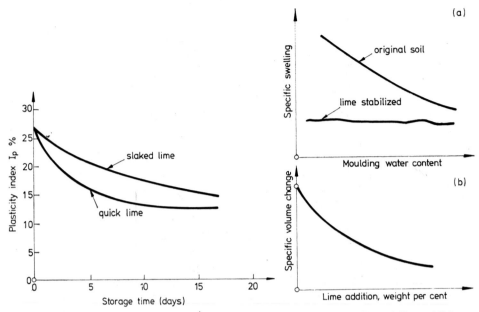

FIG. 149. Reduction with time of the plasticity index, due to the calcium effect

FIG. 150. The effect of lime addition on the volume change

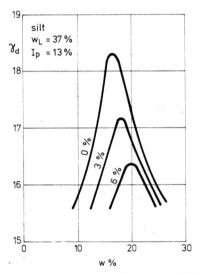

FIG. 151. The effect of lime addition on the development of the compaction curve

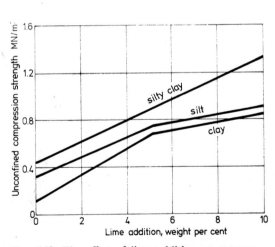

FIG. 152. The effect of lime addition on compression strength

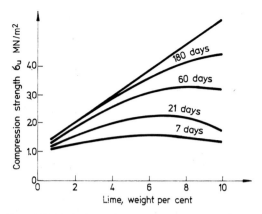

FIG. 153. Variation of the compression strength in
the function of lime addition and time

Summing up the lime admixture effects on cohesive, particularly silty, soils, the following table can be composed, with the symbols:

Table 4.16

0	no change
+	increase or improvement
+ +	significant increase or improvement
−	decrease
− −	significant decrease

soil structure	+
liquid limit	+
plastic limit	+ or + +
plasticity index	− or − −
relative consistency index at $w = $ const	+ or + +
optimum moisture content	+ or + +
maximum bulk density	−
unconfined compression strength	+ +
modulus of compression	+ or + +
water absorption	−
water resistance	+ +

5.4 Effect of various additives

Certain natural substances, such as volcanic ash, react to lime addition much better than do the ordinary soil types. These materials are usually called puzzuolanae. They are mostly of a volcanic origin, and are not crystalline but ionic in structure. They occur usually in the form of volcanic ash, tuff, or trass (silicate

171

type, trachitic tuff). The lower the degree of crystallization, the greater their activity. With such material added to the soil, the efficiency of lime stabilization may be greatly increased. The admixture of such a substance of natural origin, however, would not be economical in Hungary, but there are synthetic materials available which have a similar effect. The major example is fly-ash, mainly found accumulating in large quantities in the vicinity of thermal power stations and raising considerable storage and transport problems. Its material consists mainly of spherical non-crystalline silicate and aluminate particles, and rounded magnetic iron oxide (Fe_3O_4) grains. Calcium oxide occurs only in combination with other materials, as produced by the combustion of limestone in coal. The amount of unburnt carbon particles, whose presence is rather detrimental to both firing and fly-ash quality aspects, varies greatly with the efficiency of firing. Carbon will dilute the puzzolanic particles, increase the water demand, and reduce the maximum dry density of the stabilized soil. The puzzolanic activity of the fly-ash depends on the quality of its grain-size distribution: coarse fly-ash admixture leads to failure. The fly-ash quality can be greatly improved by grinding, but this is seldom economical.

The fly-ash particles may have an electric charge, which is rather detrimental to compaction, and can even make their use impossible. Thus in given cases a suitable discharge technique must be sought.

The greatest problem of fly-ash use is its wide quality range even under constant operational conditions. The factors causing variation include the quality of the coal fired, the temperature and efficiency of firing, and the weather conditions, which certainly cannot be controlled to give a regular advantageous outcome.

From stabilization aspects the fly-ash effect is fundamentally identical to that of calcium, involving the same reactions. Actually the pozzuolanic reaction is stronger. Consolidation and the other reactions taking place are generally slower and certain silts and clays render poorer results in the case of lime-plus-fly-ash admixture, than if only lime stabilization is carried out. Unfortunately, at present there is no way to test the fly-ash and the soil admixed separately and thus forecast the subsequent effect.

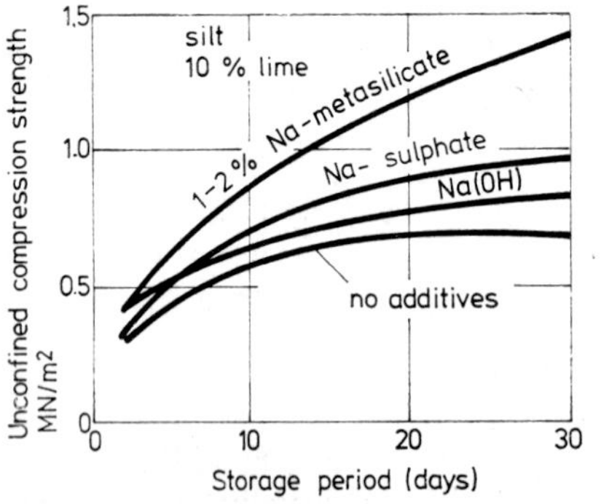

Determination of the extent of lime and fly-ash addition is discussed in the next section.

In addition to fly-ash, a variety of other materials have also been tested for the improvement of the lime-soil characteristics. The admixture of additives in small quantities is aimed at either increasing strength, or reducing the required amount of principal stabilizer. However,

FIG. 154. Compression strength increase of a lime stabilized silt on the admixture of sodium compounds

very few of these materials rendered results economically favourable. The best results were exhibited by certain Na-compounds. The strength increase upon Na-compound addition is illustrated in Fig. 154, for the case of a silt type.

5.5 Design of soil-lime mixtures

The design of lime- and fly-ash-additive stabilizations is still far from the development level seen in the case of soil cement for example. Here experience and common sense have decisive importance which of course are important factors in other stabilizations as well.

When stabilizing with lime, the amount of calcium necessary obviously depends again on the eventual use of the mix, the objectives of stabilization, and the properties required. Decisions as to whether it would be expedient to use other materials, e.g. fly-ash, in addition to lime, must be taken with economy in mind, i.e. since a given objective, such as a specified strength, can be achieved by a variety of mixtures, the composition of the preferred mix may be chosen because of its economy.

If strength is the critical factor, then the method illustrated in Fig. 155 is the best choice. If only lime is admixed, then the simple process in part (a) of this figure should be followed, involving only a few tests. For simultaneous lime and fly-ash admixture, however, the compression strength depends on two variables, so a number of mixtures must be tested if a complete pattern is to be obtained. The number of tests can be reduced by excluding a priori the uneconomical mixtures. First the maximum lime quantity still economically acceptable is determined, as shown by point A in Fig. 156.

The next step is to calculate the cost involved in the admixture of a further additive, and convert this to an equivalent calcium value, whose deduction from A will give point B. This is followed by plotting an inclined straight line whose angle corresponds to the cost unit ratio of the fly-ash and lime quantities delivered

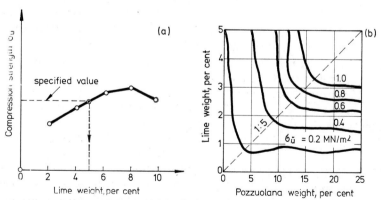

FIG. 155. Determination of the required quantity of additives on the basis of the strength of the mixture. (a) stabilization with lime; (b) simultaneous addition of lime and fly-ash

173

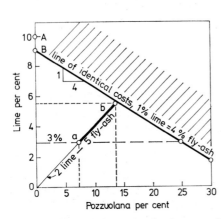

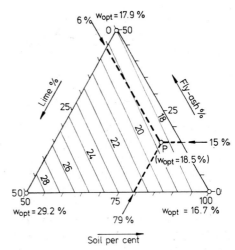

FIG. 156. Mixture design in the case of
simultaneous lime and fly-ash addition,
on the basis of economical efficiency

FIG. 157. Determination of the optimum
water content by interpolation

to the site. It should be noted that the percentages of this figure apply to the total
dry mix and not just to the soil. Points above this line indicate uneconomical mixtures. If the minimum lime-addition quantities still permissible for an acceptable
admixture are also plotted, then the feasible mixtures are limited to a fairly narrow
range from which selection may be made by testing directly the specified characteristic, e.g. strength.

The optimum water content of the mixture during construction is tested by a
reduced number of compaction tests. By interpolation we determine first, for
example, the optimum compaction water content of a 50 : 50 per cent soil-lime
mixture, then that of a similar soil and fly-ash mix, and finally that of the soil
only. The values thus obtained are associated with the vertices of a triangle diagram (see Fig. 157). Interpolation is then performed along the sides of the triangle,
whereby the corresponding points will be connected by straight lines, and the
w_{opt} pertaining to any arbitrary composition can then be read off (in the figure
referred to, the given values could be obtained after testing the three materials
separately; after interpolation, the optimum water content of a mixture of 6 per
cent lime, 15 per cent fly-ash, and 79 per cent soil would be $w_{opt} = 18.5$ per cent).

In addition to the strength specifications, certain durability and frost resistance
requirements are also applied to the mix. Lime and soil mixtures do not usually
satisfy the requirements of soil cement and no special relevant specifications have
yet been elaborated. The British recommendation of a durability index never
below 80 per cent seems to be acceptable. This value is obtained by the determination of the compression strength of the specimen after 12 freezing-thawing or wet-
ting-drying cycles, and dividing the figure thus obtained by the compression
strength of a sample produced simultaneously, but stored under wet conditions
during the entire test period.

174

6. Stabilization with bitumen and tar

6.1 Introduction

‌ Most of the soil stabilization techniques use the various road construction methods, designed originally for coarse additives like rubble or gravel alone, or with soils of fairly fine grains. As a counterpart of the "water bonded" Macadam pavement, the mechanical-stabilization technique was developed, the concrete pavement initiated the soil cement, etc. The methods of constructing black pavements made by using various asphalt, bitumen, and tar additives have also been tried in soil stabilization. In such cases, however, instead of the coarse additives, various soils were mixed with the above adhesives, thus improving the physical properties of the soil types employed. The method of soil stabilization with bitumen or tar was widely accepted, and it is still used both home and abroad, particularly as a foundation for expensive pavements. For the construction of running surfaces, however, it is not generally considered suitable. Prior to the detailed discussion of these stabilization methods, certain fundamental definitions must be agreed upon.

The active agents of the stabilization methods explained in this Chapter (hydrocarbon content, bitumen and tar) do not undergo significant changes during their use, and their main function is to cement the soil particles. The terminology of the most important materials involved is presented below, partly after Vásárhelyi (1963).

Asphalt is a natural or synthetic product in which the mineral particles are impregnated and/or cemented by bitumen.

Bitumen is a non-aqueous hydrocarbon system either natural or obtained by petroleum distillation. It can be fully dissolved in CS_2, and is a black, elastic or solid material that is insoluble in water, diluted acids and alcohol. The greater part of the bitumen used for road construction today is petroleum distillery product.

Liquid bitumen is the compound of bitumen and light-weight volatile solvents or dilutents, petroleum distillates (gasoline, kerosene, Diesel oil) or black coal-tar oils (heavy and middle oils, green oil).

Tar is a liquid or semi-solid hydrocarbon produced by the dry distillation of coal, oil, lignite, or wood. For road construction purposes, coal tar is mainly used.

Cold tar is a distilled or processed coal tar (black pitch and green oil mixture), pure or mixed with bitumen which, if a suitable solvent is admixed, will assume such a thin-liquid state that it would be adaptable directly or after warming slightly.

Black pitch is the solid or semi-solid (plastic) component of the tar left over after distillation.

Emulsion is the aqueous colloid system of bitumen or tar in which bitumen is the dispersed matter and water the dispersive agent.

The efficient admixture of bitumen to the soil may lead to several effects of which the most important are:

— reinforcement of non-cohesive granular soils, e.g. pure sand by the connection or cementation of the particles (bituminous sand);

— stabilization of the water content of cohesive fine-grain soils making them water-impermeable and reducing their water absorption capacity (bituminous soils);

— conversion of soils possessing originally only frictional resistance to cohesive and water impermeable soil types.

These hydrocarbon base materials are suitable for the following stabilization methods:

(1) Stabilization with full admixture: the individual soil particles are coated by the adhesive, so they cannot contact each other directly;

(2) Development of water impermeability by processing the mechanically stabilized soil with asphalt;

(3) Phase stabilization: the caked soil grain aggregates are coated by bitumen;

(4) Membrane stabilization: soil masses are coated by waterproof bitumen or asphalt membrane.

The following terminology applies to the stabilized products:

(1) *Soil asphalt*: water-impermeable cohesive soil;

(2) *Sand asphalt*: loose river or wind-blown sand, perhaps pit sand, whose particles are cemented by bitumen;

(3) *Waterproof mechanical stabilization*: a compound of mixed grain distribution type granular soil and a small quantity of cohesive soil, completed by bitumen admixture for water-tightness;

(4) *Oil treated soil*: if oil is sprayed onto the surface of an earth road, a stabilization effect may be easily achieved.

Recently a new terminology, different from that above and indicating its utilization, was introduced by Kari (1962), who distinguished asphalt Macadam base (AMB), asphalt concrete base (ACB), asphalt treated base (ATB), and asphalt soil base (ASB). In the first three types the asphalt has the duty of lending tensile strength to the soil, and cementing the particles. In the fourth alternative, the asphalt makes the soil water-impermeable.

176

Although the soil-bitumen mixtures are used for many different purposes, their primary field of application is to prepare the base of higher order pavements for both road and airport constructions. In the United States the basic layer of more than a total road length of 60 000 km has been constructed using bituminous stabilization.

Bitumen and tar may be used for stabilization without no other additives, or with the addition of quick lime and, perhaps certain fillers. An essential feature here, quite different from other stabilization methods, is that both bitumen and tar are thermoplastic materials and therefore the strength and deformation characteristics of the stabilized substance will depend on temperature.

It should be noted here that soil stabilization with bitumen or tar is by nature rather similar to the higher-order black pavements from both design and construction aspects, and the two categories cannot even be distinctly separated. However, since the problems of the latter are much beyond the scope of this volume, the present chapter will not describe the basic materials involved and their testing, or the design of road-construction mixtures using them, but refer to the relevant literature.* Here we will adhere strictly to the topic of soil stabilization making using of hydrocarbon base materials. However, the reader's attention is called to the various standards regulating the quality, testing, application, etc., of the different materials involved.

6.2 Stabilization with bitumen

6.2.1 Stabilizers

For the stabilizations listed in the introduction the bitumen is used as liquid bitumen or bitumen emulsion. The most important characteristics of the liquid bitumen types available in Hungary at present are summarized in Table 28.

The bitumen liquidity required for impregnation and mixing can be achieved most easily by the admixture of a solvent. Thus 8 to 12 per cent tar or green oil will reduce bitumen viscosity to a tenth. Bitumen which has been made thin-liquid using 10–50 per cent solvent will enter the small voids, promote good admixture, and when the construction is completed, with the volatile oil already evaporated, it will coat the soil particles with a thin film, cement the individual grains and thus make the soil water impermeable. If the solvent evaporates within a short period of time, the bondage will develop immediately, so this rapid curing (RC) liquid bitumen is most suitable for high-speed machine work or projects needing fast completion, and for roads on cohesive soils of a compact structure or closed base, from which the heavy oils could only evaporate after a long time. The slow-curing

* *Road Research Laboratory*: Bituminous materials in road construction, London 1962.
DURIEZ—ARRAMIDE: Nouveau traité des matériaux de construction, Paris 1962.
WIEBEL—FUHRMANN: Bitumen und Asphalt Taschenbuch, Berlin 1964.
The Asphalt Institute: The Asphalt Handbook, Maryland 1975 (USA).

(SC) liquid bitumen types are well adaptable for the impregnation of granular sands through whose voids the heavy solvent oils can readily evaporate. The Hungarian liquid bitumen varieties are medium curing (MC) as indicated by the data of the above table. For general review, Table 29 presents the American specifications (ASTM = American Society of Testing Materials, and AASHO = Amer-

Table 28

Liquid bitumen characteristics

No	Type Hungarian Standard MSZ-3268	Viscosity at 30 °C (sec)		Marcusson flash point in °C lower limit	Solvent weight % removed up to 360 °C
		10 mm mesh	4 mm mesh		
1	HB-0	—	20–40	40	24–28
2	HB-1	20–40	—	80	14–19
3	HB-2	5–150	—	120	11–13
4	HB-3	300–500	—	140	6–8

Table 29

American liquid bitumen specifications   Part I

Product	RC—0	RC—1	RC—2	RC—3	RC—4	RC—5
Flash point, °C			27°	27°	27°	27°
Furfural viscosity at 25 °C	70–150					
50 °C		70–150				
60 °C			100–200	250–500		
82 °C					125–250	300–600
Distillation to 190 °C (percentage of the	15+	10+				
225 °C distillate obtained	55+	50+	40+	25+	8+	
260 °C by distillation up	75+	70+	65+	55+	40+	25+
316 °C to 360 °C)	90+	88+	87+	83+	80+	70+
Residue of the 360 °C distillation, volume percent	50	60	67	73	78	82
Residue test Penetration at 25 °C, 100g, 5 sec	80–120	80–120	80–120	80–120	80–120	80–120
Ductility at 25 °C	100	100	100	100	100	100
Solubility in carbon tetrachloride	99.5	99.5	99.5	99.5	99.5	99.5

178

Table 29

Part II

Product	MC-0	MC-1	MC-2	MC-3	MC-4	MC-5
Flash point, °C	38 °C	38 °C	66 °C	66 °C	66 °C	66 °C
Furfural viscosity at 25 °C	75–150					
50 °C		75–150				
60 °C			100–200	250–500		
82 °C					125–250	300–600
Distillation to 190 °C (percentage of the distillate obtained by distillation up to 360 °C)	25– 40–70 75–93	20– 26–65 70–90	10– 15–55 60–87	5– 5–40 55–85	0 30– 40–80	0 20– 20–75
Residue of the 360 °C distillation, volume per cent	50	60	67	73	78	82
Residue test Penetration at 250 °C, 100 g, 5 sec	129–390	120–300	120–300	120–300	120–300	120–300
Ductility at 25 °C	100	100	100	100	100	100
Solubility in carbon tetrachloride	99.5	99.5	99.5	99.5	99.1	99.5

Product	SC-0	SC-1	SC-2	SC-3	SC-4	SC-5	SC-6
Flash point	66 °C	66 °C	80 °C	93 °C	107 °C	121 °C	135 °C
Furfural viscosity at 25 °C	75–100						
50 °C		76–100					
60 °C			100–200	250–500			
82 °C					125–250	300–600	250–500
Residue of the 360 °C distillation, volume per cent	15–40	10–30	5–25 *(total distillation to 360 °C)*	2–15	10	5	2
Residue test Ductility at 25 °C	100	100	100	100	100	100	100
Solubility in carbon tetrachloride	99.5	99.5	99.5	99.5	99.5	99.5	99.5

12*

Table 30

Liquid bitumen applications

HB type	Field of application
HB-0	Impregnation of cement or closed-grain-distribution type mechanical soil-stabilization surfaces without slackening, sand stabilization, dust removal from compact surfaces
HB-0 and HB-1	Impregnation of soils and other similar closed surfaces, spraying of levelling type spread-over and repair areas, stabilization of mixed grain-distribution soils and soil compounds under cool weather
HB-1 and HB-2	Stabilization of mixed grain-distribution type soils and soil compounds, coating closed surfaces, waterproof-surface coating, roughening, coating renewal by manual repair with stored mixture, binding loose particles, dust removal from loose surfaces
HB-2 and HB-3	Mechanical mixing of coarse-grain crushed materials

NOTE: In rainy weather or along shaded road sections an amount of adhesion-improving agent ("Evasin") corresponding to 0.2 per cent of the adhesive amount used must be admixed. The higher-viscosity version of the two can only be used in each case during the summer season.

ican Association of State Highway Officials). Interpretation of the data presented in the three parts of this table can be found in the relevant literature. The fields of application of liquid bitumens are summarized in Table 30. Generally, best stability can be achieved if the liquid bitumen is worked in at the maximum viscosity at which it can still be readily mixed.

Of the various bitumen emulsions, generally the stable, slowly breaking fine-distribution type varieties are best adaptable, but if machines mixing with a great deal of energy are applied, the emulsions of medium- and rapid-rate break-up will similarly render good results. For mixing and/or impregnation, only those types which, upon fracture, rainy weather, or clay effects, will not revert to the emulsion phase are suitable. Emulsion is best produced using a liquid bitumen corresponding to a penetration or viscosity of 50 to 200, and occasionally as much as 500. The bitumen content must be at least 50 per cent in order to prevent the emulsion water from overwetting the soil. The American specifications on emulsions are presented in Table 31.

If a heavy soil is to be treated with bitumen, it is often expedient to admix 1 or 2 per cent calcium hydrate for further improvement. Calcium hydrate will favourably change the structure of cohesive soils as described in Chapter 5, and improve adhesion between the inert soil particles and hydrocarbons. If the soil to be treated is a silt-free sand, then lime addition is required for better grain distribution.

180

Table 31

Emulsified asphalt specifications

Specification	Type	Viscosity, furfural, sec				Asphalt content		Demulsibility		
		25° min	25° max	50° min	50° max	min	max	N/50 min	CaCl₂ max	N/10 CaCl₂ max
AASHO	RS-1	20	100			55		30	90	
	RS-2			50	300	60		60		45
	MS-1	20	100			55				45
	MS-2	100				60				
	MS-3					65				
	MS-4					65				
	SS-1	20	100			57				
ASTM	RS-1	20	100			55	60	60		
	RS-2			75	400	63	68	60		
	MS-1	20	100			55	60			30
	MS-2	100				60	65			
	SS-1	20	100			57	62			
Asphalt Institute	RS-1	20	100			57	67	60		
	RS-2			75	400	62	69	50		
	MS-2	100				62	69			30
	SS-1	20	100			57	62			
	SS-1h	10	100			57	62			

6.2.2 Physico-chemical and mechanical aspects of stabilization

When mixing a particle aggregate, water, and bitumen, certain rather sophistic-ated physical and chemical processes are initiated. In such cases our aim, certainly with granular soils from Mo to fine sand, is to cover the individual grains with a bitumen film, thin enough not to overreduce the friction produced when the par-ticles are displaced, but thick enough to allow the intergranular adhesive effect to manifest itself. This takes place when the stress continuously affecting the particle aggregate is sufficient to slowly drive the bitumen out from the area around the contect points of the bitumen-coated particles (whereby the bitumen film would

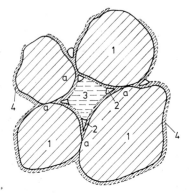

Fig. 158. Distribution of bituminous binder in sand. (1) solid particle; (2) air bubble; (3) pore water; (4) bitumen film

cover two or three grains as shown in Fig. 158), while the solid particles are almost in direct contact. If shear stresses affect such a system, then, upon the simultaneous normal and tangential stress effects, the bitumen film will be torn at several grain contact points, and considerable frictional resistances will be set up. When this movement stops, the interrupted bitumen film will gradually be restored. Since the vicinity of the contact point is "protected" by the high adhesion of the bitumen, water cannot enter that area, and the adhesive effect will be restored.

Among the bitumen-coated particles, water and air can be found. To examine qualitatively their location, let us consider the results of experiment (Buócz and Cságoly 1961) according to which a completely dry mineral-grain aggregate, or an aggregate containing less than only a few tenths of water percentage, will hardly mix with bitumen, or only at a very slow rate. The high water-content compounds will mix only with similar difficulties if at all, but the medium (4 to 12 per cent) water-content grain aggregates can be readily and efficiently mixed, whereafter the particles will be uniformly coated by bitumen.

This phenomenon can be explained by the surface-tension values and wetting energy between the individual parts of the compound. Regardless the material being dealt with, if it is to coat another material, this will only succeed if the adhesion between the two materials exceeds the cohesion of one coating material. The adhesion magnitudes at the normal temperature (about 20 °C) of the materials involved are illustrated in Fig. 159.

Accordingly, it is quite obvious that if the granular matter is dry, then a greater part of the grains are surrounded by air, and water will only be stored in certain corners. This is the case if the water content is only a few per cents as described above. However, the atmospheric gases will strongly adhere to the surface of the solid particles, so if liquid bitumen is added to this dry soil, it

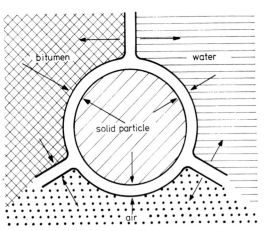

Fig. 159. Specific adhesion values between the materials of bituminous soil stabilization

will not be able to displace all the air quantity (which is limited by the internal shear resistance of the bitumen), and thus only a small fraction of the grain surface will exhibit direct contact adhesion, and a bitumen coating. If, on the other hand, too much water is involved, it will be present not only among or around the particles as corner or film water, but it will also fill up the larger intergranular voids. In order to create adhesion between the bitumen and the soil particles, this water should first be driven out of the voids, then the film water should be separated from the surface of the particles. However, this might prove impossible because of the differences in adhesion. Further, if the water and air volumes in the intergranular voids have the favourable ratio described above, then, because of the repulsive effect between water and air, the bitumen will be able to find a path along the boundary surfaces of these voids to the surface of the particles. There it will enter a bond as a result of its strong adhesion and thus bring about the adhesive action and desired effect. The rate of this process depends partly on the magnitude of the resultant specific force of attraction and, to a certain degree, on the surface of the grain assembly (the effect exerted by bitumen in heavy soils is analyzed in 6.24).

It follows that, from bituminous stabilization aspects, that the soil composition by phases (the s, v, l triplet) must have an optimum at which mixing can be most efficiently performed, and yet, in consequence, the strength of the mixture is also a maximum, as verified by a number of test results.

Similarly, a curve revealing an optimum value is obtained if the effect of the amount of bitumen is studied, as in Fig. 160 where the Hveem stability of a stabilized soil is illustrated as a function of bitumen addition. This phenomenon can be explained by the fact that the displacement of the adhesive from the vicinity of the contact points will fail at more and more points with the quantity increase: the strength of the stabilized soil is governed increasingly by the natural strength of the thickening bitumen layers, and the intergranular friction can no longer manifest itself.

Unfortunately, the available data are still insufficient for the limitation of the optimum ranges as described above to certain individual soil types. This is why the triangle diagram of Fig. 161 can offer only estimated information and cannot be used for practical purposes or, more precisely, the laboratory-test results illustrated by this figure simply cannot be generalized.

Let us discuss now the rheological properties of bitumen stabilized soils. Such examinations are based on the following assumptions:

(a) the strength of the material consists of an initial resistance and a frictional resistance, as shown in Fig. 162a;

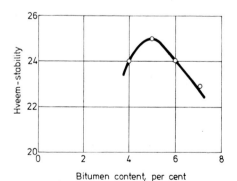

FIG. 160. Stability of a bitumen stabilized soil as a function of the bitumen content

183

(b) upon the effect of plastic deformations the τ_e and ϕ values do not change:

(c) the yield phenomenon can be described by a given viscosity whose value is independent of the rate of deformation, that is,

$$\tau = \eta \frac{\partial s}{\partial t} \tag{51}$$

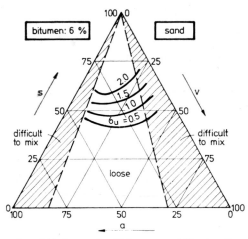

FIG. 161. Strength of bitumen stabilized soils as a function of composition by phases

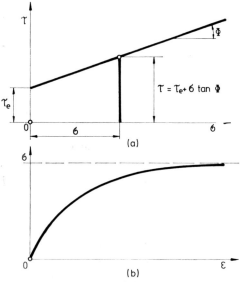

FIG. 162. Assumptions of the theoretical examination, (a) material strength; (b) deformation curve

Let us now express the stresses along the plane of an inclination in the three-dimensional stress state, when $\sigma_2 = \sigma_3$. As it is known,

$$\sigma = \frac{\sigma_1 + \sigma_3}{2} + \frac{\sigma_1 - \sigma_3}{2} \cos 2\alpha \tag{52}$$

$$\tau = \frac{\sigma_1 - \sigma_3}{2} \sin 2\alpha$$

(see Fig. 163).

The maximum shear stress will be produced over the surface having an included angle of 45° with the plane of the principal stresses, at a value of

$$\tau_{max} = \frac{\sigma_1 - \sigma_3}{2}$$

For homogeneous and isotropic materials the generalized Hooke law may be written:

$$\varepsilon_1 = \frac{1}{E} [\sigma_1 - \mu(\sigma_2 + \sigma_3)]$$

$$\varepsilon_2 = \frac{1}{E} [\sigma_2 - \mu(\sigma_1 + \sigma_3)] \tag{53}$$

$$\varepsilon_3 = \frac{1}{E} [\sigma_3 - \mu(\sigma_1 + \sigma_2)]$$

In this case $\sigma_2 = \sigma_3$, and if a constant volume is assumed, then $\mu = 0.5$ may be substituted, when

$$\varepsilon_3 = -\frac{\varepsilon_1}{2} \tag{54}$$

184

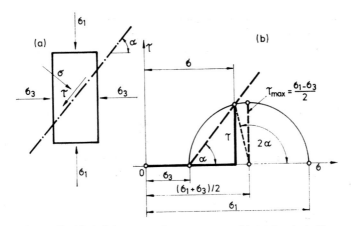

FIG. 163. (a) Axial symmetric stress state; (b) Mohr-circle illustration of the stress state

With the principal deformations produced by the principal stresses known, the shear deformation can be readily determined. The simplest way is represented by the Mohr circle of the deformations which, from Fig. 164, can be read off as

$$\left(\frac{\gamma}{2}\right)_{max} = \frac{3}{4}\varepsilon_1$$

In a homogeneous and isotropic material we get

$$\gamma_\alpha = \gamma_{max} \sin 2\alpha = \frac{3}{2}\varepsilon_1 \sin 2\alpha$$

The shear rate will be

$$\frac{d\gamma_\alpha}{dt} = \frac{d\gamma_{max}}{dt} \sin 2\alpha$$

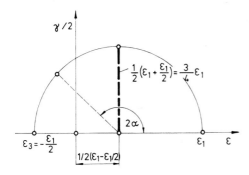

FIG. 164. Mohr circle of the deformations

Let us indicate the rate of shear deformation by D; then

$$D_\alpha = D_{max} \sin 2\alpha \qquad (55)$$

Following this introduction, the theory of the resistance of bitumen-plus-granular-additive mixtures against plastic deformation can be easily derived. According to the assumption under (a)

$$\tau_{visc} = K\eta D$$

185

where η is the viscosity of the liquid phase,

K is a factor expressing the effect of the granular additive on the viscous resistance, and

$K\eta$ is the mass viscosity, η_m.

In a granular medium, the stresses are transferred from one particle to another. If the voids contain bitumen, the effective intergranular stresses will be modified by the effect of the stresses needed for the movement of the liquid phase.

Let us take a viscous medium whose mass viscosity is $K\eta$. Let the principal stress values be σ'_1, and σ'_3. Then over the 45° inclination plane we get

$$\tau' = \frac{\sigma'_1 - \sigma'_3}{2}$$

and, on the basis of Eq. (55),

$$D'_{max} = \frac{3}{2} \frac{d\varepsilon_1}{dt}$$

whereby

$$\frac{\sigma'_1 - \sigma'_3}{2} = K\eta \frac{3}{2} \frac{d\varepsilon_1}{dt} \tag{56}$$

At a plane making an angle a with the plane of the first principal stress, we shall then have

$$\sigma' = \frac{\sigma'_1 + \sigma'_3}{2} + \frac{\sigma'_1 - \sigma'_3}{2} \cos 2\alpha = \frac{\sigma'_1 + \sigma'_3}{2} + \frac{3}{2} K\eta \frac{d\varepsilon_1}{dt} \cos 2\alpha, \tag{57}$$

$$\tau' = \frac{\sigma'_1 - \sigma'_3}{2} \sin 2\alpha = \frac{3}{2} K\eta \frac{d\varepsilon_1}{d\tau} \sin 2\alpha \tag{58}$$

It may be assumed that such (σ', τ') stresses are needed to overcome the viscous resistance of the material. Now let us look for the correlation between the total

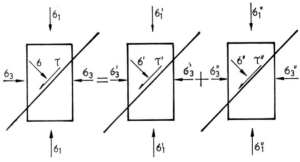

FIG. 165. Shear stress components

186

shear stress acting on the plane with angle α and the components obtained as described above. According to the schematic illustration of Fig. 165, the shear stress consists of viscous, initial, and frictional resistances or, as expressed in the form of an equation,

$$\tau = \tau' = \tau_e + (\sigma - \sigma') \tan \phi \tag{59}$$

After substitution we get

$$\frac{\sigma_1 - \sigma_3}{2} \sin 2\alpha = \frac{3}{2} K\eta \frac{d\varepsilon_1}{dt} \sin 2\alpha + \tau_e +$$

$$+ \tan \phi \left(\frac{\sigma_1 + \sigma_3}{2} + \frac{\sigma_1 - \sigma_3}{2} \cos \alpha - \frac{\sigma_1' + \sigma_3'}{2} - \frac{3}{2} K\eta \frac{d\varepsilon_1}{dt} \cos 2\alpha \right) \tag{60}$$

Differentiating the above equation with respect to α, it is easy to demonstrate that the inclination of the sliding plane will again be

$$\alpha_0 = 45° + \frac{\phi}{2}$$

independent of the initial and viscous resistances. Substituting this value, and performing trigonometric transformations, we get

$$\frac{\sigma_1 - \sigma_3}{2} \cos \phi - \frac{3}{2} K\eta \frac{d\varepsilon_1}{dt} \cos \phi =$$

$$= \tan \phi \left[\frac{\sigma_1 + \sigma_3}{2} + \frac{\sigma_1 - \sigma_3}{2} (-\sin \phi) - \frac{\sigma_1' + \sigma_3'}{2} - \frac{3}{2} K\eta \frac{d\varepsilon_1}{dt} (-\sin \phi) + \tau_e \right]$$

and, thence,

$$\frac{\sigma_1 - \sigma_3 - 3K\eta \dfrac{d\varepsilon_1}{dt}}{2} \cdot \frac{1}{\cos \phi} = \frac{\sigma_1 + \sigma_3 - \sigma_1' - \sigma_3'}{2} \tan \phi + \tau_e \tag{61}$$

Let us now perform the following transformation:

$$\sigma_1' + \sigma_2' + \sigma_3' = \frac{\sigma_1' + \sigma_2' + \sigma_3'}{3} + \frac{2(\sigma_1' + \sigma_2' + \sigma_3')}{3}$$

Assuming no volume change in the almost saturated mass, we obtain

$$\frac{\sigma_1' + \sigma_2' + \sigma_3'}{3} = 0$$

and since

$$\sigma_2' = \sigma_3' ; \qquad \sigma_1' + 2\sigma_3' = 0 ; \qquad \sigma_1' - \sigma_3' = 3K\eta \frac{d\varepsilon_1}{dt}$$

we get

$$\sigma_1' = 2K\eta \frac{d\varepsilon_1}{dt}$$

$$\sigma_3' = -K\eta \frac{d\varepsilon_1}{dt}$$

whose substitution into Eq. (61) gives

$$K\eta \frac{d\varepsilon_1}{dt} = \frac{2\cos\phi}{3-\sin\phi} \left[\frac{\sigma_1 - \sigma_3}{2\cos\phi} - \frac{\sigma_1 + \sigma_3}{2} \tan\phi - \tau_e \right] \qquad (62)$$

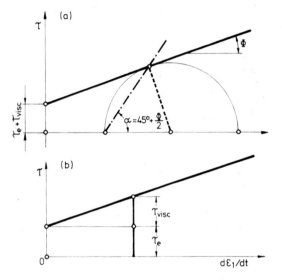

FIG. 166. (a) Shear strength of a bituminous soil; (b) determination of the two shear strength components

Equation (62) is the fundamental relation describing the behaviour of a granular matter mixed with bitumen, when the mixture is under the effect of a spatial stress state, and the rate of deformation equals $d\varepsilon/dt$. Equation (62) can be illustrated by the Mohr circle, as shown in Fig. 166a. While the ("neutral") stresses prevailing in the liquid equal zero, ϕ will remain constant and independent of the rate of load increase. If the experiment involves several different velocities, the straight lines of Fig. 166a will intersect the τ axis at different $\tau_e + \tau_{\mathrm{visc}}$ values. Plotting these intersections as a function $(d\varepsilon_1(dt)$ of the rate of deformation we can determine the value of τ_e and with τ_e known, the value of $K\eta(=\eta_m)$ can also be calculated. Finally, knowing all these data, the behaviour, strength, and slow-rate deformation of the stabilized soil can be evaluated.

6.2.3 Properties of bitumen-stabilized soils

Let us now examine the factors affecting the characteristic properties of bitumen-stabilized soils.

The first is naturally the soil-type itself. Although almost every inorganic soil that can be mixed with bitumen is suitable for stabilization, the best results can be achieved with the soil types meeting the following requirements:

188

(1) The largest grain diameter must not exceed one-third of the compacted thickness of the treated soil layer;

(2) The weight per cent of particles smaller than 4.76 mm (passing through mesh No. 4) should exceed 50 per cent;

(3) The weight per cent of particles smaller than 0.42 mm (passing through mesh No. 40) should be between 35 and 100 per cent;

(4) The weight per cent of particles smaller than 0.074 mm (passing through mesh No. 200) should be between 10 and 50 per cent;

(5) The liquid limit of the soil must not exceed $w_L = 40$ per cent;

(6) The plasticity index should be less than 18 per cent.

The grain-size distribution-curve range meeting the above requirements is illustrated in Fig. 167, where it is shown to be rather wide. More detailed relevant

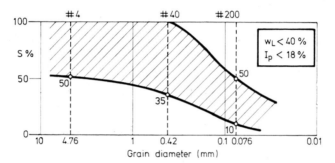

FIG. 167. Grain-size distribution range of the soils suitable for advantageous stabilization with bitumen

specifications are given by the Highway Research Board (USA), as summarized in Table 32. Mixtures advantageous from mechanical stabilization aspects can also be taken as a basis.

The Kari classification referred to in the introduction of this Chapter has selected the soils adaptable in the ATB and ASB categories considered as soil stabilization on the basis of sand-equivalent values. Accordingly, ATB (asphalt-treated base) stabilization can make good use of soils of a sand equivalent at least 30, and whose fine grains do not make this soil type plastic, whereas for ASB (asphalt-soil base) purposes the soils of a sand equivalent of minimum 20, and a plasticity index of 10 per cent maximum may be employed.

If the soil contains organic matter of acidic reaction, it cannot be stabilized with bitumen. For an inorganic soil of acidic reaction (pH < 6), stabilization must be preceded by lime addition. In dry regions of insufficient precipitation, the cohesive soils have a rather high pH, and contain much dissolved salt, so these also fail to be suitable for stabilization.

As emphasized before, one of the most important characteristics of a stabilized soil is its degree of compact. If liquid bitumen is admixed to a soil, its compactibil-

189

Table 32

Grain-distribution data of mixtures suitable for bituminous stabilization

Screen No.	Mesh mm	In-situ mixed asphalt treated base			In-situ mixed stabilized soil		
		open	compact	sand	coarse	medium	fine
	63.5	—	—	—	100	—	—
	50.8	—	—	—	90–100	100	—
	38.1	100	—	—	—	90–100	—
	25.4	90–100	—	—	—	—	100
	19	40–75	100	—	50–80	50–80	80–100
	12.7	15–35	80–100	—	—	—	—
	9.5	0–15	70–90	—	—	—	—
4		0–5	50–70	100	25–50	25–50	25–50
8		—	35–50	—	—	—	—
30		—	18–29	50–100	—	—	—
50		—	13–23	—	—	—	—
100		—	8–16	—	—	—	—
200		—	4–10	3–15	3–15	3–15	3–15

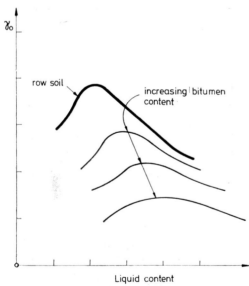

FIG. 168. The effect of bitumen addition on soil compaction

ity will usually change according to Fig. 168: upon the effect of an increasing bitumen content the feasible dry density will decrease, while the optimum liquid content (water-plus-liquid-bitumen weight per cent as related to the dry weight) will increase. An actual measurement result is shown in Fig. 169. However, this effect is not always of the same type: Puzinauskas (1961) claims that results according to Fig. 170 can also occur. —

An important point in stabilization efficiency is indicated by the strength of the compacted mixture. Usually, the correlation shown in Fig. 171 can be observed: the bitumen content has an optimum as may be concluded by examining of the structure. Up to about 4 per cent bitumen addition the strength

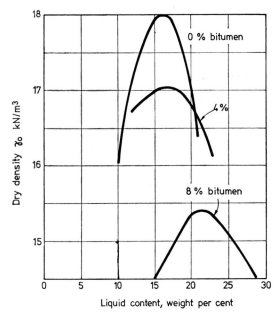

FIG. 169. Proctor curves of a sandy clay at different bitumen contents

would increase, then decrease, and then values even less than that of the non-stabilized soil strength might be obtained. This strength reduction is correlated to what was shown by Fig. 168: for an increasing bitumen content the maximum dry unit weight would decrease if only because of the lower specific gravity of the bitumen.

The strength value usually a confined compression strength figure, after the composition of the mixture, is usually not the only standard of the behaviour characterizing the mix. Particularly in the case of cohesive soils some expansion, structure destruction, loosening, or simply a strength reduction may also be observed because the small amount of bitumen could not make the soil waterproof. In order to study this effect, the samples made of the stabilized soil mix are kept under wet conditions for 4 days, then submerged for further 4 days. Based on the strength reduction of the specimens thus treated, we may then decide the bitumen admixture for which the optimum result could be achieved. Such an experimental result

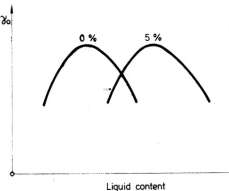

FIG. 170. A rare effect of bitumen addition on compactibility

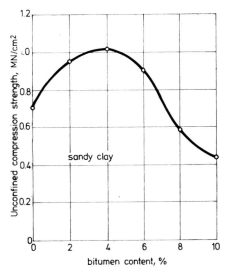

FIG. 171. The effect of bitumen addition on the unconfined compression strength of the mixture

191

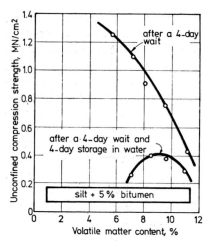

FIG. 172. The effect of storage in water on the unconfined compression strength of bitumen-stabilized silt

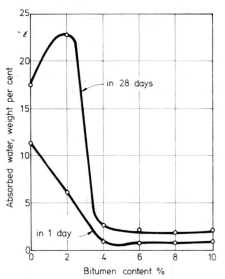

FIG. 173. Water absorption of a stabilized soil as a function of the bitumen content

of the Asphalt Institute, USA, is presented in Fig. 172. The same effect is investigated by the water-absorption test, so some relevant results must also be presented. Figure 173 illustrates the test results of the British Road Research Laboratory obtained after the water-absorption experiments described in Section 2.13, where the value of the amount of absorbed water is shown as a function of the bitumen content. It is interesting to observe that a 2 per cent bitumen addition has still increased the water quantity absorbed during 28 days, probably because such a small amount of bitumen could hardly provide any resistance to water, whereas the compactness of the soil would definitely decrease upon a bitumen admixture. Upon the effect of bitumen addition of more than 4 per cent, the water absorption might considerably decrease.

The mixing time also plays an important role. Strength, particularly of the wet samples, generally increases with the mixing time, and always when stabilizing sands. At the beginning of the mixing time, the bitumen may coat caked-particle aggregates which will disintegrate again during subsequent mixing, and increase the total surface. The result is that there is not sufficient bitumen for coating, causing a rise in water absorption (see Fig. 174).

Another effect deserving mention is that of the post-treatment. Generally, the longer the post-treatment period and the higher its temperature, the more volatile matter will be given off. A correlation rather important to stabilization-quality was demonstrated by Michaels and Puzinauskas (1956): regardless of the bituminous-soil-mixture type being dealt with, the higher its volatile-matter content during the test, the lower its compression strength. This applies to emulsions, liquid-bitumen varieties, and mixtures modified with different additives (see Section 6.24). The general character and scatter range (standard deviation) of this correlation are illustrated in Fig. 175.

For testing bitumen-stabilized soils and for their qualification, in addition to the compression strength, compactibility, density, and the extent of water absorption, a number of other test methods have also been suggested and are used today in many countries. These include, among others, the Marshall test, the Hubbard – Field method (see Fig. 176), the Florida test, and the CBR technique. Their common feature is that they are rather arbitrary, and the figures obtained as qualification results can only be correlated to the behaviour of the road or foundation made of stabilized soil by very extensive statistical data collec-

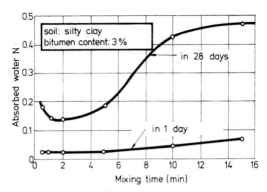

FIG. 174. Water absorption of a stabilized soil vs. mixing time

tion. Although this statement applies more or less to every procedure in road construction, in soil mechanics and, generally, in material testing as well, the author believes that there are different arbitrary character grades, and that, for example, the unconfined compression strength regardless of its dependence on the dimensions of the specimen, the rate of load application, etc. would characterize the material much more clearly and directly than e.g.

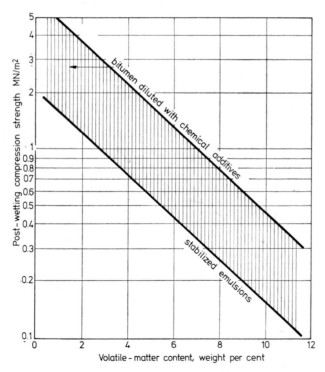

FIG. 175. Post-wetting strength of bitumen-stabilized soils as a function of the volatile matter content

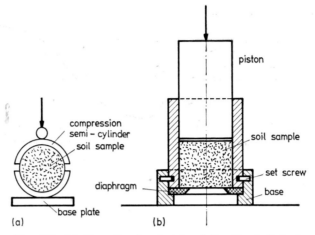

FIG. 176. (a) Operational principle of the Marshall device;
(b) Schematic illustration of the Hubbard—Field instrument

the Hubbard—Field stability In order to verify this statement, let us briefly review the methods referred to.

In the Marshall test, a 10 cm < and 6.35 cm high cylindrical specimen, produced in the Proctor equipment by precisely specified compaction, is stored at room temperature for seven days, then compressed in the device illustrated in Fig. 176a between the cylinder jacket-shaped head parts at a predetermined rate of deformation. The specimen will undergo a yield effect upon loading, after which it will not be able to withstand any more loading at all. The compression force producing this yield is the so-called Marshall stability.

The Hubbard—Field technique consists of preparing a 100 g weight and 50 mm < specimen of the bituminous mixture, with the stamping and static compaction parameters specified. The sample is then placed into a cylinder, see Fig. 176b which is placed into another cylinder having a diaphragm opening of a 44 mm diameter. The specimen is loaded by a piston causing a downward compression at a constant rate of 1 mm/sec. The compression force measured by a dynamometer is continuously increases until the material of the sample starts flowing out of the diaphragm orifice. Thus the Hubbard—Field stability is a measure of the maximum compression force.

With the stability value determined for several different bitumen contents, the best addition can be chosen empirically.

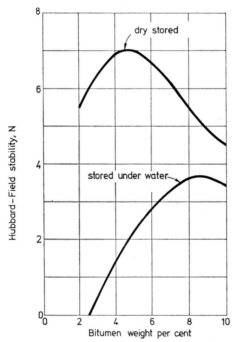

FIG. 177. Hubbard—Field stability value as a function of the bitumen addition

194

Thus, for example, according to results, the best mixture has a Hubbard—Field stability of at least 500 kp for samples stored outdoors for 24 hours, and 200 kp minimum with underwater stored samples. An experimental result is illustrated in Fig. 177 (Boromissza, 1965). During the test period, the laboratory temperature should be maintained at 18–22 °C. According to the findings of Boromissza and Gáspár (1961), although a correlation exists between the two stability indices referred to above and the CBR value, the scatter is excessive (Fig. 178).

The Florida stability test consists of ramming the bituminous mixture into a metal cube of 7.07 cm edge length, then compressing it with a static weight. After seven days a 1" diameter disc is pressed onto the centre of the top side, at a rate of 1.25 mm/min, and the force pertaining to an indentation of 3 mm depth is determined. If this is 550 kp minimum, the mixture is satisfactory.

Finally the CBR method deserves mention. It is widely known in soil mechanics for road construction and is very useful in the qualification of bituminous soil mixtures.

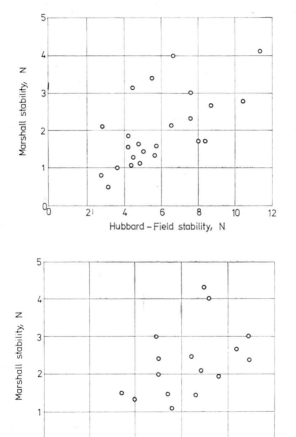

FIG. 178. Correlation between the Marshall, Hubbard—
Field, and CBR values, respectively

6.2.4 The effect of additives on bitumen-stabilized soils

Some years ago detailed investigations were conducted (Michaels and Puzi-nauskas 1956, 1958) on the improvement of the bituminous soil stabilization method using various additives. The most promising results could be achieved with phosphorus pentoxide (P_2O_5). A typical result is shown in Fig. 179, where the unconfined compression strength of a silt is indicated as a function of mixing time, with and without the addition of P_2O_5.

The results of a still more detailed test are illustrated in Fig. 180, presenting the unconfined compression strength values of five different soil types, with the addition of 10 per cent bitumen and different amounts of phosphorus pentoxide. The effect is greater for relatively coarser soils, and similarly favourable results were observed if amine compounds had been admixed, although this only occurred with fine-grain soil types. Michaels and Puzinauskas explained this considerable strength increasing effect as follows:

When a wet cohesive soil is mixed with a normal quantity of liquid bitumen, the total liquid content of the soil is usually more than that needed to fill the voids of the compacted soil. In the course of mixing, the non-wetting bitumen phase will be dispersed among the soil particles or caked-grain aggregates in the form of minute spheres or threads. The extent of admixture (that may be characterized by the average diameter of these spheres and the uniformity of their distribution) and the disintegration of the aggregates depend on the time and efficiency of the mixing

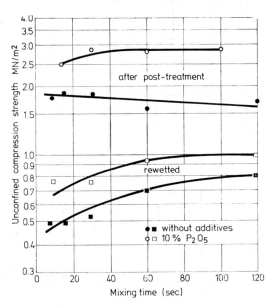

FIG. 179. The effect of mixing time and phosphorus pentoxide addition on the strength of bitumen-stabilized soils

process. During the compaction of the mixture the free void area will decrease, and part of the volatile matter (water plus solvent) will evaporate, whereas the dispersed bitumen particles are compressed into shives and filaments which occupy a considerable part of the void space. Due to the capillary forces, the asphalt phase will be limited to the major pores and ducts, while the water occupies the pores of the fine tissues in the soil mass. In this stage, the mixture is a compact aggregate of particles and grain clods wetted by water and enclosed by almost coherent bitumen particles (Figs 181 and 182). When the mixture has dried, contraction would cause further dispersion, but this is inhibited by the simultaneous increase in viscosity. If the soil has no natural cohesion, the adhesion of the bitumen to the soil particles will bring about cohesion in the whole mass during the evaporation of the water, just as that illustrated in Fig. 159. The strength thus produced will be approximately proportional to the

No	Soil type	w_L	I_p	w_{opt}	d<0.1	d<0.002
1 ○	Sandy silt	—	—	14	47	3
2 △	Clayey silt	20	6	12	62	10
3 □	Sandy clay	32	14	16	61	18
4 ●	Loess	41	15	18	100	3
5 ×	Clay	60	32	22	100	35

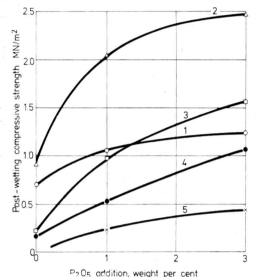

FIG. 180. Compression strength of bitumen-stabilized soils as a function of phosphorus pentoxide addition

ratio between the bitumen-filled up voids and the total void volume. If, on the other hand, the bitumen is admixed to a cohesive soil, then the presence of bitumen during the drying process will partly prevent the creation of intergranular bonds, even some of the particles will adhere. Since the strength of these bonds is much greater than the adhesion between bitumen and soil particles, the dry strength

FIG. 181. Bitumen distribution in the soil, (a) without surface-active additives; (b) with surface-active additives

197

of the mixture will be reduced. If the liquid bitumen treated soil is submerged in water, the capillary forces will cause the water to enter the sample through the open pores and channels. However, since the larger pores are filled with bitumen, and many elements of the soil mass are probably also coated by bitumen, the rate of water penetration and the saturation after a longer period of time will be much less than in the case of the original soil. The larger the specific surface of the aggregate, the smaller the probability that a given pore might be clogged or a soil particle coated by bitumen. This is why the strength of an aggregate consisting of coarser grains would decrease to a lesser degree upon the effect of submersion in water.

When the solvent has evaporated from the soil stabilized with liquid bitumen, the particles of the latter will occupy only about one-third of the void space. The resistance of the mixture to water will only be significant if the bitumen had been allocated so as to prevent, as far as possible, the water from penetrating the soil structure. This is encountered when the bitumen, as a protective film, could enclose relatively large soil particles or aggregates which have no bitumen inside. Thus a much more favourable situation ffiust develop than in the case of a "perfect" bitumen dispersion, when only one in every three voids would be filled by bitumen. It follows that in a cohesive soil the bitumen has an optimum dispersion where the water absorption is minimum. This optimum distribution can be promoted in

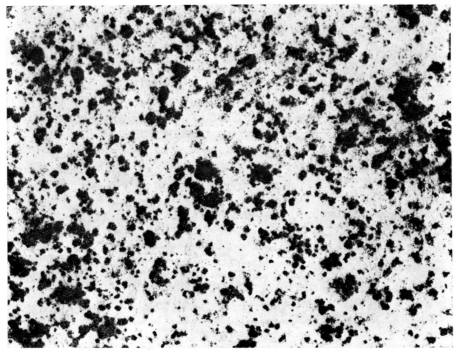

FIG. 182. Mixture of bitumen and granular soil in coarse dispersion

two ways: either a certain solvent must be used and in such a quantity provide for the "optimum" viscosity and impede excessive distribution, or the soil particles and aggregates should be stabilized to prevent them from disintegrating during the mixing process.

Another important factor in bituminous stabilization is the mobility of bitumen in the soil. If the bitumen remains sufficiently liquid after post-treatment or drying, then the water penetrating into the soil through the capillaries will attempt to remove it. Accordingly, for the stabilization of heavy soils the higher viscosity bitumen varieties are preferred. However, this effect will not manifest itself if an adhesion increasing agent is added.

The effect of the above additives can be explained as follows.

The adhesion of bitumen to the surface of the solid soil particles is relatively small. In heavy soils some of these particles are clay minerals of a considerable surface activity. Over such surfaces a water film is usually bonded. However, these are materials, including the amine compounds mentioned above, whose attraction to the grain surface is stronger than that of the water, so their molecules will displace the water. If, then, the active surface of the clay mineral exhibits an affinity to the bitumen after the transformation, the latter will adhere strongly to the particles. Thus the additives play a dual role: on one hand, they make the particle surfaces easy to wet as against the bitumen effects while, on the other, they promote the coagulation of grains and thus create larger aggregates which will then reduce the specific surface. In consequence, the bitumen quantity required for coating will similarly decrease. The first effect actually makes the soil waterproof, as the bitumen is no longer distributed in droplet form, and can much more efficiently coat the particles or their aggregates than without the additive. The structure of such a stabilized soil can be imagined as that shown in Fig. 181b, where the practically bitumen-free soil clods or particle aggregates are enclosed by an almost continuous lamellar bitumen structure. The stabilized soils of this structure are much more water resistant than those without any modifying additives admixed.

The compression strength of bitumen stabilized heavy soils is governed primarily by the strength of the bitumen-coated soil particles and aggregates. Consequently, every process or reaction that can increase the strength of these assemblies in wet condition within the soil will increase the strength of the whole stabilized soil as well and, at the same time, it will reduce expansion by preventing the individual particles from yielding to displacement. If phosphorus pentoxide is admixed to wet soil, it will form phosphoric acid with the water present:

$$P_2O_5 + 3\,H_2O = 2\,H_3PO_4$$

Since these acidic phosphorus compounds improve the strength of cohesive soils (see Chapter 7), they are capable increasing the internal strength of the particle aggregates, so increasing the strength of the stabilized soil itself. The larger the "virtual" grain size of the soil, that is, the greater number of individual grains are caked or cemented into an aggregate, the better the fine grain soils can be stabilized with bitumen.

Table 33

Selection of additives for various soil types

Character of the internal soil surface	Additives admixed
1. Complex Fe and Al silicates; the $SiO_2(Al_2O_3 + Fe_2O_3$ ratio exceeds 2; Most clay particles are of a negative charge (podsol type soil).	Organic cations produced by substituting one or more hydrogens in NH_4OH by organic roots.
2. Clay minerals, if $SiO_2/R_2O_3 < 2$, with or without Fe and Al hydroxides, typical under hot and moist climatic conditions. With increased Al_2O_3 and Fe_2O_3 quantities the negative charge of the clay mineral surfaces will decrease, and the positive charge increase.	The positive charge parts of the clay mineral surfaces can react with greasy, resinous, or other large molecule organic acids and soaps.
3. There are stable secondary grain aggregates present, coated by a humus layer rich in lignine, protein, and wax-type materials. Chernozem and other semi-arid soils.	Materials able to react with the organic matter content of the soil should be admixed, forming hydrophobic synthetic resins.
4. Desert, saline, or alkaline soils, typical wherever evaporation exceeds the amount of precipitation.	Two or more chemicals are to be admixed to the soil forming a strong water repellent film on the particles, independently of the pH and salt content of the system.

There have been many additives promoting bituminous stabilization suggested and employed, and the mechanism so produced has been described earlier. The best result is achieved, of course, if the materials added to the bitumen react with the inorganic compounds of the mineral surfaces, and form there water repellent compounds which are then bound by strong primary bonds. For the correct selection of the reactive additive, the chemical properties of the soil component mineral surfaces should be known as precisely as possible, this applying mainly to the cations bonded by the clay minerals of negative charge. This selection of the additives is greatly aided by Table 33.

To conclude the physico-chemical discussion of bituminous soil stabilization, the empirical data collected by Winterkorn (1946, 1953, 1963) should be mentioned. After experimentation for several years, he arrived at the following conclusions:

1. The greater the silicon content of the clay minerals in the soil, the more bitumen is needed for a satisfactory soil stabilization (illite and montmorillonite have a high content, the kaolinite-type clay minerals have a low silicon content).

2. The more iron and aluminum compounds the clay minerals contain, the easier the soil stabilization with bitumen.

3. The higher the valency of the exchangeable ions in the clay, the easier the soil stabilization with bitumen.

4. The effect of the soil's organic matter content depends on the conditions of its origin. Organic substances of an acidic reaction have a detrimental effect, while the neutral organic materials or those of an alkaline reaction do not.

5. Among the monovalent ions the sodium is always detrimental. The bivalent calcium may exert either a detrimental or a favourable effect.

6.2.5 Design of bituminous mixtures

There have been several different methods published in literature for designing bituminous mixtures, like the Marshall and the Hubbard-Field techniques referred to earlier, which specify the minimum stability index defined by a separate test, and determine the bitumen addition as well as the extent of compaction so as to satisfy this requirement. However, it was mentioned that bituminous soil stabilization could not be used as an independent pavement without a top cover in road construction. This means that the soil layer stabilized with bitumen will represent part of a complex pavement system, one of its several layers, so it cannot be dimensioned independently, but only as a part of the complete system. This is why the

Table 34

Bitumen types adaptable for the different soils

Mixture	Soil type	Binder (10 mm mesh consistometer)
Loose, open grain structure mix	Sand	In cool weather HB-0, above 15 °C HB-1; stable, high bitumen content emulsion
	Natural or synthetic mixture of a Macadam grain-size distribution	In cool weather HB-2, under warmer conditions HB-3
Compact mix	Most of the grains are smaller than 0.09 mm	HB-0
	Extended grain-size distribution, d_{max} — 25 mm	In cool weather HB-0
Plastic mixture	Cohesive soil, silt, lean clay	In cool weather HB-2, under warmer conditions HB-3

dimensioning methods are not discussed in this volume. It should be noted, however, that the best methods of dimensioning elastic coatings are the CBR technique and the process elaborated by the Asphalt Institute, USA. The former provides for a somewhat greater safety.

The following renders information on the approximate determination of the amount of bitumen needed. In selecting the bitumen type to be used, partly economic aspects and partly the climatic factors will be of utmost importance, as specified in Table 34.

Generally, the bitumen requirement is determined by detailed laboratory examinations, on the basis of the data by Pätzhold who claimed that the critical factor should be the grain-size distribution curve of the soil to be stabilized: the finer the grains, the greater the amount of adhesive needed. As seen before, however, this statement in the above form may be applied only to granular soils, sand, fine sand, non-plastic rock flour, and perhaps the soil mixtures of mechanical

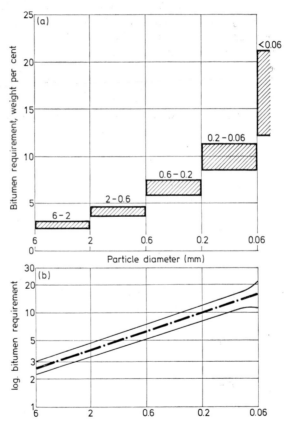

FIG. 183. Bitumen requirement of the individual grain fractions according to Pätzhold, (a) semi-log; (b) log-log scale

202

stabilization. Other important factors include the expected load on the stabilized layer, its traffic stress, and the mixer available. By testing samples taken from stabilizations proved acceptable in practice, Pätzhold suggested the determination of the adhesive requirement of the individual grain fractions according to Fig. 183. This indicates the scatter extent experienced, and the curve represents the average. If the curve connecting the mean values is plotted in a log-log system (Fig. 183b), then a straight line is obtained, that is, the bitumen requirement of the fractions tested is the exponential function of the transient maximum grain size. Figure 183b also indicates the scatter range, and it is rather conspicuous that the standard deviation is much greater in the small grain domain, because the subsequent determination of the amount of bitumen is increasingly inaccurate with an increasing particle diameter. These data apply to $40/70 - 140/240$ mp viscosity materials, and soils containing max 50 weight per cent of grains smaller than 0.2 mm.

The quantity thus calculated is taken as a starting point for further tests: the strength experiments involve the mixtures thus obtained, as well as those of approximately 0.5–1 per cent bitumen contents, respectively. Further information is supplied by the following relation, based on the detailed investigations of Johnson (1957):

$$p = 0.015\,a + 0.02\,b + 0.03\,c + 0.09\,d \qquad (63)$$

where p is the bitumen quantity expressed as a percentage of the dry weight of the soil without the solvent and/or diluent quantity,

        a, b, c, and d values are determined on the basis of the grain distribution curve of the soil, according to Fig. 184.

It should be noted here that, according to Eq. (63), the bitumen quantity to be admixed is determined primarily by the fine-grain proportion, that is, the weight per cent of particles smaller than 0.074 mm. If the calculation results are plotted as a function of quantity d, then the data of Fig. 185 will be obtained: the points lie on a straight line whose equation is

$$p\% = 2.75 + 0.064\,d \qquad (64)$$

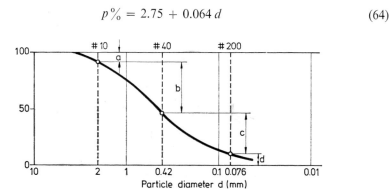

Fig. 184. Determination of the quantities of Eq. (63) from the grain-size distribution curve

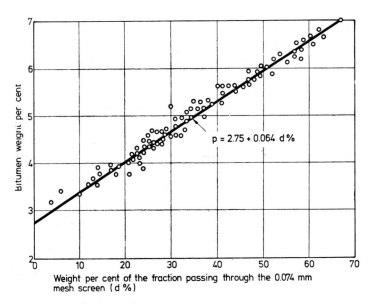

FIG. 185. The bitumen quantity required on the basis of the grain-size distribution curve

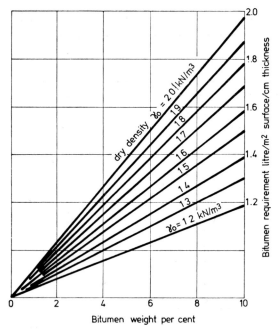

FIG. 186. Bitumen quantity to be admixed per 1 m²
road surface and 1 cm layer thickness

which is very much suitable for approximate calculations. Based on the asphalt quantity determined by weight per cent, Fig. 186 supplies the bitumen amount to be admixed per 1 cm thickness and 1 m² surface of the stabilized layer.

6.3 Stabilization with tar

Uniform grain size but poorly graduated fine sands, common in Hungary on the surface, may be stabilized with tar. Along low-traffic roads, the tar-plus-sand cover mix will provide a stabilization quite suitable for road construction purposes. However, investigations revealed that tar addition in itself will not be sufficient to bind such sands as the strength of the mixture is too low, and these mixtures cannot be compacted satisfactorily. The tar admixed to the soil (always slightly wet) will cool off rapidly, so it fails to have uniform distribution and so requires the addition of a diluent and/or an increased mixing energy.

The above disadvantages can be eliminated by adding a filler to the mixture which acts as an emulsifier, improves the unfavourable grain distribution of the basic material, and makes it easy to compact.

Apart from the very cohesive and hard soils, almost every soil type can be stabilized with tar. Particularly good results can be achieved if the grain distribution curve of the soil corresponds to mechanical stabilization. Even deficient or absolutely uniform grain distribution type soils may be tar stabilized. For soils containing larger fine-grain quantities the so-called road-tar emulsion is preferred, while for coarser soils the ordinary road tar is preferred. The relevant grain-size distribution-curve ranges are illustrated in Fig. 187.

Stabilization can make use of coal-tar products alone. The viscosity of the binder should be determined as a function of the grain-size distribution and the mixing technique. Soils easy to mix, such as uniform grain distribution type sands, fine sands, etc., may be treated with either dilute or thick road tar, fine grain soils containing silt can be best stabilized by lean road tar, whereas cohesive soils by tar emulsion or dust-absorber road tar. The most important characteristics of these tars are summarized in Table 35.

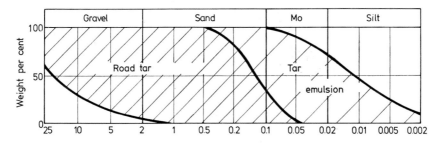

FIG. 187. The range of tar-stabilized soils

Table 35

Tar quality requirements (Hungarian Standard MSZ 3273)

Feature	Requirement							
	Distilled tars					Compounded tars		
	road tars			cold tars		green tar oils		
	UKH	UKS	UKP	HKH	HKS	AK	AK	AK
	lean	thick	no-dust	lean	thick	60/40	65/35	70/30
Appearance	Completely homogeneous, no clods or suspended solid contaminants							
Density at 25 °C	1.14–1.22	1.15–1.25	1.14–1.18	1.14–1.18	1.14–1.18	1.14–1.23	1.15–1.24	1.15–1.25
Viscosity in mp as measured with consistometer								
At 30 °C, 10 mm spout	10–40	70–100	–	–	–	20–70	–	–
40 °C, 10 mm spout	–	–	–	–	–	–	15–40	40–80
40 °C, 4 mm spout	–	–	20–35	–	–	–	–	–
30 °C, 4 mm spout	–	–	–	10.25	40–80	–	–	–
Water content, max. %	0.5	0.5	0.5	0.5	0.5	0.5	0.5	0.5
Redistilled up to 170 °C (light oil) %	max 1.5	max 1.5	max 1.5	5–15	5–15	max 0.5	max 0.5	max 0.5
170–270 °C (medium oil) %	9–17	8–16	16–30	10–13	10–13	4–12	3–10	2–8
270–300 °C (heavy oil) %	4–12	6–12	4–12	16–26	16–26	17–31	17–27	15–25
270–350 °C (heavy and green oil %)	–	–	–	–	–	–	–	–

Black pitch residue converted to 67°C Kramer–Sarnow softening point %	55–70	60–75	40–55	50–60	50–60	56–64	61–69	66–74
Black pitch residue softening point by Kramer–Sarnow, max. °C	70	70	70	70	70	70	70	70
Phenol vol %, max	4	4	6	5	5	3	2	2
Naphthalene %, max	4	4	6	4	4	3	3	2
Raw anthracene %, max	3.5	3.5	3.5	3.5	3.5	3.5	3.5	4
Benzene insoluble %, max	12	12	12	12	12	14	14	14
Ash %, max	2.5	2.5	2.5	2.5	2.5	2.5	2.5	2.5

Note:

60/40, 65/35, 70/30 are the compound ratios of coal-tar pitch and green oil.
If necessary, tar types of viscosities other than those in the table may also be used, but in such cases, the user and manufacturer should reach an agreement about the engineering requirements specified. Instead of viscosity, such an agreement should contain the Kramer–Sarnow limit of the drop point or softening point which, in turn, contains the amount of distillation water.
The figures in the table include the scattering limits.

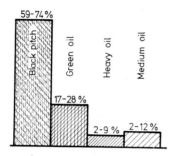

FIG. 188. The main components of road tar

An essential tar property is viscosity, used also for tar classification. The approximate composition of lean road tar is presented in Fig. 188. Its main bulk is black pitch which represents the binder, while the plastic compound of black pitch- and green oil is liquidized by other oils. A fundamental rule of the application of tar for road construction and, therefore, soil stabilization is that, allowing for the climatic conditions and the building technique employed, the thickest road tar should always be used.

The adhesive quantity required depends on the grain distribution. An addition of 3–7 weight per cent generally leads to a satisfactory strength. Addition also depends on the mixing efficiency: the more uniformly the binder is distributed, the smaller the amount is needed.

Since in Hungary stabilization with tar is used almost exclusively in the case of sands and fine sands, the following paragraphs describe in detail the experiments conducted in the Geotechnical Department Laboratory of the Budapest Technical University (Nagyváti, 1959).

Generally, the strength of a sand-tar system is governed by the following factors:
— internal friction, whose value depends on the grain distribution, grain size, and compactness;

— capillary effect, depending on the thickness of the intergranular binder coating, the specific value of the wet surface around the contact points of the individual particles, and the magnitude of the surface tension between the liquid forming this film and the grains proper;

— cohesion, determined by the viscous resistance of the film over the surface, bonding the particles involved.

If the stabilized soil is a sand of uniform grain distribution, then the joint action of these effects is small, since both the surface and structural frictions are low. The grains contact each other at a few points only, and the specific length of the contact lines between different materials will be similarly small. The resultant of the capillary effects is also rather small, and the adsorbed liquid cannot have a high viscosity, otherwise no efficient admixture is possible.

Most of the above disadvantages can be eliminated by adding a filler to the mix, which will have several duties. To clarify these actions, let us examine the physical processes taking place during stabilization with tar, and the behaviour of the solid particles–water–tar system. Three sand particles are illustrated in Fig. 189.

The particles are surrounded by an adsorptive coating, and at the contact points certain stresses will be produced which, in turn, generate forces from the surface tension. These forces, like the virtual cohesion of the wet sand, press the particles together and this effect, along with the shear strength of the adsorptive coating, will lend a compression strength to the soil. The higher the dynamic viscosity of the adsorptive coating, the greater the forces referred to. This effect is a maximum at a certain optimum thickness of the coating. Thus the optimum binder quantity depends on the specific surface of the particles, and will increase in the case of smaller grains. If this is exceeded, the superfluous non-adsorbed binder will have a lubricating effect, and the particles may readily be displaced relatively. At an optimum adsorptive coating thickness, the higher viscosity binder will ensure greater cohesion.

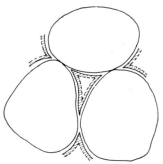

FIG. 189. Adsorbed film over the surface of the particles

In order to increase the capillary effect, the contact surface should be sufficiently wet, and the adsorptive coating of an optimum thickness, whereas for increased cohesion the binder must be as viscous as possible. If these two requirements are satisfied simultaneously, and the hot viscous binder is admixed to the cold soil, then the adhesive will obviously not adhere to the surface of the wet soil particles. A thermal-state modification is impossible, and below 65 °C not even the lean road tar can be admixed to the soil appropriately. When admixed to the soil, the tar may cool off to 20 °C, its viscosity will greatly increase, so that a coating film simply cannot be produced. Mixing must therefore be achieved differently: the adhesive is introduced to between the particles, either in solution or in the form of an emulsion. However, with the oily tar solutions there have been some very bad experiences: the oil leaves the mixture very slowly, so that it remains quite soft for a fairly long time, which means that the road cannot be used for a considerable period after the completion of construction. The situation is similar with the anion-active emulsions, since the application of aqueous emulsions introduces a great deal of superfluous water to the mix which makes efficient mixing and compaction impossible, and permits only a very slow strength increase.

Let us examine now what happens after adding the hot tar to the wet soil, whereby the temperature of the former is rapidly decreasing. In the loose mixture the tar will be located among the soil particles in smaller and larger drops, or enclose certain particles and grain aggregates too thickly, whilst totally avoiding other points. Compaction after admixture greatly reduce the void volume of the loose soil, the grains and grain aggregates then approach each other and displace some of the tar drops. The amount of tar-coating of the grains increases, and part of the tar is pressed into the leftover pores by the external force. When the already cooled binder and the soil particles are compressed, another process starts.

When admixing tar to the soil, emulsification sets in if an emulsifier is present and sufficient mechanical energy is available. Sand structures consisting of separate particles do not contain any emulsifier, so they must be supplemented with a fine-grain additive which acts as an emulsifier in the whole system and, from a binder viewpoint and also with respect to the unfavourable grain distribution of the basic soil material, as a filler. In the presence of such fine grains, considerable

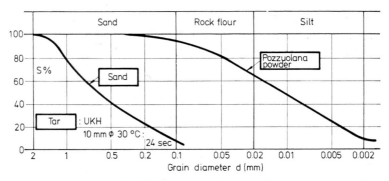

FIG. 190. Test material properties

emulsification begins, the soil particles are coated by the adhesive, and each of the three strength factors increases, giving rise to a significant stabilizing effect. This fine grain filler, however, does not improve the grain distribution of the mix critically. In other words, it does not exert a major mechanical stabilization effect, which would need much greater quantities and a distribution of much coarser grains. The optimum filler quantity depends mainly on the viscosity and softening point of the tar, then on the means and method of compaction, while the grain distribution of the basic soil is of a lesser importance.

Any material of sufficiently fine grains and easy to pulverize, e.g. loess, too, should be adaptable as a filler. The use of pozzuolana, however, is preferred from a number of aspects such as its commercial availability in the desired grade and powder form, its providing certain hydraulic bonds, binding the excess water of the mixture, and increasing the strength of the latter.

The optimum mixing ratio of sand, pozzuolana, and tar can be determined by compaction, strength, and water-absorption tests. The following paragraphs describe an actual example of the examination and study referred to above.

The characteristic properties of the basic materials used are shown in Fig. 190. The composition of various mixtures was tested, to find the optimum one. The additive quantity was varied in the percentage of the dry-sand weight between the following limit values:

$$
\begin{aligned}
\text{pozzuolana:} \quad & 2-4-6-8 \text{ per cent} \\
\text{tar:} \quad & 4-5-6-7 \text{ per cent} \\
\text{water:} \quad & 11 \text{ per cent}
\end{aligned}
$$

The given water content was that most favourable of the mixture at compaction.

First the air-dry sand and the pozzuolana were mixed, and the tar was added to this mixture. The compacted cylinders ($d = 96$ mm, $h = 134$ mm) were stored outdoors (18–20 °C), and after seven days the unconfined compression strength was determined. The results of this test are presented in Fig. 191, which confirms that, from the aspect of compression strength, there is an optimum mixing ratio. The various mixtures were then used for laboratory traffic tests, and it was found

210

that for road behaviour, the 5 per cent tar and 6 per cent pozzuolana mixture proved to be most advantageous. The examinations also included water absorption and drying. A set of such results is illustrated in Fig. 192.

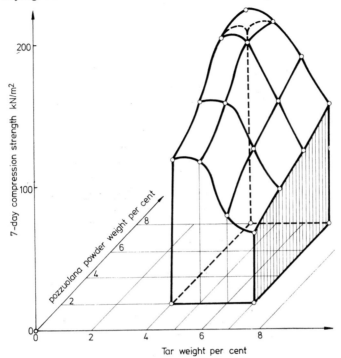

FIG. 191. Strength of the sand-tar-pozzuolana mixture as illustrated in a spatial co-ordinate system

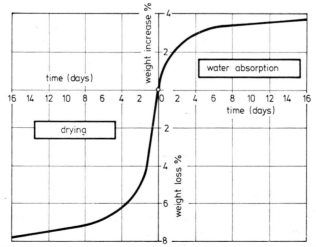

FIG. 192. Water absorption and dry-out curves of the optimum mixture

7. Chemical soil stabilization

7.1 Chemical soil-stabilization methods

Although the various chemical processes play an important role in almost every type of stabilization, there are certain techniques whose most essential feature is a chemical transformation taking place either in an interaction with the soil particles, or independently, with only their inert involvement. In recent years, research was focused on practices in this category, and researchers studied a great number of chemicals and chemical processes, with the objective of use in stabilization. This type of research had a major upsurge during the Second World War, when the rapid construction of military routes gained primary importance. Vast numbers of papers, reports, and studies have continue to deal with the problems of chemical stabilization in a vast number ever since, and details of a wide variety of most different techniques are published, so that summary and assessment of the entire problem scope is almost impossible. With a very few exceptions, however, the chemical soil stabilization methods still cannot be fully evaluated from the aspects of soil physics, technology, and economic efficiency, and there are only a few such methods that have been generally accepted. Thus the present Chapter cannot offer more than to explain, in parallel, the methods proved to be acceptable from certain viewpoints from previous research and practical applications, to point out the main trends, and to discuss the physico-chemical relations of the various procedures. There is still much research, experimentation, practical observation and experience needed before the mass introduction of these methods.

Almost every problem related to soil use is due to the unfavourable interactions between water and soil. From engineering aspects, increased water content has a number of disadvantageous consequences: cohesion decreases, the soil swells, the alternating dry-out shrinkage and wetting/swelling effects destroy the soil structure, as do frost-thaw variations. The main objective of chemical soil stabilization, therefore is, that the soil should maintain its characteristics, favourable from the aspects of the given engineering target, regardless of the moisture in its environment. Chemical soil stabilization is intended to modify the interactions between water and soil by surface reactions in such a manner as to make the behaviour of the soil with respect to water effects most favourable for the given purpose. In such stabilizations, therefore, the surface activity of the soil particles, the polarity of the surfaces and their water absorption, and the entire adsorption complex play the most important roles. Of similar importance are the aggregation extent of the particles and the changes in the degree of aggregation, achieved by the modification of the equilibrium of intergranular repulsive and attractive forces. Since the chemical soil stabilization methods produce chemical modifications over the surface of the soil particles, it follows that mainly cohesive soil-stabilization techniques will be discussed in this chapter. This is because the combined effect of the different chemical reactions in sands cannot bring about critical changes of the characteristic soil properties, owing to the small specific surface.

As mentioned above, the main objective of chemical stabilization is to favourably change the soil-water interactions. For this purpose the following methods are most suitable:

1. The soil is treated with a chemical compound having a stronger bond to the surface of the soil particles than that of the water, whereby water sensitivity is eliminated. The additive "displaces" the water molecules from the grain surface and does not permit the bondage of new ones, thus making the soil "non-wetting". Such an effect can be achieved by treating the soil, for example, with methyl chlorosilane gas.

2. The soil is treated by non-hydrated positive charge ions attracted to surfaces of a generally negative charge, and substituting other ions. Through such a transformation the sensitivity of the soil to water will decrease and, once dried, the soil cannot be wetted again. This process can be accomplished, for example, by the application of ammonium salts.

3. The soil is treated with large molecule type ionic compounds. These macromolecule chains connect the soil particles with electrostatic and polar forces whereby aggregates are produced. The soil becomes porous, but remains water-impermeable and structurally stable.

4. The interaction between water and soil can be modified, finally, by separating the polyvalent cations (Mg, Ca) bound to the surface of the soil particles through the addition of certain chemicals. Thereby, in the presence of free water, the solvated water layer may increase and the soil turns liquid, to some advantage. For example, the soil thus treated can be readily compacted and made water-impermeable, or easily processed even at extremely small water contents, since its contraction will be very small. Such an effect can often be achieved by the addition of very small amounts.

Modification of the soil behaviour against detrimental water effects (but certainly not of the interaction between water and soil) is feasible, of course, by filling the intergranular voids with a water-repellent, inert material of good adherence to the particles (e.g. some resin), whereby the water producing otherwise certain reactions will be prevented from contacting and interacting with the grain surfaces. Although some chemical effect is again involved, such techniques consist mainly of void-filling.

According to the character of the interaction between the chemical employed and the soil particles, the chemical soil-stabilization methods may be categorized as follows:

(a) The chemical exerts an effect via its interaction with the soil or the soil particles. In such cases, the physical properties of the chemical employed are barely significant.

(b) The interaction and the physical properties of the chemical exert a joint effect.

(c) The physical properties of the additive used are of decisive importance, while those of the soil matter little.

Let us examine now through what mechanism the different stabilizers are able to have a favourable effect. In this context, two fundamental alternatives must be distinguished. In the first case the stabilizer creates a continuous matrix, and the soil particles are then completely embedded in either the chemical additive, or the material produced by the chemical process. In the second case, the stabilizer does not form a continuous matrix.

In the first case the characteristics of the system thus produced are always governed by the stabilizer. If the soil particles float in the consolidated stabilizer as an inert filler, then on loading, the fracture will obviously take place in the stabilizer which creates a coherent skeleton whereas the "filler" particles are not even loaded. If, on the other hand, the stabilizer and the soil particle surface create a bond whose strength exceeds that of the stabilizer, then with an increasing load the stabilizer itself will first be destroyed. If, on the other hand, the strength of the bond is lower, then the bond will naturally be destroyed first. Thus the soil particles become an inert filler and, from the viewpoint of the strength of the entire system, that of the stabilizer will again be decisive.

In the case of a non-continuous matrix, the stabilizing effect may be brought about in three different ways. The first is the modification of the surface properties of the soil particles, as discussed in connection with the modified water-soil interaction. In such cases chemicals which simply change the surface properties of the soil particles are used. The other possibility is to fill up the intergranular voids with an inert material. In mechanical stabilization this effect ensures strength. It is possible, however, that such a void fill-up may also be achieved through a chemical reaction, as well, in the soil, and this is why it must be mentioned also in the Chapter on chemical stabilization.

The third mechanism capable to accomplish stabilization in the case of a non-continuous matrix is the connection of the soil particles at certain points, resembling "spot welding". In such a system two cohesion types exist: a natural cohesion of the soil particles and the stabilizer and an adhesion between them. Fracture may occur in two ways: if the adhesion exceeds the two cohesion types, then the fracture takes place either in the stabilizer or in the soil particles (or, furthermore, in grain aggregates where the bonding force had been produced by something other

214

than the effect of the stabilizer). If, on the other hand, the cohesion exceeds the force of adhesion, then the fracture will occur over the contact interface between the particles and the stabilizer. Familiarity with the various fracture modes is important from practical aspects since if, for example, a fracture occurred in the stabilized soil as a result of insufficient adhesion, then a cohesion increase would not be associated with an increased strength.

According to the above considerations, the characteristic features of the various grain bond types are illustrated in Fig. 193, while in Fig. 194 an attempt to explain the different fracture mechanisms is shown.

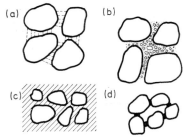

FIG. 193. Soil-particle relations in the different stabilizations. (a) cohesion is produced by the intergranular surface forces; (b) the intergranular voids are filled by an inert material; (c) the soil particles are embedded in a continuous matrix; (d) the strength of intergranular connection is ensured by "spot welding" contact

Table 36

Reactions in the various stabilization processes

Stabilization technique	Cause of hardening	The matrix developed	The bond between soil and stabilizer	The bond producing stabilizer strength	Properties
Cement	Hydration	Non-continuous	Ionic, polarized	Ionic, covalent	Strong, brittle
Bitumen	Temperature	Non-continuous	Van der Waals, polarized	Van der Waals, polarized	Weak, brittle
Liquid bitumen	Evaporation	Non-continuous	Van der Waals, polarized	Van der Waals, polarized	Weak, brittle
Bitumen emulsion	Evaporation	Non-continuous	Van der Waals, polarized	Van der Waals, polarized	Weak, brittle
Sodium silicate	Precipitation	Continuous	Ionic, polarized	Ionic, polarized	Strong, brittle
Aniline furfural	Condensing polymerization	Non-continuous	Van der Waals, polarized	Covalent	Strong, brittle
Calcium acrylate	Additive polymerization	Continuous	Ionic, polarized	Covalent, ionic	Strong and brittle when dry, strong and elastic under wet conditions

215

In connection with chemical soil stabilization we must know the chemical reactions by which the stabilizing effect is brought about after the admixture of the stabilizer to the soil (see Table 36). In the course of this chemical reaction, a new material having certain properties very different from those of the original additive will be formed, so that there is not only a phase change, like that providing in the case of bituminous stabilization.

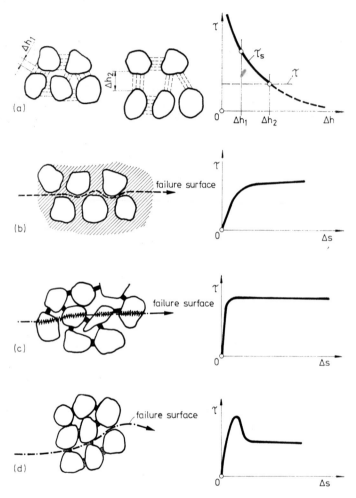

FIG. 194. Fracture mechanisms in stabilized soils. (a) Due to the displacement of certain soil particles, the shear strength produced by the intergranular forces of attraction will be reduced to the value of the shear stress caused by external forces; (b) Strength is determined by the natural strength of the binder; (c) Strength is determined by the natural strength of the soil particles; the attractive force of the bonds is greater; (d) Strength is determined by that of the intergranular bondages

The chemical reactions affecting soil stabilization are as follows:

Ion exchange

Many clay properties depend on the type of the cations adsorbed over the surface of the soil particles, thus a change in the adsorption complex will be associated with the same in the soil characteristics.

Precipitation

If contacting in the form of a solution, many compounds under certain conditions create new, water-insoluble substances which will then be separated or precipitated from the original solution. Some of these precipitates are suitable for acting as stabilizers. Such a process, for example, takes place during the interaction of sodium silicate and calcium chloride, when calcium silicate is produced.

Polymerization

In the course of the reaction of some simple compounds, certain heavy-weight large-size molecules are produced. This process is known as polymerization, with two main types: additional and condensing polymerization. In the former the two compounds interact without any losses whatsoever, while in the latter either water, ammonia, or alcohol is precipitated.

Oxidation

In certain stabilizations, it is most likely that the stabilizer is produced through oxidation, but this process is not fully understood.

The various stabilization methods can be classified with respect to the type of the reactions involved, according to Table 36. Their description can be found partly in the previous chapters, and partly hereafter. The present chapter additionally discusses the problems of improving mechanical soil stabilization by the admixture of sodium or calcium chloride, and the possibilities of changing the soil properties most important from frost aspects, by trace chemicals.

7.2 Soil stabilization with chlorides

Calcium and sodium chloride have now been used for dust removal from earth road for about 30 or 40 years. Data on the first application originate from 1913, when these materials were used for dust-adsorption along water-bound Macadam roads.

When Macadam or earth roads were treated with chlorides, it was found that the road stayed moist even under dry weather conditions, since the salt reduced evaporation and the road absorbed water from the atmosphere because of its hygroscopic character. In 1931, observations were made along experimental sections to determine the extent of evaporation from calcium-chloride treated roads, and it was ascertained that the reduction of the water content was much slower than along the untreated sections. Since then these materials have been used for stabilization, in addition to dust adsorption.

The greatest advantage of the calcium chloride application was obviously the reduced water loss through evaporation during construction, from the substance of a mechanically stabilized earth road. Since, furthermore, the stabilization of the water content is extremely important with respect to the compaction of any granular soil, the moisture-retaining action of calcium chloride might be a very great advantage.

From the vertical axis (0 per cent concentration), the vapour pressure of pure clean water can be read off as a function of relative humidity.

Among the characteristic properties of calcium chloride, the following features are of the greatest importance in connection with soil stabilization:

It will greatly attract water, and upon the effect of the latter it will readily flow and spread, being highly hygroscopic in nature. The minimum relative humidity and temperature values at which calcium chloride would still spread are shown in Fig. 195a, while the extent of its hygroscopic nature (the water quantity absorbed by 1 kg $CaCl_2$ at 25 °C as a function of relative humidity) is illustrated in Fig. 195b. The surface tension of calcium chloride exceeds that of the water, whereas it has a lower vapour pressure than water. Figure 196 presents the vapour-pressure variation as a function of the concentration exhibited by the solution. Owing to these properties, $CaCl_2$ will greatly reduce evaporation. Thus, for example, the vapour pressure of a saturated $CaCl_2$ solution at 25 °C is 7.0 mmHg while that of pure water is 23.8 mmHg, giving the rate of evaporation from the free surface as 23.8 : 7.0 = 3.4-times less. The relative humidity above which $CaCl_2 \cdot 2H_2O$ can adsorb moisture from the atmosphere is 7 : 23.8 = 29.4 per cent (see Fig. 195a). Water absorption will then continue until the vapour pressure of the solu-

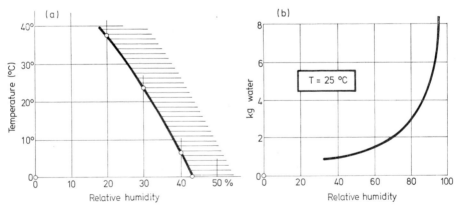

FIG. 195. (a) Minimum temperature and relative humidity values at which $CaCl_2$ would still spread; (b) water uptake by $CaCl_2$ at 25 °C as a function of temperature

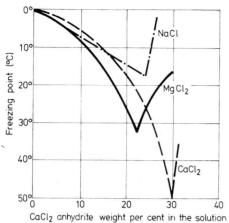

FIG. 196. Vapour pressure of CaCl₂ solutions as a function of concentration

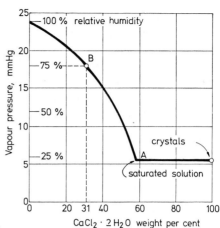

FIG. 197. Chloride solution freezing points as a function of concentration

tion thus produced is reduced to that of the water in the atmosphere. If, for example, the relative humidity is 75 per cent, then the calcium chloride will adsorb the necessary water quantity to make the concentration of the solution correspond to B in Fig. 196. If, then, this solution exists at less than 75 per cent relative humidity, adsorption will stop and evaporation start.

Another important characteristic of chloride solutions is the reduced freezing point. The extent of this reduction is illustrated in Fig. 197. Owing to this property, chlorides can be used to thaw frozen soils or roads.

As shown in the figure referred to, the $CaCl_2 - H_2O$ system has a eutectic point, that is, there is a concentration at which the freezing point assumes a minimum value. For the case of a still lower concentration, although started at the temperature revealed in the figure, freezing will not be completed because only pure water is "freezing out" of the solution, so its concentration increases while the freezing point decreases. If the temperature continues to decrease, the water "freeze-out" also continues until the concentration of the non-frozen solution arrives at the value corresponding to the eutectic point, where the entire compound then freezes. If freezing begins at a concentration higher

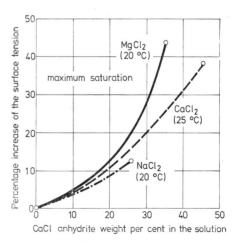

FIG. 198. Surface tension increase of chloride solutions as a function of the latter's concentration

than that corresponding to the eutectic point, then calcium chloride crystals will separate until the concentration of the eutectic point is finally developed.

According to the figure, if the soil of an earth road is treated, for example, with NaCl, then complete freezing will only take place at -18 °C. The temperature in the case of a $MgCl_2$ treatment is -32.7 °C, while if $CaCl_2$ is used it is -51 °C. Thus chloride treatment for frost effect aspects means not only a lower freezing point, but also a gradual freezing and the absence of complete freezing-thaw cycles.

Figure 198 illustrates the surface tension as a function of the concentration of the solution. The effect of the increase shown is an increase in the cohesion produced by the water films.

We must note that the $CaCl_2$ solutions have the drawback of increasing and accelerating the corrosion of metals. In road traffic, this is particularly detrimental where calcium chloride is used for snow removal or de-icing. (In the United States, for example, the chassis of a car is likely to be in a much better condition in California than in the Eastern states, where the salt solutions can almost destroy the contacted metal parts within a few winter seasons.) This effect is partly due to the acidic reaction of calcium and magnesium chloride when dissolved in water, through the following chemical process:

$$MgCl_2 + H_2O \rightleftarrows Mg(OH)_2 + 2HCl$$

$$\text{weak base} \qquad \text{strong acid}$$

If, because of the presence of HCl, the pH of the solution is decreased to below 3.5–4.5, then free hydrogen is produced, associated with the initiation of a rapid rate of corrosion. The pH of $CaCl_2$ solutions is about 4.5 to 5.0 and, therefore, much less harmful than that of $MgCl_2$ which amounts to about 3.9; thus the damaging effect of sea water, too, is due mainly to the $MgCl_2$ content.

From a corrosion viewpoint the hygroscopic character is still more detrimental since, thereby, the active rust formation period is considerably extended. This can be remedied only by frequent chassis washings.

The various salts, if dissolved in the pore water of the soil, supply cations which are capable of participating in the following reactions:

— exchange with the ions already present in the soil;
— adsorption over the surface of the particles;
— supply of ions connecting the soil particles (e.g. the K^+ will be embedded between two clay sheets and connects them permanently during dry-out);
— ion concentration increase, whereby the intergranular electric repulsion will be reduced.

Usually, more than one of these reactions take place simultaneously, so it is rather difficult to determine the role they play separately. However, their essential common feature is an aggregator or coagulator action whereby they increase the electric force of attraction between the adjacent fine soil particles,

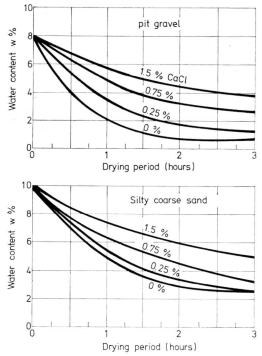

FIG. 199. Dry-out curves of calcium chloride treated soils as a function of concentration (a) pit gravel, (b) coarse sand

although no cementing effect can be observed. From all these findings, it follows that any such effect is feasible only in fine-grain soil types.

A number of laboratory experiments have already involved calcium chloride for testing the strength and compactness of soils, and it was used also for the construction of experimental road sections. All these have led to the following conclusions:

The reduction of evaporation, one of the most important effects of $CaCl_2$ addition, applies to the water in the soil as well, of course, as exampled by Fig. 199 which illustrates the dry-out curves of a silty pit gravel type and a coarse sand, as a function of calcium chloride admixture. Chlorides change, though to a limited extent, the plastic properties of soils and cause their plastic indices to decrease slightly (Fig. 200).

This effect is due to the adhesion of the particles, increasing the virtual grain size. These adhered particles will then be located in a loose irregular network. The phenomenon is well known from laboratory experiments on soil mechanics, when coagulation occurs in the course of the wet analysis, and the particles thus adhered and coagulated will settle in a loose flocculent structure within a short period of time.

This loose, irregular structure will increase the permeability of the soils thus treated 2 to 20-fold whereby, in turn, the frost hazards of such soils will be reduced. Lambe (1956) claims that, upon the admixture of 1/2 per cent iron chloride, the extent of frost expansion could be reduced to 1/2–1/5.

The dry-volume weight of the compacted soil will slightly increase upon chloride addition, although the difference is usually slight,

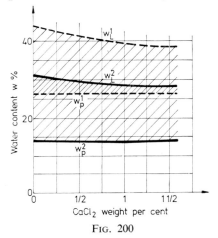

FIG. 200

221

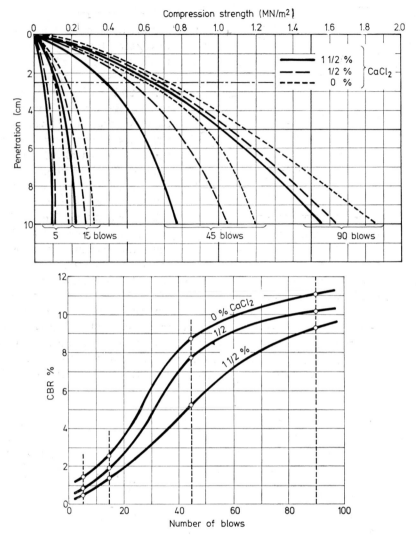

FIG. 201. (a) Penetration curves obtained in the course of CBR
tests, with different $CaCl_2$ additions; (b) CBR-value variations
against $CaCl_2$ additions

and the increase itself is almost identical to the quantity of the calcium chloride
added. This means that the salt will fill up the voids or remains dissolved in the
pore water, increasing compactness only virtually, since its weight will only
be manifested in the dry weight.

   $CaCl_2$ addition generally decreases soil strength. At an increased soil compactness this decrease is not too much, but in loose soils it may assume excessive values.
Some CBR test results are presented in Fig. 201, where the extent of the above

222

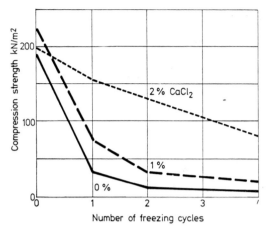

FIG. 202. Strength reduction after a number of freezing cycles

decrease is illustrated as a function of compactness, and the figure also indicates the CBR values calculated from the penetration resistance.

The most favourable effect is the freezing point reduction, and the similarly reduced frost hazards due to the above physical properties, as verified by Fig. 202, illustrating the compression strength of calcium chloride-treated cylindrical soil samples, after a certain number of freezing test cycles. It is clearly seen that the strength reduction is much less if $CaCl_2$ is admixed. The effect, as mentioned above, is due mainly to the increased permeability.

Since calcium chloride is water soluble, one must reckon with the possibility of its being leached by rain, and also the variation of its amount by other water movements. The rain water carries the salt from the treated top layer of the road to greater depths. Under dry weather conditions the solution (the pore water) will move upwards through the capillaries, then the water will evaporate from the surface and the salt crystallizes, to be washed off by the next rainfall. In addition to these phenomena, calcium-chloride migration in the soil is promoted by the downward diffusion of the ions. This explains the measurement results in Fig. 203 (Woods and Yoder, 1952): the two curves illustrate the calcium-chloride content of the soil at the same place, as a function of depth, but two years have passed between the two measurements. The downward migration of the salt can be clearly observed. If, therefore, the calcium chloride is added to a mechanical stabilization without a protective layer, the treatment must be repeated periodically.

The extent of migration and of the losses greatly depend, of course, on the local climatic conditions, the variation of rainy and dry seasons, the ground water level, and its fluctuations. Soil permeability and compactness also play an important role. If the surface of the earth road is sealed by a bituminous layer, then the extent of migration will certainly decrease, although

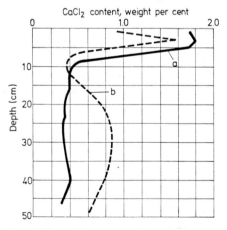

FIG. 203. $CaCl_2$ content of the soil as a function of depth, (a) measurement after construction, (b) measurement two years later

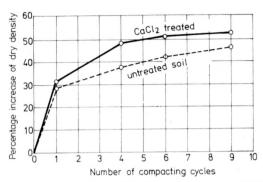

FIG. 204. The effect of CaCl$_2$ on the compactibility of silt

not cease completely: ion diffusion and the horizontal water movement toward the banks will be maintained.

Chlorides, mainly calcium chloride, are used primarily for mechanically stabilized earth roads to preserve their favourable moisture content and to reduce dust formation. With respect to grain distribution and the Atterberg limit values, the Calcium Chloride Institute (USA) recommends adherence to the specifications presented in Table 37. Addition should be, on the basis of the hitherto research results and experience of previous research, 20 dkg per 1 m road surface and 1 cm thickness of the compacted layer, which corresponds to about 1 per cent of the wet weight. The salt is added to and admixed with the dry mixture, and the water is only admixed afterwards. The final step is compaction. The optimum water content of compaction is somewhat less than that of the untreated soil. The compaction energy required is favourably affected by the addition of calcium chloride since, as shown in Fig. 204, the same degree of compaction can be achieved with a lower number of compacting cycles. The road crown should be constructed with a uniform lateral slope of at least 4 per cent.

Table 37

Soils suitable for stabilization
with calcium chloride

Grain diameter, mm	Weight per cent	
	Surface layer (1)	Basic layer (2)
25	100	100
18.3	85–100	70–100
9.2	65–100	50–80
4.76	55–85	35–65
2.00	40–70	25–50
0.42	25–45	15–30
0.076	10–25	5–15

NOTES: (1) The weight per cent of grains smaller than 0.076 mm must not exceed 2/3 of that of the particles smaller than 0.42 mm. The plasticity index of the grains smaller than 0.42 mm should be 4-9 per cent, with a liquid limit of 35 per cent maximum.
(2) The weight per cent of grains smaller than 0.076 mm must not exceed 2/3 of that of particles smaller than 0.42 mm. The plasticity index of the grains smaller than 0.42 mm may be a maximum of 6 per cent, with a liquid limit maximum of 25 per cent.

7.3 Stabilization with phosphoric acid

The application of phosphoric acid for soil-stabilization purposes is a fairly new method. Based on soil science and ceramics practices, the idea was raised by Winterkorn in 1940, but the first successful stabilization of this type was completed only in 1957 (Lyons, 1957). The addition of phosphoric acid or other phosphoric compounds, perhaps together with other chemicals, certainly increases the strength and water resistance of soils.

Phosphoric acid is produced by the dissolving in water the phosphoric anhydride (P_2O_5) produced when burning phosphorus:

$$P_2O_5 + 3H_2O + 2H_3PO_4$$

For industrial production, the calcium phosphate is treated with sulphuric acid (wet process):

$$Ca_3(PO_4)_2 + 3H_2SO_4 = 3CaSO_4 + 2H_2PO_4$$

If phosphoric acid (H_3PO_4) is added to a soil containing clay minerals, the reaction forms certain Al and Fe compounds, the most important being aluminum metaphosphate.

$$Al^{3+} + 2(OH)^- + H_3PO_4^- + XH_2O \rightarrow Al_2(OH)\,H_3PO_4 \cdot XH_2O$$

The aluminum metaphosphate thus produced is hard and water insoluble, so readily capable of exerting a stabilizing effect. It can be produced using any aluminum compound. The rate of reaction depends on the concentration of the compounds involved.

In soils, aluminum for this reaction is available from three sources:

- clay mineral structures,
- exchangeable aluminum ions,
- free aluminum oxide.

The solubility of aluminum metaphosphate depends on the pH of the solvent, and it is optimum if this pH is between 2 and 4.

While only part of the phosphoric acid present has been transformed into aluminum metaphosphate, the metaphosphate will continue to dissolve in the residual acid. Then, as the acid quantity gradually decreases in the mixture, the aluminum metaphosphate precipitating in the form of left-over gel will be able to exert a cementing action, which increases considerably if the water content of the gel decreases. In the first post-admixture phase, during dissolution, the phosphoric acid will act in the soil as a dispersing agent while later on, in the course of gel formation, as a coagulator. The (virtually) larger grain size produced during coagu-

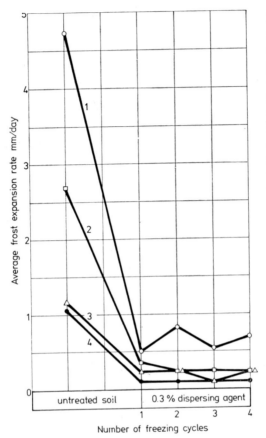

FIG. 205. Results of freezing-thaw tests involving
clay-gravel types

lation, the stronger skeleton, and the reduced capillarity throughout the dispersion phase all explain the reduced frost hazards of the soils thus treated, as confirmed through a test by Lambe (1956): Fig. 205 illustrates the frost expansion of a clayey gravel as a function of the number of freezing-thaw cycles. The treated soil again exhibited a greatly advantageous behaviour.

The quantity admixed in the laboratory experiments varied between 2 and 5 per cent, which affected the soil properties as follows:

Plasticity and the Atterberg values did not reveal changes easy to forecast, nor were the results of volume variation unequivocal. As regards the mixing energy, it was rather interesting to observe that phosphoric acid, as already mentioned, exerted a dispersive effect initially but a later coagulating action. If this mixing energy, necessary for maintaining of a continuous uniform admixture, is plotted as a function of the mixing time, then the curve presented in Fig. 206 is obtained.

The effect of phosphoric acid on soil strength has already been studied on several different soil types, but no certain correlation has yet been discovered. The preparation, feeding, and admixture techniques, as well as the post-treatment conditions seem to play an important role. The results published in the literature have been processed by Barenburg (1963), and reveal excessive scatter. Detailed investigations were conducted by Michaels and Tausch (1960) who added a small amount of fluorine compounds to the mixture and observed their advantageous strength-increasing effects. In the stabilization of a soil type containing illite and exhibiting an $I_p = 6$ per cent plastic index, the laboratory experiments rendered the results shown in Fig. 207. At a given acid concentration, the strength of the samples stored under wet conditions for 24 hours increased almost linearly with the amount of sodium fluosilicate (Na_2SiF_6) quantity admixed. It is most likely

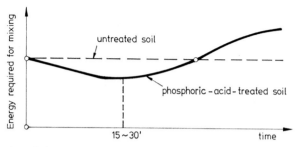

FIG. 206. The energy required for mixing, in the function
of the mixing time

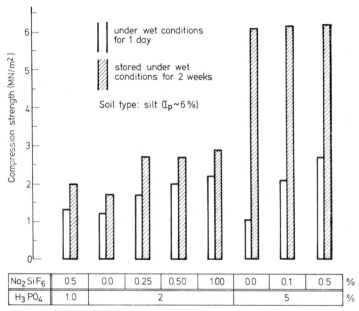

Na₂SiF₆	0.5	0.0	0.25	0.50	1.00	0.0	0.1	0.5	%
H₃PO₄	1.0	2				5			%

FIG. 207. The effect of sodium fluosilicate addition on the strength
of a silty sand stabilized with phosphoric acid

that this significant effect is due to the fact that fluorides greatly accelerate the dissolution of aluminum metal in phosphoric acid. In such cases the aluminum metal
becomes covered by a hydrated aluminum oxide layer, of a composition resembling
the soil particles and the substances in the clay minerals. Although phosphates
would be adsorbed over these surfaces, resembling a stabilization effect, the process
could not advance. The fluorides assist in the separation of this inhibiting passive
film, whereby the chemical process has an increased efficiency. The same effect
could be achieved with a number of different fluorine compounds (K_2SiF_6,
$ZnSiF_6$, AlF_3, etc.).

15*

Stabilization with phosphoric acid fails if the soil contains much calcium since then a major part of the phosphoric acid will be consumed to neutralize the calcium carbonate, and no stabilization will take place (the neutralization of 1 per cent $CaCO_3$ requires 1.25 per cent H_3PO_4).

7.4 Natural and synthetic polymers

7.4.1 Polymer-stabilization types

The polymers are chain-type large molecules produced by linkage from monomer-class organic compounds, a process called polymerization. This phenomenon, as a chemical reaction, can be utilized for soil stabilization in two ways. In the first case, certain monomers and a catalyzer system are added to the soil. The catalyst brings about the polymerization and, simultaneously, some chemical reactions take place between the soil and the monomer or polymer. In the second alternative, a polymer already prepared is added to the soil in a solid, dissolved, or emulsion form, and the reaction between the polymer and the soil will start immediately after the dissolution of the polymer or, in the case of an emulsion, its breakup.

A number of natural and synthetic resins, plastics, etc., have already been tested for soil stabilization purposes. Often excellent laboratory test results can be achieved but these cannot be reproduced on site, or else they proved to be prohibitively expensive. Three of these experiments deserve special mention since, although the difficulties referred to above still pertain they must certainly be discussed with a view to future development. This is why stabilization by resins, calcium acrylate, aniline and furfural, respectively, are described below. The first one does not increase strength, but renders the fine-grain soil thus treated water-impermeable, while the second and third increase strength and reduce water permability.

7.4.2 Stabilization with resins

The following paragraphs describe the results obtained during the British "*Vinsol*" resin (Clare, 1949). This resin is a dark brown solid, melting at a temperature of 110–115 °C, with a specific gravity of about 1.25; it can be produced during the course of turpentine manufacture, making use of the residual resinous matter obtained through pine or fire distillation. The residue is extracted by benzene or toluene, then removed, and the mixture is treated with a kerosene solvent. The remaining substance is the Vinsol resin, commercially available in powder form. Its chemical composition is only suspected, with a probable empirical formula of $C_{27}H_{30}O_5$, and a measured molecular weight of about 450.

Resins are used mainly for rendering the fine-grain soils waterproof, since the resin encloses the soil particles with a thin water repellent film, thereby preventing the reduction of cohesion.

228

The major characteristics of resin-treated soils are:

The most favourable effect of resin addition is the considerable reduction of water absorption. Figure 208 illustrates the results of a capillary-absorption test involving a sandy silt, indicating the amount of water absorbed as a function of the resin content and the time taken by absorption. The figure presents the experimental method, and the soil-physical characteristics. Samples were produced by mixing the soil dried at 105 °C with an amount of water 2 per cent less than the optimum moisture content of compaction, and then, after mixing for 10 min, the admixture of the resin for another 10 min. The mixture was then pressed into moulds 5 cm diameter and 7.5 cm in height using a 1600 kp static weight.

According to the curves obtained, even a 1 per cent resin admixture critically reduces water absorption, but there is an optimum added quantity giving a minimum water absorption. This characteristic can be observed consistently in Clare's experiments (1949), although it was found that the resin would never made the soil completely impervious.

Clare studied, using ingenious methods, the mechanism giving rise to water impermeability. He made use of the Koženy formula (1927), according to which the height (h) of the capillary ascension within a period of time t in soils is approximately

$$h = C \sqrt{t}$$

Assuming that in the tests the weight (G) of the water absorption was proportional to the capillary rise, the formula may be written as

$$G = C' \sqrt{t}$$

Koženy proved that this constant would depend on the surface tension σ of the absorbed liquid and the angle of intergranular wetting (Θ):

$$C = K \sqrt{\sigma \cos \Theta}$$

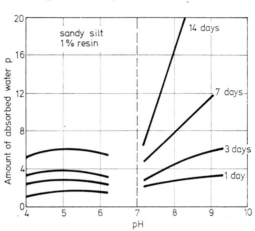

FIG. 208. Water uptake of a sandy silt as a function of resin content and time elapsed

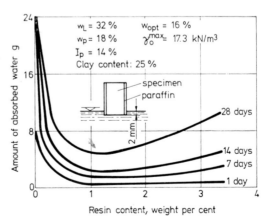

FIG. 209. Water absorption of a sandy silt vs. the pH value

According to these test results, the constant C should decrease by almost 100 per cent as a result of resin admixture. Measurements of the surface tension and the contact angle, on the other hand, revealed that the variation of these values could not have caused the significant changes in absorption. It was discovered, furthermore, that the resin made the soil almost impermeable by a mechanism other than clogging the larger pores. Measurements of the wetting heat disclosed that water impermeability did not result from adsorption over the interface between a solid soil particle and the liquid, although the resin formed a monomolecular film on the surface of the liquid. In such layers, the hydrophillic carboxyl and phenol groups present in the resin are attracted by the water, and the larger hydrophobic hydrocarbonates by the air, thus producing a hydrophobic surface. This is why the l value decreases. This means that the resin could exert an optimum effect if it contained an optimum amount of water. Such a monomolecular film, produced by the acidic polar molecules of the resin, explains the dependence of the water uptake on the pH of the pore water, at least according to the experimental results, as shown in Fig. 209. Accordingly, the system waterproofed by resin admixture may be considered as the soil particles or aggregates being enclosed by a water film, with several of these water films merge in the vicinity of the contact points, but there will be a considerable water/air contact surface left inside the soil. If powdered resin is added to the soil, this surface would be coated by the film described. The system thus developed is illustrated in Fig. 210. The mechanism of waterproofing on the basis of the presence of such a resin layer may be as follows:

During the progress of capillary absorption, the air/water contact area will continuously decrease, restricting the resin layer to a similarly diminishing area. Thus it will be compressed in the plane of the contact surface, and the counteracting resistance will reduce surface tension, in turn leading to a capillary water increase. This explains why the extent of water adsorption is greatly reduced.

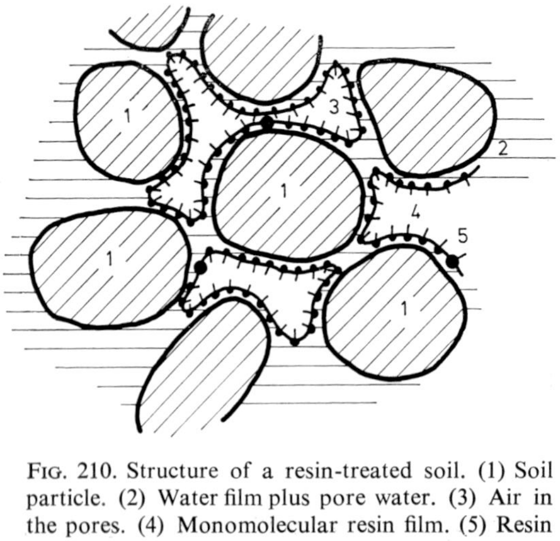

This explanation was strongly supported by Clare's surface-pressure measurements.

As regards the other physical characteristics, any effect on them, it may be mentioned that the presence of a resin does not reduce shear strength. Not will the proctor curve change, except when the resin-treated soil is left to rest for an extended period of time in a loose condition. Thus is why compaction immediately after mixing is recommended.

The resin-treated soil may be attacked by bacteria and fungi.

FIG. 210. Structure of a resin-treated soil. (1) Soil particle. (2) Water film plus pore water. (3) Air in the pores. (4) Monomolecular resin film. (5) Resin particle

This, in turn, may be particularly detrimental if the mixture coontains to much air, but can be readily prevented by adding of certain antiseptics like sodium pentachlorophenate. No such hazards are encountered when the resin is added to cement-stabilized soils to give increased water impermeability.

7.4.3 Stabilization with calcium acrylate

Calcium acrylate, an organic salt, has the following composition:

$$\underset{H-C=C-C-O-Ca-O-C-C=C-H}{\overset{\text{H H O}\qquad\qquad\text{O H H}}{}}$$

It can be produced by compounding calcium carbonate and acrylic acid. If it is added to a soil, together with a redox catalyst system, then polymerization takes place and, as a result, the soil particles become enclosed by strong and flexible polymer chains to which the soil particles are linked.

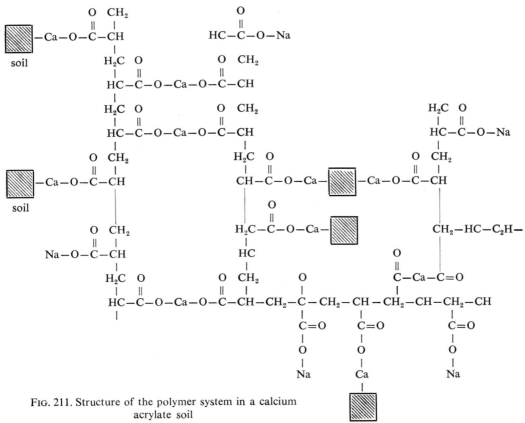

FIG. 211. Structure of the polymer system in a calcium acrylate soil

231

FIG. 212. Calcium-acrylate-stabilized soil of a satisfactory bending strength and a considerable deformation capacity

The structure of a sodium-clay system treated with calcium acrylate, i.e. the soil-particle polymer chain system is presented in Fig. 211 (Lambe, 1953).

The effect of calcium acrylate is based on the following processes:

1. Ion exchange: when the acrylate is dissolved in water, large organic cations are produced, capable of substituting the exchangeable ions over the surface of the clay minerals.

2. The calcium acrylate monomer will be polymerized into long chains even without dissolving in water, which incorporates the large organic cations bound to the soil particles. These molecular chains will then be cross-linked by the free Ca^{2+} ions (see Fig. 211), forming a strong three-dimensional network of soil particles. In consequence, the soil will gain certain tensile and bending strength and, under special conditions, even the outstanding effect illustrated in Fig. 212 may develop.

A strength increase is due mainly to the second effect. It can be accomplished by adding to the soil a redox system, consisting of an oxidizing catalyst and a reducing accelerator. The best quantity for the chemical is between 4 and 10 per cent. Any less cannot be admixed sufficiently, whereas using more is not economical. As a catalyst mainly ammonium persulphate, and as an accelerator in most cases sodium thiosulphate, proved to be most suitable.

Table 38

Tensile strength of calcium acrylate-treated soils

Soil	Liquid limit %	Water content %	Tensile strength kN/m^2	Deformation at fracture %
Loess	27	25	200	73
Greyish-brown silt	28	25	270	43
Clayey silt	35	30	270	96
Sandy clay	59	35	280	16
Clay	67	45	100	34

The stabilized soil properties develop as follows:

After polymerization, soil strength is greatly increased, as exampled in Table 38. Before treatment none of the soils tested exhibited a tensile strength at the given water content. The smaller the amount of mixing water within the limitations of the mixing possibilities, the greater this increase. Compression strength similarly increases, though not at the same rapid rate, and the soil becomes elastic. The polymer locks the water particles, stops water seepage, decreasing the permeability of the soil almost to zero. Calcium acrylate treatment practically eliminates soil-freezing hazards. Water permeability can be radically reduced even for the case of sands,

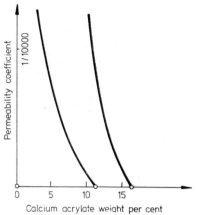

FIG. 213. Permeability of non-cohesive soils vs. the amount of the stabilizing agent

so as to make the soil completely waterproof, as attested by Fig. 213. With pea gravel, waterproofing was only feasible using much more chemical.

Other physical characteristics, the Atterberg values and the plasticity index were found to decrease, just like the optimum water content, while the maximum dry density increased.

The calcium-acrylate production costs are still rather high, so this material cannot yet be used for soil stabilization aimed at serving road-construction purposes.

7.4.4 Stabilization with aniline furfural

Numerous test results show that clay particles may be made water repellent by means of water-soluble organic cations. This is achieved by causing the cations, through base exchange, to substitute the metallic cations (Na^+, Ca^{++}, etc.) in the absorption complex of the clay particles. The water-absorption capacity and expansion of the soil thus produced are much smaller than those of an untreated soil. The organic cations to be considered here include amines (ammonia types in which one or more atoms are replaced by an organic molecule group), aniline furfural, and others. The coverage of the grain surfaces is proportional to the size and quantity of the cations added. The more intense this coverage, the more resistant the soil will be to water effects.

Among the stabilization alternatives based on the above principle, the aniline-furfural technique has gained considerable attention, upon the initiative by Winterkorn. Aniline is a primary aromatic amine, produced by substituting a hydrogen atom of benzene by a NH_2 root. It hardly dissolves in water, and exhibits a slightly basic character. Furfural is a primary aldehyde, the main derivative of furfurane. It can be produced by distilling oat chaff or other agricultural by-

233

products like corn cobs in the presence of sulphuric acid. It is an oily reddish-brown substance, boils at 162 °C, and produces a synthetic resin with phenols, amines, or ketones.

Condensation of the aniline and furfural takes place in the presence of certain acidic (oxalic acid) or basic catalysts. When used for stabilization, 50 per cent of the water required for the compaction of the soil to be stabilized is added with aniline, and the other 50 per cent by furfural, and the soil is then sprinkled with the aqueous emulsions obtained successively. The aniline/furfural ratio is 2 : 1 or 3 : 2, while the required amount is 1 weight per cent.

Thus stabilization may be due to one of two actions. Firstly, the two additives may react and produce a resin or a polymer which exerts its effect as discussed in the previous paragraphs, by reducing water permeability, bringing about strong bonds and, thereby, increasing strength, etc. For this purpose, secondly, at the above weight ratio, only part of the aniline is used, while the residue initiates an exchange with the adsorption complex of the soil, as pointed out before, in the form of large organic cations. When stabilizing sands, only the first effect will manifest itself, of course.

A chemical discussion of the aniline-furfural reaction would go much beyond the scope of this volume (see e.g. Geiseking and Goebel, 1955), so the formula of this chemical reaction will be presented here just to verify the above statement. In a neutral environment, an aniline molecule reacts with a furfural molecule whereby a furfuraldehyde-ammonia type compound is produced:

This compound is unstable and has a great tendency to polymerization. During resin production the furfural ring opens up.

The reaction needs only one molecule of each component, while the weight ratio approximates 1 : 1 (the molecular weight of aniline is 93, and that of the furfural is 96). If, therefore, a ratio of 2 : 1 or 70 : 30 is used, then the exchange with clay minerals leaves about 50 per cent of the aniline available.

The numerical effect of aniline and furfural additions on the physical characteristics is still not well understood. This is probably due to the fact that such a stabilization is not at all economical. The following paragraphs describe, therefore, only two details of a rather interesting test series (Ogilvie, Sheeler and Davidson, 1957). These authors performed experiments with Iowa loess samples (USA), using 2 : 1 volume ratio aniline-furfural mixtures. First they compacted the 5 cm diameter specimens and then, after a storage of 10 days, they subjected their samples to different tests (unconfined compression, compressibility, dryout-wetting, freezing-thaw, etc.). Compaction of the samples of different compositions specified the optimum water content at compaction, and the maximum dry density.

234

Two details of the results are shown in Fig. 214. Since during processing it was soon discovered that the clay content of the samples ($d < 2\mu$) greatly affected the properties under discussion (all the more understandable as the reactions involved take place with clay minerals), a method of illustration was selected such that the characteristic feature under examination was given as a parameter of a function of the aniline-furfural and clay contents, respectively. Thus Fig. 214a indicates the optimum water content, and Fig. 214b the values of unconfined compression strength. The water-absorption test gave similarly interesting results: at an addition of about 22 per cent clay content and five per cent aniline-furfural mixture (in a 2 : 1 ratio), the water-absorption value was at a minimum (2 per cent) level. According to the DTA experiments, the resin formation was closely connected with the effect exerted by the clay minerals. The disadvantage

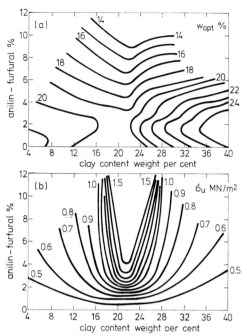

FIG. 214. Properties of an aniline-furfural-plus-loess mixture as a function of amount of stabilizer and clay content; (a) the optimum water content at compaction, (b) unconfined compression strength

of aniline-furfural stabilization is its inadmissibly low economic efficiency: it requires an admixture of about 4 weight per cent, whereas an addition as low as only 1/2 per cent would be needed to compete with processes such as cement stabilization. Moreover, its durability is still not supported by sufficient data, and furthermore, aniline is hazardous to health.

7.4.5 Stabilization with sulphite liquor

When discussing stabilization with synthetic resins, one must include the procedures using sulphite liquor, a by-product of the paper industry. This material has now been used for quite some time to treat and remove dust from earth-road surfaces, since by means of the fire or pine resin it contains, it creates a certain bondage among the particles of mechanical soil stabilization. However, this bond only has a temporary nature, as the material separated through evaporation is water soluble (in cellulose production, after sulphuric acid digestion, exactly the water soluble subtances are washed off), so it is washed off by precipitation, and the stabilization effect thus fails under wet weather conditions. This is why the method of producing calcium lignosulphonate by means of the sulphite liquor through lime addition was experimented with, giving, by sodium or calcium bichromate addition, an insoluble resin. The chromium ions would transform the lignosulphonate into a water-absorbent gel-type substance of a rather dark colour, capable of considerable expansion and thereby filling up the pores of the soil. This chromium-lignine process was first suggested for soil stabilization in 1910.

From the cellulose-plant wastes of the timber-processing industry, the following materials have been made good use of in soil stabilization so far:

1. Acidic raw sulphite liquor,
2. Condensed sulphite liquor,
?. CaO lignine (alkaline calcium salt of the lignine sulpho-acids).

The raw sulphite liquor, the actual by-product of timber processing, is greatly acidic (with a pH of 3 to 3.5), so it is rather reactive particularly at high temperatures. Its density is low (7°Bé), and contains only about 10 per cent solids. This is why its application has been completely abandoned, although it had been tested experimentally.

It is still used, however, in the form of a condensed and neutralized liquid, concentrated to a 30 to 35°Bé density in evaporators, leaving about 50 to 60 per cent of the solids in the liquid phase. The fluid thus produced is not reactive having a pH of 5.5 to 6.5; it can be readily transported, rediluted usually to 25°Bé, i.e. to a 40 per cent content of solids, and sprayed readily on the road surface. The capacity of the evaporators is unfortunately very limited, and the completely condensed powder substances are still used in the experimental stage only.

Recently, practice has drawn attention to the material called CaO lignine, a raw sulphite liquor completely neutralized by the excessive addition of calcium hydroxide. These liquids can be condensed into thixotropic substances, which are still sufficiently fluid by sedimentation or centrifuging.

The role played by calcium-alkali mixtures in soil stabilization is still not understood. Some chemistry experts claim that, under highly alkaline conditions, lignine and similar materials would form a gel type skeleton practically water-insoluble but readily softened, with the assistance of the calcium ions. Using this binder will changes the soil properties as follows:

— cohesion increases,
— the soil is easier to work with and compact,
— permeability, water absorption capacity, and frost sensitivity decrease,
— soil hygroscopy increases.

In road construction, this binder is generally used for building water-bound gravel roads, including both the foundation and 3–5 cm stabilized pavements, with the objective of using the stabilized rubble-mixed soil-layer to make the gravel surface last for at least 3 to 5 years. The grain-distribution curve of such stabilized soils

236

is more or less identical to the optimum earth for roads, except that grains larger than 3 mm are replaced by rubble.

Admixture involves 2–4 per cent sulphite liquor (the solids in the sulphite liquor related to the dry weight of the soil), and 5 to 10 per cent powdered lime, depending on quality and other aspects. In such an addition the optimum mixtures would result, under laboratory conditions, in a compression strength of 40 to 50 kp/cm (10 cm diameter and 10 cm height cylinders), while the in-situ strength figure, measured after complete adsorption, would be about 15 kp/cm .

This method is suggested periodically, but experiences on durability are unfortunately rather discouraging. According to our own experiments the different mixtures (manganese-lignine technique) exhibited some consolidation only under dry conditions, and the strength achieved was insufficient. Further, the mixture did not prove to be waterproof and disintegrated completely under the effect of water under pressure or flowing. This suggests that the expected chemical effects, including an interaction with the soil structure, did not transpire. Similar unfavourable experiences have been collected in the United States, though by briquetting certain soil mixtures resembling that described above, some desired results could still be achieved.

7.4.6 Stabilization with other synthetic resins

Synthetic resins are also used for stabilizing purposes. In the following the results of a test series performed in the laboratory of the Department for Geotechnique (Technical University of Budapest) will be discussed. The resins had a Carbamid

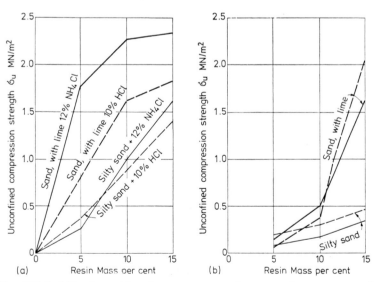

FIG. 215. Stabilization with polymers; compression strength vs. amount of stabilizing agent, (a) storing in dry air; (b) storing in moist air

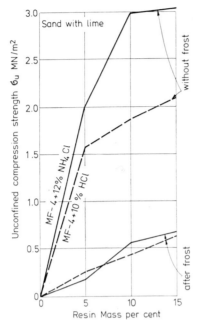

FIG. 216. Effect of frost on the compression strength

and a Melamin basis, respectively, they were produced with formaldehyde. The viscosity was exceptionally low just slightly higher than that of the water. By adding a catalysator, solidification occurs, the structure becomes foamy. On the action of heat, solidification occurs without reagents; a three-dimensional network will be formed.

For the tests, two soils were selected: a fine sand, with some lime content, and a silty fine sand. The soils were pulverized in an air dry state, then water, resin (5, 10, 15 mass per cent) and catalysator added. The samples were stored under different conditions, and after 21 days, their compressive strenght tested. Some results are given in Figs 215 and 216. The frost susceptibility of the samples has also been investigated. The following conclusions could be drawn:

The influence of the grain-size distribution on the solidification is rather high. Fine soils will have a higher strength; however, if the fines are clay minerals, the strength becomes lower. pH values over 7 to 8 are detrimental: a lime content is also disadvantageous. Frost effect is very detrimental: the strength will be one sixth of the original value. Storage under water only caused a slight drop of strength. It was an important finding that no solidification occurred, if the moisture content of the untreated soil was above $w = 10$ per cent. At $w = 5$ per cent significant compressive strength was achieved with 15 per cent resin added.

7.4.7 Soil treatment with RRP

The chemical treatment of the soil has been in use for 15 years. The chemical which is used most frequently is the so-called RRP (Reynolds Road Packer 233). This is a strong acidic material which alters effectively, through ion exchange, the water-absorptive capacity of the fine soil particles. The hydrated shell will be thinner, therefore the soil can be easier compacted and the volume change, the capillarity, the frost susceptibility and water sensitivity decreases and the bearing capacity increases. The RRP does not produce binding forces between the particles, it does not stabilize the soil. Another similar chemical is CBV (Chemische Bodenverbesserung).

The method of application consists in spraying simply the diluted chemical on the surface of the road; mixing is not required. After a certain amount of time the wetted soil is compacted in a moist state. The preliminary investigations include only the determination of the grain-size distribution and of the compactibility; required amount of chemical is determined by the percentage of the particles smaller than 0.06 mm.

Since 1968, several low-traffic roads have been treated with this chemical in the Federal Republic of Germany. On rural and forestry roads the treated soil was covered by a thin granular wearing course. In housing estates and community roads, often an asphaltic layer or carpet is applied.

The preliminary laboratory investigation of the soil to be treated includes the determination of its grain-size distribution curve, liquid and plastic limits, compactibility and pH value.

The treatment starts with scarifying the soil in a depth of 5 cm.

If necessary, 3 to 5 thick granular wearing course material is spread over the surface. Before treatment, the moisture content of the upper soil layer be somewhat below the Proctor optimum.

The chemical will added in two doses

(a) 2 to 6 kg RRP, with 200 l water;
(b) 1 kg RRP, mixed with 4 to 500 l water.

The treated soil remains in a loose state for at least two weeks. If there was not a precipitation of 20 to 30 mm in the meantime, then the still required amount of water will be added in several doses. Then we wait until the moisture content of the upper soil layer is closely around the optimum; if the soil is dry, moistening is required. The cross-fall of road formation has to be checked. Compaction will be made by using a pneumatic tyre roller; the achieved degree of compaction has to be checked regularly. The required value is at least 93 to 95%. Uniform spreeding of the chemical and through compaction are indispensable for successful treatment.

The effect of chemicals on several soils has been investigated in the Hungarian Road Research Institute (Dr. Gáspár). He suggested to judge the suitability of the soil to chemical treatment on the basis of the following tests:

— drop of the liquid limit on treatment with a small amount of chemical (1/10 to 1/100 of the material likely to be used);
— changes in the compactibility properties;
— CBR investigations (along with the measurement of water absorption and swelling) on samples compacted at optimum moisture content, after 4 days of capillary water absorption;
— pH value of the original soil.

According to the investigations made by Dr. Gáspár, treatment can be beneficial, if the following requirements are met:

— the application of a small amount of chemical is sufficient to cause a major drop of the liquid limit

239

- due to the treatment, the maximum dry density and the optimum moisture content are increased;
- CBR value of treated samples, compacted at w_{opt} and exposed to capillary action for 4 days is min 15 to 20 per cent, and the accompanying swelling is not more than 2 to 3 mm;
- pH value is not greater than 7.5.

Advantages of chemical soil treatment are:

- it requires the use of a very small amount of chemical (30 to 70 g/m^2);
- the application is simple, no complete pulverisation and mixing is needed;
- there is no definite setting time; water will not elutriate the material; consequences of eventual bad weather can be eliminated by appropriate organization;
- in regions where granular soils are scarce, the treatment can substitute the base course;
- simply adding a thin granular wearing course will permit low traffic to be carried.

The disadvantages:

- not all cohesive soils can be successfully treated;
- 2 to 3 weeks waiting time cannot always be ensured;
- effective compaction of the treated and moistened soil is a prerequisite for successful application.

8. Design of stabilized earth roads

8.1 Introduction

8.1.1 Fields of application of the various stabilization methods

The roads in a country are usually classified according to their traffic and economic importance, the authority in charge of road construction and maintenance, or the character of the traffic turnover. In this book, no such classification has prime importance since soil stabilization is adaptable for any road type, even in the case of roads constructed for maximum traffic and requirements, in a deeper layer if not elsewhere, to increase the load-bearing capacity of the soil. In the following paragraphs we discuss the road types where we think stabilization can be practised successfully and economically.

The most important field of application of stabilized roads is, undoubtedly, the construction of an agricultural road network. About 55–60 per cent of the total value of agricultural production is due to commodity transport and, therefore, good organization of deliveries as well as their expedient and economical implementation represent some of the fundamental problems in directing agricultural plant operations. Falling short of the optimum transport times, or using the wrong transport type leads to losses in the quantity of the commodities delivered, quality reduction, transport and other operational peak difficulties, and considerable cost increase. Moreover, failure to deliver certain agricultural requirements (feed, water, plant protectives, fertilizers or farmyard manure, etc.) might completely paralyze farming and cause tremendous damage almost impossible to predict.

Agricultural transport is aggravated by the dependence of agricultural production on the existing weather conditions. This is why certain agricultural operations become overcrowded, the products to be transported accumulate, and the relevant tasks have to be accomplished by the rather limited transport capacities, within a shorter time and under still less favourable conditions.

Agricultural roads may be categorized according to Fig. 217.

The agricultural enterprises are connected to the national road network by roads which lead to the farms, that is, the centres of the individual agricultural plants. The farms have their in-plant routes — feed and fertilizer distribution — as well as numbered subsidiary roads, while the rest is represented by the so-called external roads, including main and ordinary feeder lines along which the agricultural products are transported to the centres, and the by-lanes along the fields serving their cultivation. The length of the main and ordinary feeder roads,

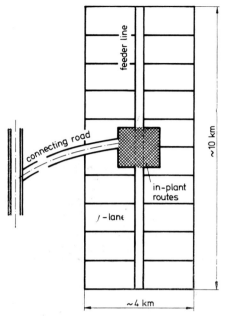

FIG. 217. Roads of an agricultural enterprise

and the by-lanes depends on the size, shape, and location of the area concerned. Per 1000 ha approximately 4–5 km by-lanes, 1–2 km secondary feeder lines, and 2–4 km main feeder roads are needed. The average length of the connecting roads is 2–3 km.

With co-ordinated agricultural and engineering aspects, the loading and classification of the individual road categories are given in Table 39. This loading is distributed rather irregularly throughout the year: the early products like cereals, vegetables, etc. are harvested and transported mainly in July and August (Category No. I), corn, potato, silage, hay and other feed plants from the middle of August to Mid-October (Category No. II), while the late crops, e.g. sugar beet, the other industrial plants, grape, apple, etc., mainly in October and November (Category No. III). Certain goods (for example farmyard manure, fertilizers, seed stock, soil amelioration agents, building materials, etc.) are transported fairly regularly throughout the year (Category No. IV).

In order to illustrate the quantity and distribution as functions of time of transports, Fig. 218 presents data on the in-plant deliveries to a fictitious 4000 ha farm, while Fig. 219 shows the distribution of transptorts among the different road types.

Another area where stabilized earth roads may play an important role is forestry.

Table 39

Classification of agricultural roads
by character and loading

Type	Load, tons/day	Category
Connecting roads	> 1500	I
Primary and secondary feeder lines	400–1500	II
By-lanes	200– 400	III
	100– 200	IV
	< 100	V

Efforts to reduce the work and thus the costs required for transport, and to make deliveries independent of the current weather conditions, and many other requirements of an intensive forestry operation demand the construction of a forest road network. Where rock is hardly or not at all available for forestry operations, transport is increasingly implemented over earth-stabilized routes.

Other fields of stabilized earth-road applications include the routes of mining areas, where often only temporary roads are needed for e.g. shaft sinking, machine transports, etc. A further opportunity is the construction of industrial in-plant roads, since such internal transport routes passable throughout the year can considerably increase the efficiency of the plant operations. A similar category includes the construction of residential district roads and sidewalks. Here high-load traffic is envisaged only if people are moving or their fuel is delivered, otherwise only very light traffic need be considered — these roads lend an urban character to the area. Sidewalk construction may increase the permeability of transition zones. A final field of application, similar to the roads in mining areas, is represented by provisional roads for preliminary operations and transports, readily constructed within a very short time inexpensively, and area pavements for storage purposes.

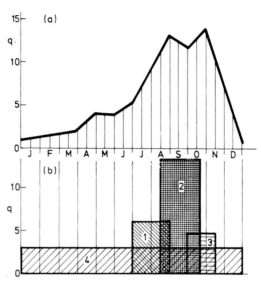

FIG. 218. Quantities to be transported in a 4000 ha agricultural enterprise. (a) Distribution of the quantities to be transported; (b) distribution by categories

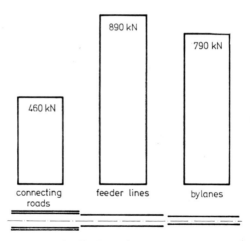

FIG. 219. Distribution of the transports among the different road types in a 4000 ha agricultural enterprise

Finally, soil stabilization has a significant economic importance in constructing load bearing foundations for higher-order road surfaces, but the discussion of this theme belongs to general road construction textbooks.

8.1.2 Effect of climatic factors on design

For the assessment of the meteorological conditions of the individual regions, the following data are most useful:

- map of the average total precipitation annually,
- the probable number of rainy days in the May–September period, and
- the annual amount of sunshine hours.

Here we should mention certain research projects, started some time ago, aimed at determining the factors on which the properties of the soil found now at a given site had been developed. Wherever erosion is the main factor, as in the hilly western parts of Europe, the soils are rather "young", and the experts of soil science consider geological and mineralogical conditions to be most essential and of a primary influence, while in the European part of the Soviet Union, where there is no erosion to prevent the soils from "ageing", Dokutchayev and his school emphasize the importance of climatic factors. According to Dokutchayev, the properties of a soil depend on the following factors:

$$T = f(K, O, G, t)$$

where T is an optional soil property,
K means the climatic effect,
O indicates the influence of living organisms,
G represents the geological factors, and
t is time.

Jenny (USA) has expressed this equation in an extended form:

$$T = f(K, O, D, A, t)$$

where, additionally
D means the topographic conditions and
A is the parent rock.

Climate is one of the most important factors, since the soil which develops from the parent rock depends on the fluctuation and extreme values of the temperature, as well as the total amount of precipitation. This is clearly illustrated in Fig. 220.

Under cold and wet climatic conditions, where infiltration usually exceeds evaporation, the eluvial A-horizon creates an acidic environment which the iron and aluminium compounds will be washed out. Underneath an accumulation level will develop, often of quite considerable strength. The soil over the terrain is generally ash grey, and rather poor in mineral matter.

244

Under a hot and humid climate, if infiltration exceeds evaporation then the organic parts will be rapidly oxidized. The iron and aluminium oxides released as a result of the absence of protective colloids will precipitate from the dispersed state, and accumulate. Here the effect destroying the compounds is represented by hydrolysis, which weathers much more intensively than the acidic environment does, and the situation is further aggravated by higher temperatures and the wet-dry cycles. Under such conditions, the aluminum and iron silicates will weather into a colloid solution, then be washed out. The soil thus produced is laterite.

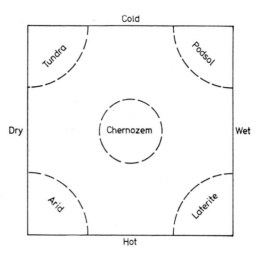

FIG. 220. The effect of climatic factors on the development of soils

If the precipitation is sufficient for the vegetation, but not enough for an intensive infiltration so that no leaching takes place, a very fertile soil type, most favourable from agricultural aspects will be produced: chernozem. In the presence of calcium, the acidic-type organic matter will be neutralized, or decomposed throughout to carbon dioxide, thus the reaction of this soil will be either neutral or alkaline. In the presence of moisture, and at a relatively high atmospheric carbon-dioxide content, some carbonates and bicarbonates will be produced, and an accumulation horizon rich in calcium is formed, at a depth depending on the evaporation/infiltration ratio.

A hot and dry climate creates desert soils, while cold and dry climatic conditions develop tundra or, perhaps, steppe areas. As mentioned above, the character of the soil type produced is greatly affected by infiltration and evaporation, as shown oversimplified in Fig. 221.

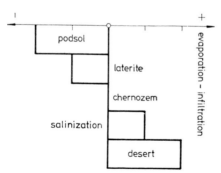

FIG. 221. The effect of evaporation and infiltration on soil development

245

8.2 Engineering characteristics of stabilized earth roads

8.2.1 Profile design

The width of roads is determined by the vehicles expected to travel along them. Data on the types of transport most frequently used at present are given in Table 40, while the design of agricultural road cross sections is exampled in Fig. 222. By-lanes separating fields (a) may be constructed as grader-planed earth roads having about a 5 m wide crown. In the case of granular soils an additional ditch is never needed except when the amount of surface water exceeds the average. With cohesive subsoils, on the other hand, the method of raising the road from the terrain by constructing an embankment may be adopted, always with a waste ditch. The feeder lines (b), internal farm roads, may be constructed as stabilized roads, with dimensions corresponding to section (b) in Fig. 222. Along these roads, however, no tracked or caterpillar tractors are allowed to travel as they would completely ruin them, since these vehicles are designed to move on the terrain or over the fields. If tractor movements must also be catered for, then a separate tractor route should be constructed next to the stabilized road, but at a lower level. Built-road and tractor-lane intersections deserve special attention. These intersections should be covered by quarry or cobble stone, precast concrete slabs, etc. according to Fig. 223.

Cross section of a connecting road may be designed according to the detail (c) of Fig. 222. In certain cases, the construction of a connecting road with a higher-order pavement may also be justified, of course. Otherwise stabilized earth roads

Table 40

Transport characteristics

Vehicle	Dead-weight tons	Net weight load tons	Dead-weight load ratio, tons net weight	Wheel load tons	Load per road surface kp/cm²
Cart (1.2–3.2 t) useful load	0.4–0.8	1.2–3.2	0.33–0.25	0.5–1.0	10–60
Tractor	4.552–5.770	—	—	2.712–1.840 3.218–2.552	1.5–1.8 2.0–2.4
Trailer (3 t)	1.650	3.000	0.55	1.160	4.5
Tractor + 1 trailer	6.202	3.000	—	—	—
Tractor + 2 trailers	7.852	6.000	—	—	—
Truck ("Csepel") D-350 D-700	3.7 7.0	3.5 6.8	1.06 1.15	4.5 4.25	max 2.6 5.34
Truck + trailer	5.350 8.650	6.500 9.800	0.820 0.895	— —	— —

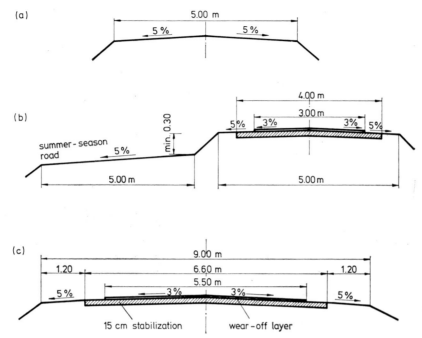

FIG. 222. Agricultural road sections. (a) By-lane separating fields; (b) feeder line or in-plant farm road; (c) connecting road with public traffic

will be satisfactory with, perhaps, a greater width and load bearing capacity than those of the feeder lines.

Forestry road cross sections are exampled in Fig. 224. In such cases single tracks will often suffice, according to section (a), with siding ensured at intervals by the construction of section (b).

The cross section of a "ribbon" road is illustrated in Fig. 225. Such single-track roads were constructed in some of the sandy regions of the Hungarian Great Plain: in dry weather the traffic travels along the "ribbon", the middle lane being made of 0.30 m alkaline surface-improved sand, and under wet conditions along the sand banks.

The salt content of the alkaline soil protects the road from disintegration during the summer heat, while in rainy weather or snow, the sand of a good water permeability keeps the running surface sufficiently dry. These roads are extremely well-suited to tyred traffic.

In addition to soil stabilization, other solutions have also been suggested for ribbon road construction. Thus concrete ribbon roads, for examples, were experimented with (Wárlám, 1938), starting from the idea of utilizing the otherwise detrimental feature of cart traffic to follow the same single track if possible. The ribbons are supposed to protect the road surface mainly against the disintegrating action of iron wheel bands, so their width and distance are determined

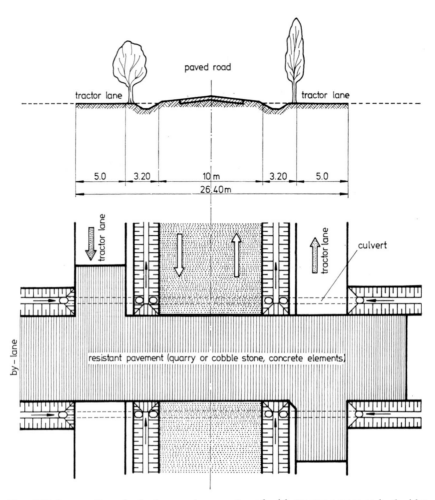

FIG. 223. Intersection of a by-lane and a paved road with tractor routes at both sides

by the most common local cart tread (Fig. 226). The maximum 2.5 per cent slope of the ribbons and 4 per cent decline of the adjacent road parts will cause the carts to use the improved earth road only for siding or overtaking. The resisting force and jolting effect of the ribbon road must be less than those of the earth road, otherwise the carts will avoid it. In Rhodesia asphalt ribbon roads are used extensively. Our experiences with experimental concrete ribbon roads were not favourable enough, so these roads could not be generally accepted.

As a last comment in connection with the design of stabilized earth road sections, it should be noted that their width must be determined with respect to the building machinery available, so this width will be the same as the operational width of the machines, or its multiple.

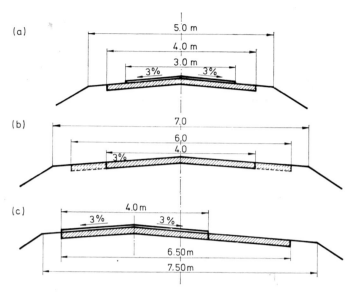

FIG. 224. Forestry road sections. (a) Single-track road; (b) provision for continuous or periodical siding; (c) siding for empty vehicles

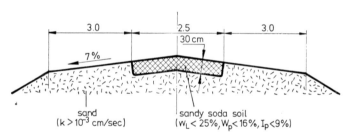

FIG. 225. Alkaline "ribbon" road cross section

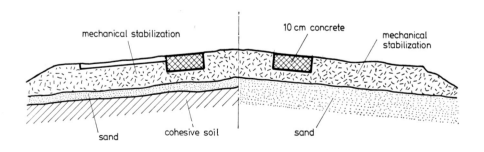

FIG. 226. Concrete "ribbon" road cross section

8.2.2 Horizontal and vertical alignment

Over flat terrain, the horizontal alignment of agricultural roads should correspond to the in-plant transport requirements of the enterprises. Junction points, ramps and rundowns, entrances, etc., must enable the vehicles to turn in. The minimum radii needed are

tractor + trailer	5 m
light trucks	8–9 m
heavy trucks	11 m

Along the individual road stretches the turning radius of the machines doing the stabilization job will determine the minimum radii which should not be less

Table 41

Road type	Plains				
	Design speed km/h	Maximum turning radius m	Maximum slope p%	Pavement width m	Bank width m
External part of connecting roads	60	300	3	4.0–6.0	1.0–2.5
Transition zones of connecting roads in communities	30	30	3	6.0–7.0	1.5–2.0
Internal main lines	40	125	4	3.0–4.0	1.0
Internal by-lanes	20	10	4	3.0–4.0	1.0
	Hilly country				
External part of connecting roads	30	70	6	4.0–6.0	1.0–1.5
Transition zones of connecting roads in communities	25	30	4	6.0–7.0	1.0–1.5
Internal main lines	25	50	6	3.0–4.0	0.5–1.0
Internal by-lanes	15	10	8	3.0–4.0	0.5
	Highland				
External part of connecting roads	25	50	7	4.0–5.0	1.0–1.5
Transition zones of connecting roads in communities	20	20	5	5.0–6.0	1.0–1.5
Internal main lines	20	20	7	3.0–4.0	0.5–1.0
Internal by-lanes	15	10	8	3.0	1.0

than 60 to 80 m, otherwise construction might be rather awkward, with much time needed to turn the machines, and leading to a much poorer pavement quality than along the straight sections, while later on the torsional forces transmitted to the road surface under traffic would rapidly wear off the pavement.

As for the vertical alignment, it is best to design uniformly increasing slopes. In plains, the road is usually elevated 25 to 40 cm to facilitate drainage and snow removal. Slopes must not exceed $p = 8$ per cent even in extreme cases. If surface cover is employed, then maximum 3 per cent slopes may be included to avoid the vehicles sliding or slipping. In order to promote good drainage, we should avoid excessive horizontal sections. A detailed summary of the engineering characteristics of agricultural roads is presented in Table 41, with separates data on plains, hilly country, and highland.

8.2.3 Traction forces and velocities

Among the engineering parameters, data on the traction force or haulage capacity and on the velocities involved are of particular importance as economic investigations simply cannot be carried out without them. In addition, they are indispensable if the stresses and loads on the pavement are to be understood accurately.

Table 42 presents specific resistance figures. This information is most important for transport cost calculations since, as pointed out in Chapter 1.1 (Eq. (2)), the transport cost is proportional to the specific resistance.

The hauling capacity of the most common transport means is illustrated by detailed data in Table 43, while Fig. 227 presents horse-drawn total weight in the function of the gradient along different roads (Wárlám 1938), and Fig. 228 supplies data on mechanical transport means.

Here the so-called "starting resistance", having considerable importance in the case of earth roads must also be mentioned. Each soil type has a certain water content at which the traction or haulage resistance is minimum. This value

Table 42

Specific resistance values

Road surface	μ, permill
Concrete	10
Asphalt	15
Stone or brick	20
Macadam	30
Gravel	40
Grader planed earth road	50
Dry earth road with potholes	75
Muddy or sandy earth road	150

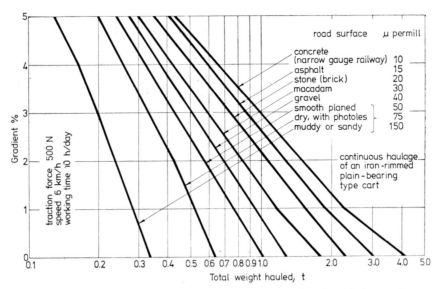

FIG. 227. Maximum weight hauled by a 500 kg horse as a function of the gradient and travelling resistance

will obviously be near the optimum water content of compaction, on which some measurement data are presented in Fig. 229 (Járay 1955). Since the starting resistance exceeds the travelling resistance, the loadability of the vehicles will be determined by the former. This effect is taken into account by the data presented in Fig. 227.

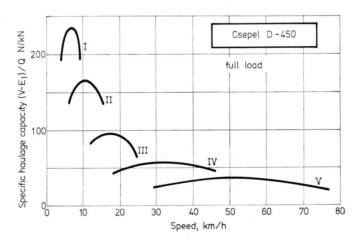

FIG. 228. Specific haulage capacity of a CSEPEL D-450 truck under full load (I—V = gears)

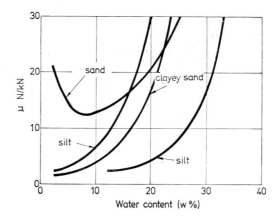

FIG. 229. Starting resistance on earth roads vs. the moisture content of the soil

8.3 Pavement design

8.3.1 General

Pavement design of stabilized earth roads demands the accomplishment of the following duties:

(a) Determination of the pavement thickness with the strength characteristics of the pavement and the subsoil, as well as known wheel load of the vehicles involved;

(b) Determination of the quantity and build-in technique of the stabilizer, at given subsoil and pavement thicknesses, and with known wheel load of the

Table 43

Traction force requirement of transport means along a horizontal road surface (kp)

Road	Cart	Tractor VÖCSI D-4k	Trailer 3 t	Tractor + 1 tr.	Tractor + 2 tr.	Truck	Truck + trailer
Concrete	16– 40	46– 58	46	92	138	72–140	118– 184
Asphalt	24– 60	69– 87	69	138	207	108	177– 276
Stone, brick	32– 80	92–116	92	184	276	144–280	236– 368
Macadam	48–120	138–174	138	276	414	216–420	351– 552
Gravel	64–160	184–232	184	368	552	288–560	472– 726
Planed earth	80–200	230–290	230	460	690	360–700	590– 920
Dry with potholes	120–300	345–435	345	690	1185	540–1050	960–1380
Muddy or sandy earth	240–600	690–870	690	1380	2070	1080	1770–2760

253

vehicles, according to the required pavement strength and, on this basis, to the peculiar features of the given stabilization method;

(c) Determination of the pavement thickness or amount of stabilizer, on the basis of other effects independent of the load, such as the pulverizing or kneading action of the wheels, frost or soak-through effects, etc.

Dimensioning of the stabilized earth roads will differ considerably from that of both the elastic and rigid pavements, except for case (a). This difference will increase more since the design and construction of stabilized earth roads cannot and does not rely on such rational bases as those available for the design of higher-order pavements. Soil stabilization is still said to be an "art" to some extent, not completely an engineering science. We do not yet have a full knowledge of basic quantitative details, such as wheel load or the strength and elasticity characteristics of the soil which are absolutely necessary for developing a rational dimensioning method. Accordingly, dimensioning still involves a number of empirical and intuitive elements. The only reason why these do not have major disadvantageous effects is that, for earth roads, the changes in design and construction during implementation do not represent the great problems involved with other road types. Thus batching, the number of compaction cycles, and even the thickness of the stabilized layer, for example, may be readily changed during the in-situ operations. On the other hand, an experienced professional engineering control of construction is vital in suiting the process to the changing conditions.

In the following paragraphs we discuss the dimensioning of stabilized earth roads within a rather narrow framework with respect to the above comments, and only those methods particularly important for stabilized earth roads are explained. As for the other pavement-dimensioning techniques, we refer to the literature.

Prior to discuss the various dimensioning methods, let us examine how a stabilized earth road can be destroyed.

8.3.2 Stabilized earth-road destruction

From destruction aspects, just as in the case of higher-order pavements, elastic and rigid types must be distinguished. Bitumen, tar, lime, and the various chemical stabilizations are elastic, while cement stabilization supplies a rigid cover. A separate third category is represented by mechanical stabilization, since vehicle wheels will produce here the same indentations as for ordinary earth roads, because in these cases no "foreign crust" having very different properties forms over the subsoil surface.

Rigid pavements like the soil cement may be destroyed when its own strength or that of the subsoil becomes insufficient. In the first case the top layer is crushed, then broken into small pieces, whereas in the second case deep indentations are formed, and then the cover cracks into large parts.

254

With flexible stabilizations the low natural strength can also cause destruction. Since this is usually the consequence of the low compactness of the stabilized mixture, destruction is preceded by intensive post-compaction, then the formation of potholes, which the surface undergoes rapid destruction. If the strength of the subsoil is too low, the flexible pavement will suffer from deep bucklings which also produce potholes. This, however, can be clearly distinguished from pothole formation by post-compaction. If the strength of the subsoil is very low, the stabilized "road" will be "upset" or "turned upside down".

In the case of flexible pavements, but particularly with mechanical stabilization, destruction by wheel-track formation may occur. A pavement or, more precisely, a mechanically stabilized soil layer of increased strength, quite sufficient for a single static effect of the standard wheel load, may quickly be destroyed by the kneading action of moving wheels and their repeated loading effect. In the stabilized layer of a relatively low strength, upon the latter action the wheel track produced by the first vehicle will afterwards deepen increasingly quickly until the surface is finally destroyed. This process is particularly rapid if the maintenance of the road is poor, or if the strength of the subsoil under the stabilized layer is not sufficient.

The pavement may also be destroyed by the effect of water, through capillary adsorption, downward soaking via developing potholes, normal water uptake, or frost. Particular attention is deserved by the pumping or suction effect due to repeated transient traffic. Tyres above irregularities in the road surface compress the air in these pits and as the wheels travel along the trapped air will suddenly expand, exerting a strong suction effect on the surface. In extreme cases this effect may be as intensive as 1 kp/cm². Such action will damage the material of the earth road and, if the ground water level is near the bottom of the pavement, may cause an upward vertical water movement. After the wheel has passed this action is no longer exerted so water movement in alternating directions may develop, exerting an extremely destructive effect on strength. The same destructive effect will appear if the bottom surface of the pavement is affected by water pressure, as with slack water in the ditch along the road (Fig. 230).

Suction is detrimental to the road surface even if no water is present. If the surface material cannot withstand this action, then the surface starts to decompose, some particles are removed, and the subsequent traffic will continue to destroy rapidly the surface thus attacked. It is particularly disadvantageous if vehicles with iron-rimmed wheels travel along the same road, since a joint effect such as

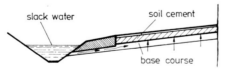

FIG. 230. Detrimental effect of the water stagnating in ditches along the road

255

 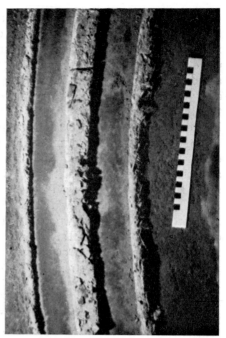

FIG. 231. Silt and sand mixture of a 3 : 1 weight ratio, with 15 kg/m² for 15 cm thickness No. 500 cement addition, after 50 000 motor vehicle wheel revolutions. The coating was repeatedly watered during the test. With hardly indented wheel tracks, the first few mm oft op layer have become quite plastic. Moderate grain removal prior to irrigation

FIG. 232. Following several 10 000 tyre revolutions, the soil-cement surface was exposed to a traffic of several 100 carts. 5–8 mm wheel tracks could then be observed, with the stabilized soil appreciably loosened between them

this will cause extremely rapid destruction. Assuming an average suction force of about 0.5 kp/cm², it can easily be calculated that the suction effect will not be able to attack the surface if the cohesion Φ of the latter, at a friction angle of 25 to 30 deg, is not less than $c = 5$ to 7 Mp/m². Thus the material of improved earth roads must either satisfy this requirement, or be made resistant to the suction effect by the addition of a suitable adhesive.

The different modes of road surface destructions are illustrated by the accompanying photographs, taken during the experiments conducted with the machine shown in Fig. 30 (Figs 231–234). The legends describe in detail the experimental conditions and the type of destruction.

Soil cement without a protective coating is not suitable for iron-wheel traffic, as shown in the relevant photograph. Either a mat cover must be constructed, or the top 5 cm layer should be supplemented with 50 weight per cent 20/25 rubble, since the experiments with this material showed favourable results.

FIG. 233. Wheel ruts on a tar-stabilized clay-type gravel road (sandy gravel to red clay = 3 : 2, with weight per cent tar). The soil was exposed to 15 000 tyre revolution

FIG. 234. Soil cement completely destroyed by upward water pressure and simultaneous traffic

8.3.3 Pavement and subsoil strength control

Under the effect of wheel load, certain stresses will be generated in both the pavement and the subsoil. While the deformations thus caused are small enough, and the stresses generated are three or four times the safety factor against failure, they may be calculated by the formulae derived from on the basis of the theory of elasticity. (See Handbook of Soil Mechanics, Vol. 2.) Such a stress calculation requires information on the standard wheel weight, and on the contact surface between tyre and road. When new, and under the operational pressure as specified by the manufacturer, and under the maximum permissible load, the contact surface of certain tyres is elliptical, and the ratio of the axes is about 1 : 1.5, as evidenced by measurements performed over soil-cement surfaces with normal tyres of 6" width and 22" diameter (Kézdi, 1951). At lower tyre pressures the ellipse is somewhat elongated (Fig. 235). If the surface is determined at different axle loads and plotted as a function of these pressures, then the curve illustrated

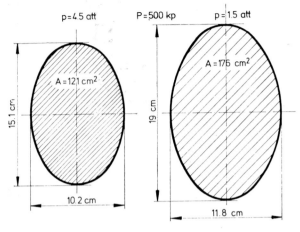

FIG. 235

in Fig. 236 is obtained, revealing that the stress affecting the pavement does not coincide with the internal overpressure. Calculation and plotting of the average stress leads to an almost linear correlation. In the case of perfectly elastic tyres of no natural rigidity, the two above values will be equal, will occur at the specified operational pressure as shown in the figure. According to test results, distribution of the stress caused by the wheels having tyres over the contact surface in the case of tyres may be considered. as uniform. This was confirmed by the stress values measured in both the pavement and the subsoil.

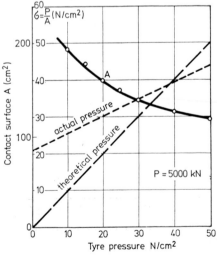

FIG. 236. Relation between the tyre pressure and the contact surface

The effect exerted on the pavement by iron-rimmed wheels is very undesirable as they penetrate excessively into flexible pavements or earth roads, while over a rigid pavement the surface irregularities cause stress peaks, so the stress distribution is unquestionably non-uniform, as shown by the test result illustrated in Fig. 237. If a piece of blotting paper is placed on a slightly wetted soil-cement road subsequently exposed to the action of an iron-rimmed wheel, the paper will suffer indentation and discoloration, depending on the stress, so the imprint will characterize the stress differences. The maximum stress will amount, presumably, to a

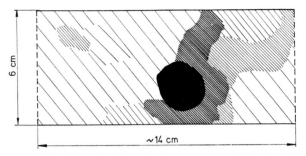

FIG. 237. Cart-wheel imprint in a cement stabilized earth road. Wheel diameter: 87 cm; wheel load: 524 kp; $F = 83$ cm^2; $p_{average} \approx 6.3$ kp/cm^2; $p_{max} = 15$–18 kp/cm^2

multiple of the average. Differences between the tyre and iron-rimmed wheel stress distributions are illustrated in Fig. 238. Under cart wheels, a rigid pavement such as cement soil will be destroyed mainly by a crushing pulverizing effect due to excessive local stresses.

As mentioned above, the stresses generated in both the soil layer and the subsoil can be calculated on the basis of the Theory of Elasticity. The theoretical basis of the calculations has had detailed elaboration in recent years. In addition, a number of Tables and graphs are also available in many cases. Thus solutions are already known for the homogeneous infinite half-space as well as for the double and triple-layer systems (Fig. 239), to calculate either the stresses or the deformations. (For the details of the theoretical investigations and practical applications see Handbook of Soil Mechanics, Vol. 2.) Here only the stresses caused in the sub-

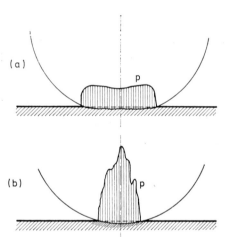

FIG. 238. Stress distribution over the road surface

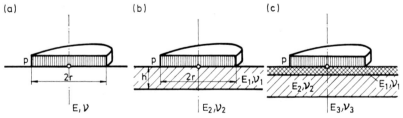

FIG. 239. Stresses in layered systems. In the given cases, tables and graphs are available for calculation

soil by a uniformly loaded circular surface are given. For a double-layer system, the stresses acting in the axis of the loaded surface will be determined, since in the case of a stabilized earth road only these are important.

Whenever the Young modulus of the stabilized soil is at maximum 5 to 10 times that of the subsoil, the stresses can be reliably calculated by making use of the homogeneous half-space theory by Boussinesq. This was clearly evidenced by the Vesić investigation (1963), according which to the Burmister theory on layered systems does not give reliably the stresses caused in an elastic pavement. This is because firstly the subsoil never has the tensile strength assumed by theory, and secondly the deformation modulus, critical from tensile aspects, is usually much lower than the assumed figure. Furthermore, we should remember that in stabilized soils the traffic itself and other effects may bring about changes which will act detrimentally upon the tensile strength and the deformation characteristics. Such effects are, for example, the formation of cracks in soil-cement ,or the softening of bituminous stabilization under extreme temperature conditions.

Accordingly, in the case of stabilized earth roads the application of the results obtained with double-layer systems may only be used for the determination of stresses produced in soil-cement-pavements and their subsoils, and even in these cases only if the soil-cement has a protective coating. In any other case the results of the Boussinesq theory should be used. The wheel-rut formation mentioned

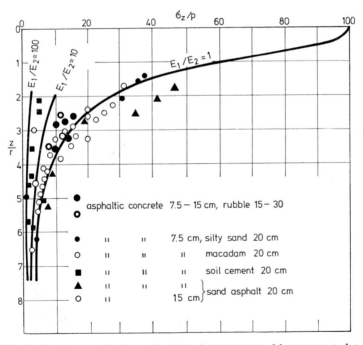

FIG. 240. Vertical stresses in the soil under the pavement. Measurement data, and calculations on the basis of a double-layer system

above, however, deserves special investigation as it follows an entirely different mechanism.

To verify the statement above, Fig. 240 presents, after Vesić, the results of some relevant stress measurements. This figure specifies the various pavement thicknesses involved, the pavement materials, and the theoretical curves: the vertical stress distribution for a homogeneous half-space, according to Boussinesq, and the curves based on the Burmister–Fox theory, for the $E_1/E_2 = 10$ and 100 ratios of the Young moduli. From the homogeneous half-space curve, only the stresses measured in asphalt concrete pavements based on soil-cement and beneath have deviated significantly.

Results of the Boussinesq solution applied to the homogeneous half-space are illustrated by the diagram in Fig. 241. The vertical stress effect values (σ_z/p) along the axis of the loaded surface and along the vertical lines at different distances are here given.

Figure 242 assists in the determination of the radial horizontal and annular stresses, while Fig. 243 presents the shear stresses (the curves of Figs 242 and 243 are associated with a $\mu = 0.5$ Poisson number). Exact formulae can only be given for the axial stresses. These are, with the symbols of Fig. 239, as follows:

$$\sigma_{zo} = p\left[1 - \frac{z^3}{(r^2 + z^2)^{3/2}}\right] = p(1 - \cos 3\alpha),$$

$$\sigma_{xo} = \sigma_{yo} = \frac{p}{2}\left[(1 + 2\mu) - \frac{2(1 + \mu)z}{(r^2 + z^2)^{1/2}} + \frac{z^3}{(r^2 + z^2)^{3/2}}\right],$$

$$\bar{u}_{max} = \frac{\sigma_2 - \sigma_x}{2} = p\left[\frac{1 - 2\mu}{4} + \frac{(1 + \mu)z}{2(r^2 + z^2)^{1/2}} - \frac{3z^3}{4(r^2 + z^2)^{3/2}}\right].$$

The stress effect values calculated with the above formulae are illustrated graphically in Figs 241–243. The maximum shear stress occurs along the axis of the loaded surface with the radius disc at a depth of 0.71 r.

Using these formulae and diagrams it is easy to assess whether or not in a given case the stresses produced in the pavement of known strength characteristics are still allowable at a given static wheel weight, or more precisely, how far the given stress state is from the limit condition of failure. To make such a decision, it is best to illustrate the stresses according to Mohr: the principal stress circles for the stress conditions produced along the axis are plotted, and then the envelope of the circles pertaining to the different depths define the shear-stress variation (see Fig. 244). If this curve is compared to the Coulomb line expressing the failure condition, a correct picture may be obtained on the failure safety limit. Thus the strength of the pavement may be considered satisfactory if the envelope curve referred to is only tangential to the so-called "proportional Coulomb line" of the soil (Kézdi, 1963). This can be determined according to Fig. 245, on the basis of a direct shear test.

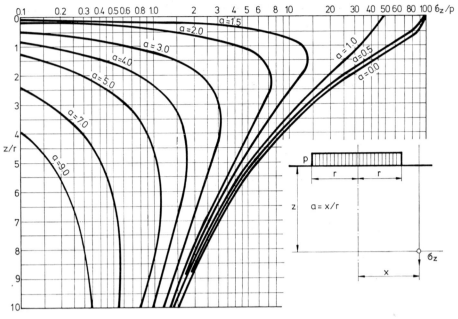

FIG. 241

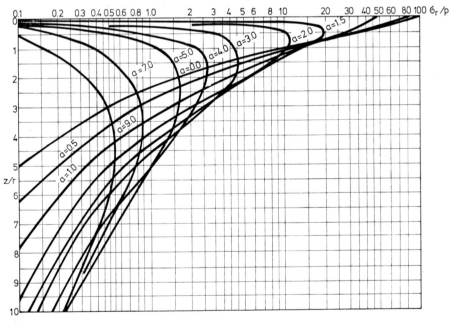

FIG. 242

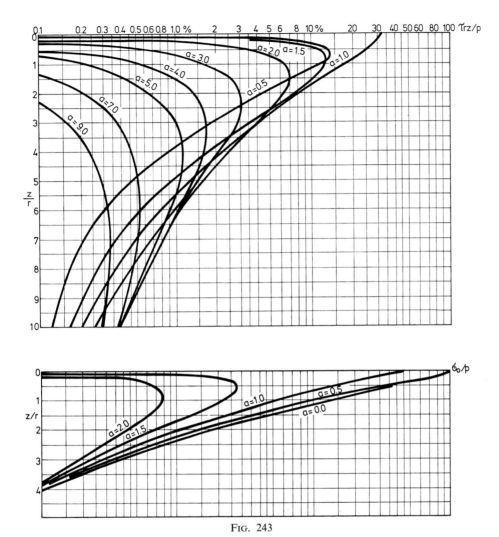

FIG. 243

For calculating stresses caused in double-layer systems (see Fig. 239b) the nec-essary tables and graphs are also available. Here two alternatives must be distinguished: in one case the contact surface of the two layers shows a perfect continuity of stresses and deflections, whereas in the other case the contact surface is frictionless, so there no horizontal stresses can be transferred. Obviously, only the first case applies to stabilized earth roads, when the vertical and horizontal stresses caused along the axis of loading, that is, at the boundary, can be readily determined from the graph of Fig. 246 (see the derivation in Kézdi, 1951). This figure reveals that, for a more rigid top layer, the stresses in the layer of the higher Young modulus E will increase, whereas in the much more compressible lower

263

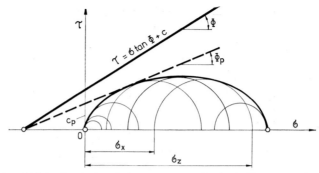

FIG. 244. Mohr circles of the stress states in the half-space under a load uniformly distributed on a circular surface, the envelope curve of these circles, and its comparison with the Coulomb line of failure

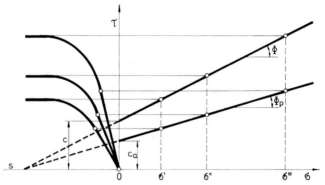

FIG. 245. Determination of the proportional Coulomb line by direct shear test

layer much smaller stresses will be produced. The horizontal stresses will differ in the upper and lower layers at the boundary surface. However, since the horizontal stress at the surface of the lower layer is always compressive, the given stress distribution may be considered valid even if the basic layer has no tensile strength, although in the lower part of the upper layer there certain tensile stresses will always act.

Figure 247 illustrates the vertical stresses produced in a double-layer system as a function of depth. The curves clearly portray the effect of the rigid upper layer, that is, the stress "accumulation" in the layer of a greater rigidity.

With known stresses produced in the pavement the strength of a rigid pavement (soil-cement) can be checked upon in the following way (see 4.3.2):

First the unconfined compression and tensile strength values of the mixture containing the predetermined quantity of cement, or its strength at a failure in

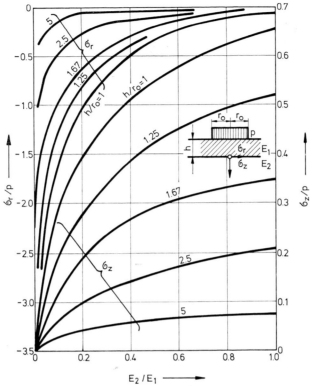

FIG. 246. Stresses in a double-layer system, as a function of the ratio E_2/E_1, at the boundary of the two layers

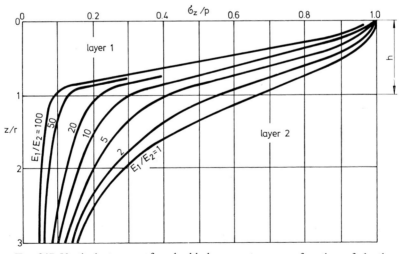

FIG. 247. Vertical stresses of a double-layer system as a function of depth

265

the Brasilien test are determined. On the basis of these data the Coulomb failure line (Fig. 248) of the pavement can then be plotted. Furthermore, it is useful to determine the "proportional" Coulomb line as shown in the figure, which is

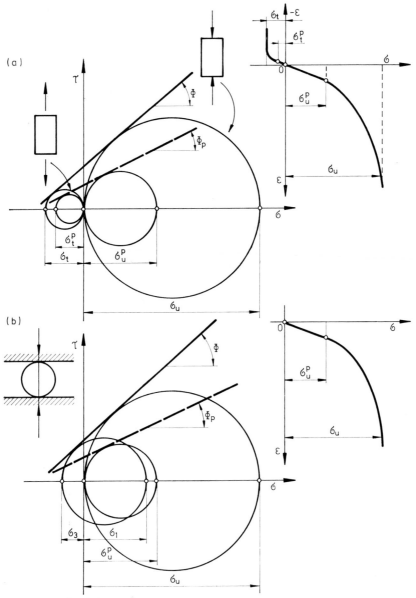

FIG. 248. Determination of the Coulomb failure line of the pavement on the basis of (a) unconfined compression and tension, (b) unconfined compression and a failure in the Brasilien test

associated to the stress states where the deformations taking place are actually proportional to the stresses involved (see Fig. 245).

Then the Young moduli E_1 and E_2 of the pavement and the subsoil are determined as described in Chapter 4.

Here first the stress transferred to the pavement is first determined for a known wheel load, then the size of the load-transfer surface (usually elliptical and is

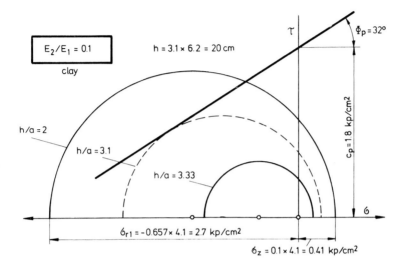

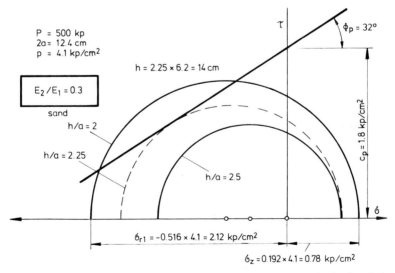

FIG. 249. Strength check of a rigid soil-cement pavement, on the basis of the stress state exhibited by the double-layer system

substituted by a circle of identical area) and, from the stress diagram and with known parameter E_1/E_2, the stress limits $(\sigma_r/p, \sigma_z/p)$ are found. Since σ_z and σ_r produced along the axis are the principal stresses, the Mohr circle can be readily plotted, and a comparison with the Coulomb line or the straight line pertaining to the proportionality limits will supply sufficient information on whether or not the strength of the pavement is satisfactory. An economical solution is obtained when the principal stress circle thus obtained is tangential to the Coulomb line of (Φ_a, c_a) parameters (Fig. 249). If, then, the principal stress circles are plotted for different h/r values, then the thickness providing a satisfactory strength of pavement at the given strength parameters can also be determined.

The same investigation can also be performed, of course, through an analytical method for the lower surface of the pavement the condition of fracture will assume the following form:

$$\sigma_{r1} = \sigma_z \tan^2(45° - \Phi/2) - 2c \tan(45° - \Phi/2)$$

Substituting the relation

$$2c = \sigma_u \tan(45° - \Phi/2)$$

we obtain

$$\sigma_z = \sigma_u + \sigma_{r1} \tan^2(45° - \Phi/2)$$

It follows that the strength of the pavement is satisfactory if the following inequality holds:

$$\sigma_u > \sigma_z - \sigma_{r1} \tan^2(45° + \Phi/2)$$

8.3.4 Deflection of soil-cement pavements

As usual in soil mechanics, when testing stabilized roads involving quantities calculated by the Theory of Elasticity, the stress values have a significant importance, whereas deformation is usually calculated on a basis other than elasticity. Theoretical data on deflection are useful mainly for the determination of the Young modulus for a static weight, and other load-bearing or deformation characteristics, by making use of the data measured accordingly.

In the case of a homogeneous half-space, the vertical displacements below the uniformly loaded circular surface, along and outside the axis and outside thereof at different depths, can be determined by means of Fig. 250. Such a displacement can be calculated from the following relation (see the accompanying figure):

$$y = \frac{pr}{E} F_1$$

where F_1 is the displacement influence given by the figure. Figure 251 enables the calculation of the same displacement but in a double-layer system, as a func-

268

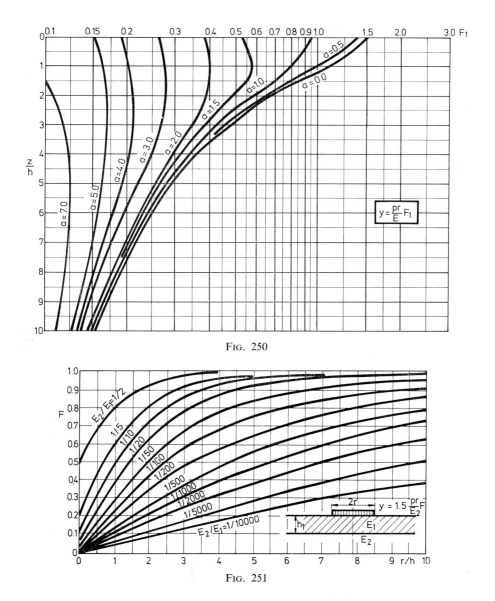

FIG. 250

FIG. 251

tion of parameters r/h and E_2/E_1. The subsidence along the axis of the load can be calculated from the following expression:

$$y = 1.5 \frac{pr}{E_2} F$$

where E_2 is the Young modulus of the lower layer.

269

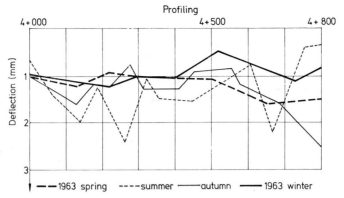

FIG. 252. Measured deflections of a soil-cement pavement

If the above formulae and diagrams are to be used to determine the E values, then the deflections must be measured, preferably using the so-called "Benkelman beam". The measurement results are best illustrated in a longitudinal section form. Comparison of the measurement results obtained at different times of the year will render an illustrative pattern of the load-bearing-capacity variations, as exampled in Fig. 252.

For the investigation of soil-cement deflections, detailed research was conducted by the Portland Cement Association (Nüssbaum and Larsen 1964), whose results may be summarized as follows:

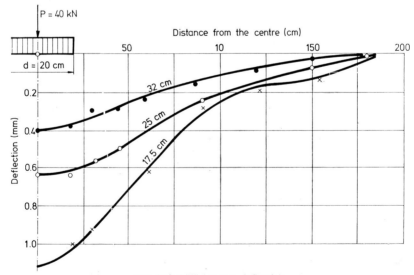

FIG. 253. Soil-cement deflection

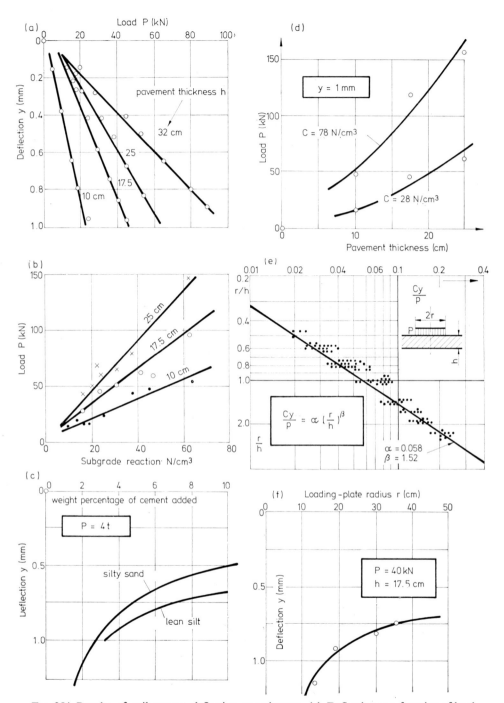

FIG. 254. Results of soil-cement deflection experiments. (a) Deflection as a function of load, for different pavement thicknesses; (b) Load bearing as a function of coefficient of subgrade reaction; (c) The effect of cement addition on deflection; (d) Load value pertaining to a given deflection as a function of pavement thickness; (e) Illustration of the experimental results using dimensionless parameters; (f) The value of deflection in the function of the loading plate diameter

Table 44

Data of subsoils used in soil-cement deflection experiments

Subsoil	Unit	A	B	C	D
Gravel	weight-	0	29	0	0
Coarse sand, 2–0.42 mm	per cent,	2	32	4	4
Fine sand, 0.42–0.074 mm	S, %	8	26	16	9
Silt, 0.074–0.005		32	8	40	35
Clay, <0.005		58	5	40	52
Colloid, <0.001		44	—	20	40
Yield point	%	38	—	36	39
Plastic index		13	—	19	22

Soil-cement pavements of a 3×3 m^2 area and 10, 17.5 and 25 cm thickness, respectively, were prepared and then loaded statically with plates of 20, 30, 40, and 60 cm diameters. The test involved four different subsoils, and the calculated coefficients of subgrade reaction varied between $C = 2$ and 8 kp/cm^3. These characteristic soil data are presented in Table 44, while a typical test result is shown in Fig. 253. The self-evidently crucial correlations obtained by processing these data are illustrated in Fig. 254.

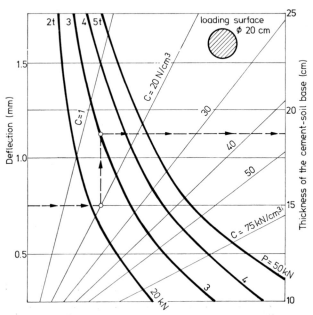

FIG. 255. Diagram for the determination of soil-cement pavement thickness on the basis of specified deflections

Attention is called to Fig. 254e, illustrating the test results using dimensionless parameters. This relation gave, to good approximation, a straight line, and may thus be expressed as:

$$\frac{Cy}{P} = \alpha \left(\frac{r}{h}\right)^{\beta}$$

This relation is valid in the $r/h = 0.5 < 2.0$ range. The experiments gave $\alpha = 0.058$ and $\beta = 1.52$. The coefficient C of subgrade reaction was determined with a 75 cm diameter loading plate, from the equation $C = p/y$, based on the settlement pertaining to a $p = 0.7$ kp/cm² load. This formula does not contain the soil type and the cement content, and the pavement strength is only indirectly involved. Based on this equation, the dimensioning diagram of Fig. 255 could be plotted to supply the pavement thickness pertaining to the given deflection.

8.3.5 Thickness of mechanical soil stabilization

The load-bearing capacity of mechanical stabilization is not governed primarily by its thickness, so in design it is far from being the critical problem of dimensioning. The strength of the pavement surface, its wear resistance, and the prevention of water penetration, etc. are much more important, so design must specify, above all, the optimum composition of the mixture. The thickness is governed by the equipment available. Moreover, the "construction" itself, that is, the mixing, compaction, and levelling of the bound and granular components may be entrusted more or less to the traffic, whereby the ultimate thickness will "develop". Thickness deserves increased attention when mechanical stabilization represents the foundation of higher order pavements, or if the road is to be constructed stepwise

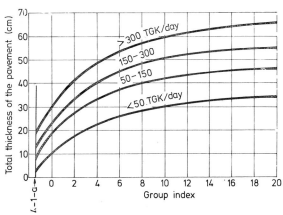

FIG. 256. Required thickness of mechanical stabilization,
according to Aichhorn

and only the stabilized base layer is completed in the first stage. For such cases Aichhorn (1956) has elaborated dimensioning curves, as shown in Fig. 256. These curves specify the total thickness of the superstructure (+ foundation + pavement) for a $P = 4$ t wheel weight, as a function of the group index and traffic density. For other wheel loads, the thickness specified by this figure should be multiplied by the $n = 0.15\ P + 0.4$ factor.

8.3.6 Wheel-rut formation

Every wheeled vehicle travelling over a soil surface or an earth road will leave a permanent rut in the ground. The energy required for its production will cause a resistance to the surface movement of the soil. Deformation of the soil surface is brought about by the vertical weight loading the wheel and, in the case of driving wheels, the torque, whereas in the case of driven or running wheels by the traction force or haulage capacity (see Fig. 257).

The wheel always rotates about the instantaneous point of support. The vertical and horizontal forces create stress fields whose effect must be studied jointly. Total deformation during wheel-rut formation is produced by a horizontal dis-

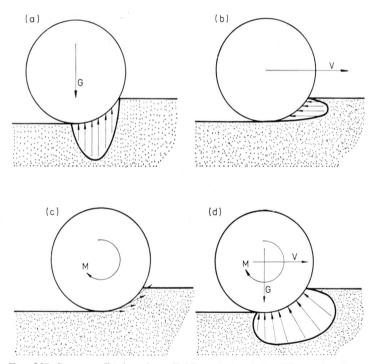

FIG. 257. Stresses affecting the soil (a) vertical weight; (b) traction force; (c) under a wheel loaded by driving moment; (d) joint effect

placement in the direction of movement, and by a vertical compaction. The horizontal displacement increases with the rate of movement, whereas the vertical compaction decreases with this rate, since the soil cannot be compacted under the effect of such a short period of loading.

During wheel-rut formation the resistance increases with increase in indentation, whose measure may be characterized by the following empirical expression:

$$p = kz^n$$

where z is the depth of the rut, and k and n are constants. According to the measurements by Birulya (1950), in compacted cohesive soils, and also in compacted but granular soil types $n = 1$, whereas in a soft clay $n = 0$. If, finally, the soil is of a medium resistance due partly to cohesion and partly to friction, then $n = 1/2$.

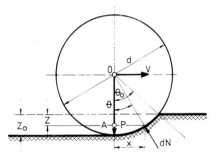

FIG. 258. Determination of the running resistance of a wheel pressed into the soil

Let us now determine, with the validity of the above correlation still assumed, the travelling resistance of the wheel, i.e. the relation between wheel weight and indentation, using the wheel illustrated in Fig. 258. Let us assume only a vertical displacement of the soil under the wheel. The work required for an indentation to a depth of z_0, at a road length l and surface width b, will amount to

$$M_1 = bl \int_0^{z_0} p \, dz = bl \int_0^{z_0} kz^n \, dz = kbl \frac{z_0^{n+1}}{n+1}$$

It may also be assumed, again as an approximately, that the work per unit surface thus calculated will equal the rolling resistance overcome by the traction force acting along the wheel axis. If the wheel of a width b is rolling along a length l, then the traction force V will perform work $M_2 = Vl$ work, and from $M_1 = M_2$ we get

$$V = kb \frac{z_0^{n+1}}{n+1}$$

According to Fig. 258, the traction force is

$$V = \int_0^{\theta_0} dN \sin \Theta = \int_0^{z_0} pb \, dz$$

18*

275

while the wheel weight amounts to

$$P = \int_0^\theta dN \cos \Theta = - \int_0^{z_0} pb \, dx$$

The geometrical relations may be written:

$$\overline{OA} = \frac{d}{2} - (z_0 - z); \quad x^2 = \left(\frac{d}{2}\right)^2 - \overline{OA}^2 = [d - (z_0 - z)](z_0 - z) \sim d(z_0 - z),$$

and $2x \, dx = -d \, dz$.

Substituting into the above wheel-weight formula we obtain

$$P = kb \int_0^{z_0} z^n \frac{\sqrt{d} \, dz}{\sqrt{z_0 - z}} = k^b \sqrt{d} \int_0^t (z_0 - t)^n \, dt$$

where $t^2 = z_0 - z$, $dt = -dz/2t$.

Series expansion, taking only the first two terms into account, will give

$$P = \frac{kb \sqrt{d}}{3} z_0^{n+1/2}(3 - n).$$

Although the above relation is probably unsuitable for direct numerical calculations, it illustrates quite clearly the effect of the various factors on indentation, and the connection between the force, the wheel width and diameter, and the indentation.

Figure 259 defines the relations between force and indentation (wheel-rut depth), and stress and indentation, respectively, for three typical n values: $n = 0$, 1/2, and 1. With these known, the relation of traction force to weight, i.e. the specific resistance, can also be expressed. With these three n values the following relations are obtained:

$$n = 1: \quad \mu = \frac{V}{P} = 0.86 \sqrt{\frac{P}{kbd^2}}$$

$$n = 1/2: \quad \mu = 0.876 \sqrt{\frac{P}{kbd^{3/2}}}$$

$$n = 0: \quad \mu = \frac{P}{kbd}$$

or, expressed as a function of indentation,

$$\mu = \frac{3}{(n + 1)(3 - n)} \sqrt{\frac{z_0}{d}}$$

276

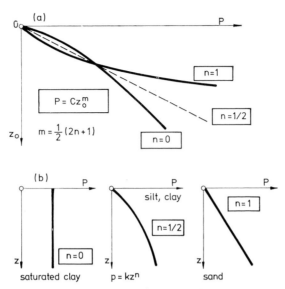

FIG. 259. (a) Correlation between wheel weight and indentation, (b) Correlation between stress and indentation, at three characteristic values of the exponent n

so that for the three cases we have

$$\mu = 0.75 \sqrt{\frac{z_0}{d}}\;;\quad \mu = 0.8 \sqrt{\frac{z_0}{d}}\;;\quad \mu = \sqrt{\frac{z_0}{d}}$$

Accordingly, if a 60–70 cm diameter wheel sinks to a depth of 1 cm in an earth road, then the specific resistance is $\mu \approx 120$–130 kg/t, in good agreement with the empirical findings.

The problems of wheel-rut formation are currently being dealt with thoroughly again these days within the frame of general earthwork and tillage machinery development, and interesting new results have already been achieved in this field from both theoretical and experimental aspects (see, for example, Mészáros and Sitkei, 1965). A detailed description of these results, however, would go much beyond the scope of this volume.

However, we should mention, on the other hand, that, according to the investigations by Rázsó (1951), if the central angle pertaining to the wheel are contacting the soil is twice the friction angle between soil and wheel, then the soil resistance will increase suddenly, since the wheel continues to move a greater soil mass than that kneaded beneath. Consequently, the surplus soil will accumulate in front of the wheel which, in turn, will have to start to rise. This is equivalent to the wheel sinking by this pile-up depth into the soil below the actual track depth. The continuous lifting of the accumulated soil particles, the increasing wheel surface contacting the soil, the movement of larger soil masses, and the enhanced compaction work, produce a signinificant increase.

9. Construction of stabilized earth roads

9.1 Introduction

This chapter deals with the various stabilized earth road construction techniques, the machines designed for such work, and the application of this machine pool. The consecutive construction phases, then the required post-treatment, and finally the relevant maintenance methods are discussed. However, no detailed instructions are given for implementing the different stabilization procedures, being out of character with this book, and since this purpose might be best served by official regulations, standards, and guidelines. Thus, for practical construction, the problems of soil physics are again emphasized, since such knowledge may promote the correct use of the machines available, and assist the issue of relevant building specifications.

Stabilized earth roads can be constructed in one of three different ways. The first method consists of driving a series of machines along the route to be constructed. These machines build the stabilized road by using the soil thus produced, perhaps with the admixture of other soils or additives. First the soil is disintegrated by ploughs, rippers, etc. to the depth specified, and then follows pulverization by machines designed specifically for the purpose. To this pulverized material the liquid or powder stabilizer is then added plus enough water for a good consistency. This is followed by wet mixing, compaction, levelling, profile formation, and post-treatment (Fig. 260), though one or more of the stages may be omitted depending on the soil type involved, or the stabilization method employed.

The second technique involves construction with a moving machine pool. Here the soil first loosened up is lifted, then pulverized by the plant advancing

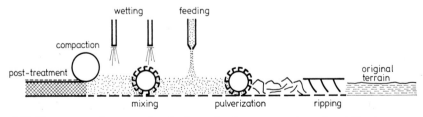

FIG. 260. The consecutive operational phases in the construction of stabilized earth roads using individual machines

along the route under construction. This is followed by stabilizer and water addition, wet mixing and, finally, the spreading and the compaction of the mixture. This means that the machines do not advance along the road surface, but the soil moves through the forward moving plant (a cartoon illustrating this technique is presented in Fig. 261, which was the cover of the Proceedings of the 1952 "Conference on Soil Stabilization", organized by the Massachusetts Institute of Technology, dealing scientifically for the very first time with the problems of soil stabilization). In practice, the first method is usually preferred since the cost and rather com-

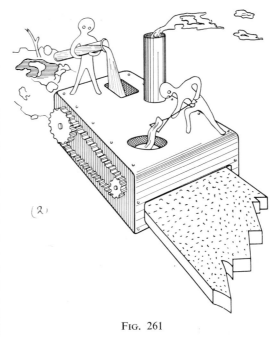

FIG. 261

plex organisation of the moving plant is only economical in such cases where a great deal of work is involved.

For the third possibility, stabilized earth roads can be constructed using a stationary mixing plant, where mixing itself may be either continuous or intermittent. The former resembles a moving plant, whereas the latter is similar to the usual concrete mixing operation.

Let us now list the advantages and disadvantages of the three methods to determine the best fields of application for each:

Stationary mixing

Advantages	Disadvantages
Simple, relatively inexpensive, easy to transport machines.	The achievement of a uniform thickness for the stabilized layer is quite difficult as precise setting of the machines is not easy. Mixing is less uniform than in a permanent plant.
The number of machines employed may be adjusted to the size of the job.	
The entire stabilized section may be compacted immediately.	
High average output is feasible.	A sudden major shower can spoil a whole section (2 mm precipitation would increase the water content of a 15 cm layer by 1 per cent). Under dry climatic conditions it is rather difficult to replace the evaporation losses.
Under wet climatic conditions the evaporation losses represent an advantage, since this is the only means of removing the surplus water.	

279

It should be added that the advantages listed above apply mainly to agricultura machinery (plus a pulverizer-mixer). Certain large machines performing stationary mixing, although rather expensive, too heavy, and difficult to transport, do not suffer from the disadvantages referred to.

Moving mixer plant

Advantages	Disadvantages

Advantages:
Precise water addition
Uniform mixing
Short mixing time
Uniform road surface and surface thickness feasible
Maximum output feasible

Disadvantages:
Excessive investment cost
With continuous use of the excessive machine capacity difficulties will often be encounter
If any machine component breaks, the entire operation must be stopped

Stationary mixing plant

Advantages:
Precise mixture feeding readily feasible
Precise production of the coating thickness specified
Normal concrete mixers adaptable
No superfluous transport if the soil is recovered from pits
Suitable for work between finisher rails as well.

Disadvantages:
Too expensive when used for in-situ soil stabilization

Compaction is feasible only intermittently, according to transport

The output figures achieved by the various methods under favourable conditions are presented in Table 45.

Table 45

Output of the various stabilization techniques
per 10-hour working,
with a 15 cm pavement thickness

Method	Average output, m²	Max output, m²
In-situ mixing	1 500– 6 000	11 000
Moving plant	15 000–25 000	50 000
Stationary plant	400– 1 500	—

In principle, it may be stated that no stabilization can be performed efficiently by manual techniques. Manually, uniformity and efficiency are lacking in the following: soil crushing and pulverization, mixing with the stabilizer or other material, and the compaction of the mixture: thus the stabilized soil obtained does not have the desired properties. Thus manual work must be excluded a priori, and it may be stated that the requirement of a successful soil stabilization is mechanization of the individual operations.

FIG. 262. Soil-cement road construction. Heavy soil ploughing by a multirow plough. The ploughing depth can hardly be maintained

During the initial development stages of soil stabilization it became obvious to use for implementation the agricultural machines available, since a number of operations like ripping, crushing, pulverization, batching, etc., were also involved in agriculture. Ripping or loosening may be done by common agricultural ploughs, readily turning a soil layer of 20–25 cm depth. The soil thus ploughed is then further disintegrated and mixed by disc harrows, having 8 to 12 opposite layout spherical-section discs. Two disc rows are usually employed consecutively. The angle included by the discs and the axis of the road, and the setting of the discs are varied in each run if required. Light soils require 4 or 5, and heavy soils 8 to 10, pulverizing runs. In loose soils tillers or grubber hoes may also be used. Haulage requires 28–35 HP tractors.

When agricultural machines are used, the cement or lime is distributed in bags at predetermined distances over the pulverized soil surface. Mixing is done by the same machines. Water is added by tankers supplying it under pressure.

Agriculture has recently undergone rapid development. Consequently, the tractor supply greatly improved. These tractors are suitable for hauling graders, feeding units, compactors, etc., and since they themselves represent expensive machinery, agriculture might mechanize soil stabilization for relatively low investments, and so this is expected to be the future trend of development in

281

FIG. 263. Pulverization of the ploughed-up cloggy clay by a disc harrow. The unloaded discs cannot penetrate to the desired depth

this field. Until such conditions are reached the agricultural machines may be used occasionally since their use will normally yield acceptable results. Besides, use of agricultural machines has the advantage of promoting a better exploitation of the machine pool owned by the farms and the agricultural repair stations, since these machines could be used for road construction if it not convenient or timely to perform, agricultural operations to be performed (possibly at the most suitable, usually very short time viewpoints) from road-construction.

Undoubtedly, however, agricultural machines must soon be barred from the field of soil stabilization, since each machine is best suited for its designed and constructed purpose. Nevertheless, as a record, we will publish some photographs of the construction of certain experimental roads in Hungary, about 25 years ago, upon the initiatives of the Army and under the control of author, involving a stabilized-cement soil layer as load-bearing pavement. The results achieved (Kézdi 1954; Nagyváti 1955; Kézdi 1957b) were described in detail by foreign literature (see Beér 1957, Road Abstracts 1955, Annales de l'Institut Technique, Paris 1958). These pavements were tested by several thousand 10 t truck runs, and their behaviour was studied for a number of years. Construction of the three experimental sections, each about 400 m in length is illustrated by Figs 262–267, while one of the finished road sections is shown in Fig. 6.

282

FIG. 265. Mixing cement to the pulverized soil in dry condition

FIG. 264. Distribution of the cement bags over the pulverized soil surface by means of a knotted rope

FIG. 266. Mixture wetting by a tanker supplying water under pressure

FIG. 267. Compaction by a tyred unit

The following chapters describe the soil-physics and technological aspects of the various operational phases of actual construction, such as mixing and compaction. Further, they present the machines and technology of both in-situ mixing and by moving plants.

9.2 Soil mixing

In-situ, laboratory as well as research results have clearly verified that the critical requirement of successful soil stabilization is uniform and efficient mixing. The employment of agricultural machines as referred to above is, therefore, rather disadvantageous since the stabilizer distributed over the surface of the pulverized soil thus loosened cannot be mixed well enough with the soil using these units, and so the distribution will become uneven, and the stabilizer will fail to reach the desired depth. In Chapter 4, Fig. 126 illustrated the character of in-depth cement distribution within the thickness of the stabilized layer. Now Fig. 268 illustrates given measurement results from an actual site, and the in-depth distribution of the cement along a section of satisfactory load-bearing capacity, and in the pavement of a destroyed section. It is clearly seen that hardly any cement could penetrate below 10 cm.

To indicate mixing efficiency, Michaels and Puzinauskas (1956) introduced the concept of the mixing index, which indicates the ratio illustrated in Fig. 268.

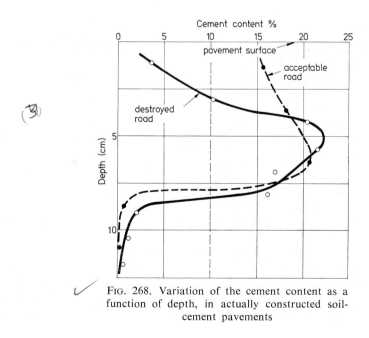

FIG. 268. Variation of the cement content as a function of depth, in actually constructed soil-cement pavements

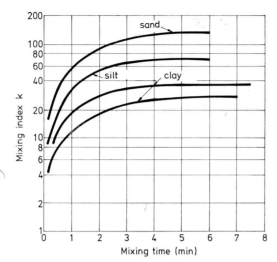

FIG. 269. Variation of the mixing index as a function of mixing time

If n optional samples are taken from a mixture containing, on the average, a weight per cent additive a, then the standard deviation is

$$\sigma = \left[\frac{\sum_{i=1}^{n} (a_i - a_0)^2}{n} \right]^{1/2}$$

Before mixing, the soil and the additive are located adjacently without admixture or compounding. However, owing to measurement errors and differences in soil-particle dimensions, the measurements will reveal a certain additive content, whose standard deviation is

$$\sigma_0 = [a_0(1 - a_0)]^{1/2}$$

The mixing index implies the following quantity:

$$k = \frac{\sigma}{\sigma_0}$$

In the case of a non-mixed material $k = 1$, while the index of a material perfectly mixed in theory would be infinite.

The mixing-index value can be determined experimentally by mixing a radio-active labelling substance to the stabilizer to be added to the soil. The distribution and amount of this substance in the soil are then determined after different mixing times. The curves of Fig. 269 were obtained on the basis of such measurements, performed with a laboratory test mixer. The increase of this index is still insignificant after a mixing time of 4–5 min.

The best practical measure of the efficiency of a mixer is the behaviour of the material thus mixed. Thus, for instance, in the case of soil cement the unconfined compression strength will increase with increased mixing time, as exampled by Fig. 270. A similar correlation can be observed between compression strength and the mixing index.

The efficiency of in-situ mixing is usually characterized as follows: the sample taken from the mixed loose material is divided in two; one part is used for the production of a specimen by ramming the material in this condition, for the unconfined compression test, while the other part is mixed for 10 min in a laboratory mixer, and then the specimen is made of this material (see Eq. (52) in

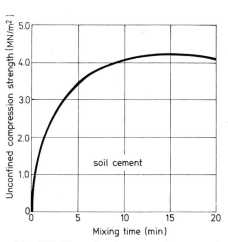

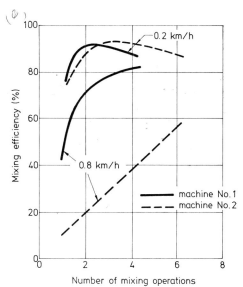

FIG. 270. Unconfined compression strength of a soil cement vs. mixing time

FIG. 271. Mixing efficiency as a function of the number of mixing runs, in the case of two different mixers

Section 4.4). The ratio of the compression strength values exhibited by the two samples define the efficiency of in-situ mixing. The results of such a test performed with a uniform fine-grain sand are illustrated in Fig. 271.

It seems that, for example, a slower speed affects efficiency. Accordingly, it was suggested (Robinson 1952) that the drum of the mixer should be rotated in the direction opposite to that of the advancement, since in this case the material would move much more vigorously (Fig. 272).

The experiments verified the assumption that the efficiency thus achieved was twice that for the case of rotating in the direction of advancement. The shaft of the Ringhoffer mixer also rotates opposite to the direction of advancement, at 550 rpm (Fig. 273). The importance of good mixing from an economic view-

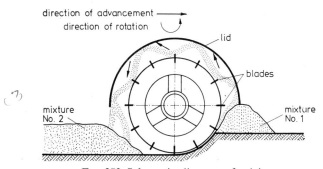

FIG. 272. Schematic diagram of mixing

287

point is verified by Fig. 274, illustrating the amount of cement required for the compression strength specified, in this case $\sigma_u = 17.5 \text{ kp/cm}^2$, as a function of mixing efficiency. If the number of mixings is increased, or machines providing better mixing are used, considerable cement saving is possible.

As demonstrated numerically by the examples presented so far, the longer the mixing time, the more uniform the mixture, and the more favourable its properties. There are, however, two exceptions: one is that certain overmixing will take place, separating the particles or grains of the mixture will be separated by size, impairing the quality of stabilization, and the other is

FIG. 273. Ringhoffer mixer shaft. Rotation is opposite to the direction of advancement in order to increase mixing intensity. The speed involved is 550 rpm

that of the soil cement. The hydration of cement will start at the moment of contacting water, and the bonds thus developed will be destroyed during the extended period of mixing, thus reducing the strength will be reduced again. This effect is produced by mixing for more than 15 min shown in Fig. 270, where strength decreases somewhat. (The effect of a mixing wait has already been dealt with under 4.4).

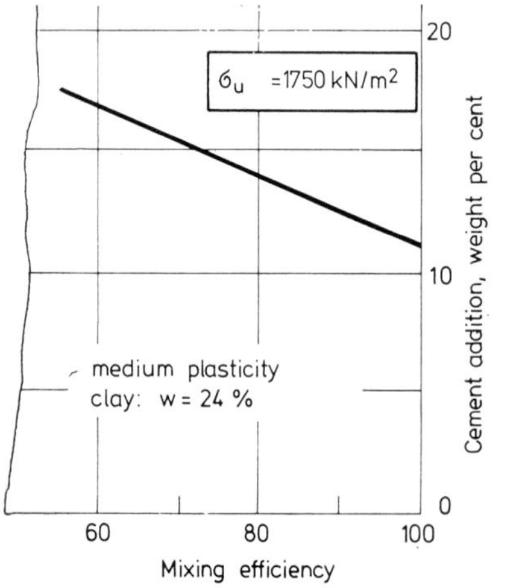

The effect of the water content of the mixture on mixing also deserves mention. Generally, we endeavour to mix and compact the material at such a water content that the maximum dry density is obtained, altough it is not certain that the best result is obtained in this case. As seen in the chapter discussing the properties of soil cement, sand stabilization is the most advantageous, if the water content is somewhat less than the optimum moisture content of compaction, and in the case of clay if the soil is slightly wetter. Bituminous stabilizations should involve mixing under wetter conditions than the optimum.

FIG. 274. Cement quantity required for a predetermined compression strength, as a function of mixing efficiency

[chart: $\sigma_u = 1750 \text{ kN/m}^2$; medium plasticity clay: w = 24 %; y-axis: Cement addition, weight per cent (0, 10, 20); x-axis: Mixing efficiency (60, 80, 100)]

So far it has been assumed that mixing was done by scrapers, but it can be performed by graders, although they would provide much less efficient mixing. The machines adaptable for mixing are described later in 9.42.

9.3 Compaction

The importance of compaction was repeatedly emphasized earlier, by pointing out that a satisfactory compaction is essential for successful soil stabilization, although compaction also plays an important role in fields other than soil stabilization. An earthwork can satisfy the requirements of its intended use only if its compactness and its strength — as a function of that compactness or, perhaps, its water impermeability — conforms to that same use. The general and detailed problems of compaction are explained in the Handbook of Soil Mechanics, Vol. 2, so only those problems closely related to the construction of stabilized earth roads will be discussed here.

First of all, it should be pointed out that stabilized soils are compacted almost exclusively by either static pressure or kneading, using roller-type tools such as the smooth or plain road roller, the sheep-foot unit, the tyred compactor with the exception of the vibro-

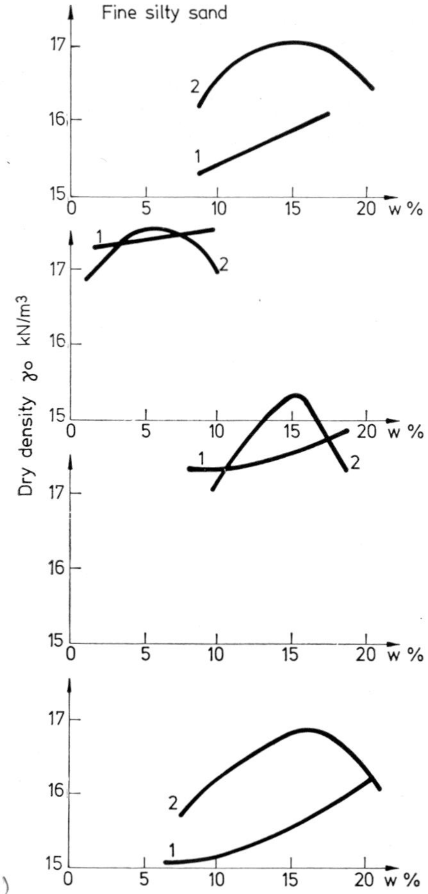

FIG. 275. Dry densities achieved by static (1) and dynamic (2) compaction — fine silty sand, medium grade sand, sandy silt, loess

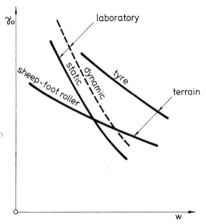

FIG. 276. Relation between water content and dry density by compaction, at different compaction techniques

machine compact. Both effects differ considerably from the dynamic action of the Proctor test employed in laboratory experiments, so the soil cannot be expected to behave identically during the laboratory and in-situ investigations. This assumption is verified by the laboratory test result presented in Fig. 275, and the in-situ experimental data illustrated in Fig. 276. In addition to the laboratory Proctor curves of four different soils, Fig. 275 indicates those dry density values which could be obtained after the compression of soils with different water content by a static weight of 5 kp/cm² for 10 sec but where the characteristic optimum water content did not manifest itself. Figure 276 compares laboratory and in-situ data. These figures reveal that it would be rather important to introduce separate laboratory methods for compactors operating statically and dynamically.

The effect of the compactness of stabilized soils on the various physical characteristics has been discussed in connection with the different techniques. The optimum water content of compaction in the case of major projects is best determined, according to the above, by in-situ experiments, using the machine employed for mass compaction.

During the travel of a compactor along the surface of the layer to be compacted, no immediate time-dependent deformations in the given cross-section will be produced, according to Fig. 277, where the ratio of the two parts will depend on the initial degree of saturation of the soil layer to be compacted, as shown in Fig. 278. If loading is applied gradually as when the compactor is rolling along over the cross-section at a set speed, and the vertical stresses in the given cross-section of the layer are time-dependent, the compressions will develop according to Fig. 279. With known values of the constants in the consolidation theory,

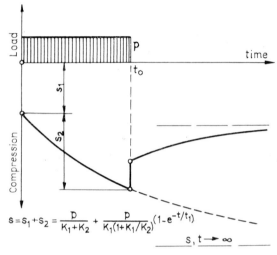

$$s = s_1 + s_2 = \frac{p}{K_1 + K_2} + \frac{p}{K_1(1 + K_1/K_2)}(1 - e^{-t/t_1})$$

FIG. 277. Deformations in the compacted layer

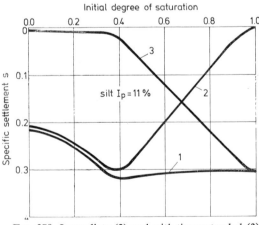

FIG. 278. Immediate (2) and with time extended (3) part of the total compression within 10 sec (1)

290

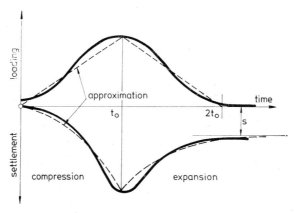

FIG. 279. Stresses and during the passing over of the compactor roller

Table 46

Hungarian specifications on the required compactness

Earthwork destination	$D_{r\gamma}$ (modified Proctor test)	
	$\gamma_0 \geq 1.75$ Mp/m³	$\gamma_0 < 1.75$ Mp/m³
Foundation of rigid and semi-rigid pavements, soil replacement, backup of engineering structures	95%	100%
Foundation of elastic pavements	90%	95%
Other earthworks	85%	90%

Table 47

Compaction specifications for embankments
(USA, Ohio Department of Highways)

Embankments lower than 3 m and not exposed to water pressure effects		Embankments higher than 3 m or exposed to water pressure	
Max. lab. dry density (Proctor test)	Desired compactness value	Max. lab. dry density (Proctor test)	Desired compactness value
$\gamma_d^{max} < 1.45$	avoid the use of	$\gamma_d^{max} < 1.52$	avoid the use of
1.45–1.65	$D_d \geq$ 100%	1.52–1.65	$D_{r\gamma} \geq$ 102%
1.65–1.75	98%	1.65–1.76	100%
1.75–1.92	96%	1.76–1.92	98%
>1.92	95%	>1.92	96%

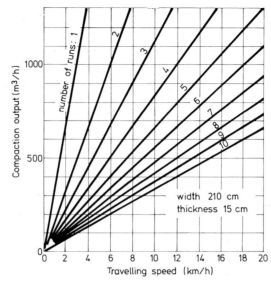

FIG. 280. Diagram for the determination of the maximum theoretical output of tyred compactors

the expected compressions (i.e. feasible compaction) can also be determined by calculation.

To conclude the discussion on compaction, we present specifications on compactness being in Table 46 Hungarian, and in Table 47 United States. Figure 280 illustrates the maximum theoretical output-capacity of tyred compactors.

9.4 Construction of stabilized earth roads by in-situ mixing

9.4.1 Preparatory operations

The preparation of stabilized earth road construction, including layout or pegging, removal of the vegetation and humus from the terrain, earthwork, and the formation of the crown or profile, does not differ significantly from similar operations for any other road construction, except that every part of the operation may be carried out much more simply, with much less preparation. Thus the relevant problems need not be discussed here, except those related especially to stabilization.

The machines required for stabilization are combined into a line, consisting of digger ploughs, pulverizer-mixers, water-feed tankers, compactors, graders, and the stabilizer-feeder units. If well organized, and under favourable conditions, the output of such a machine line is considerable. If continuous operation is ensured, about 30 to 40 km stabilized roads can thus be constructed annually

292

and more if the machine line is reinforced by a number of compactors, binder distributors, etc. This, however, requires high-level on-site organization, and involves so many duties that an experienced engineer of sufficient organizational ability plus a skilled foreman and a well-trained staff are required.

The minimum machine-line composition is as follows:

1. mixer
2. tanker + tractor
3. motor grader
4. compactors
5. binder transport or, eventually, spreading unit
6. surface bitumen spray equipment
7. minor auxiliary equipment

The above machine line must be supplemented by quality control and other laboratory equipment requiring, in addition to the machine operators, 3 or 4 unskilled worker and a technician to perform the necessary control measurements in the laboratory.

When multishift mixers are used, sections of 100 to 300 m length are stabilized and, therefore, the construction stretch must be divided into working sections, whose length may be determined according to the figure below.

Taking into account the output of the entire stabilizer machine line, the length must be determined so that the interval between the distribution of the binder and the completion of compacting is less than 3–4 hours. Particular attention should be paid here to vehicle turning facilities. In the case of narrow roads, the turning of hauled machines (mixers, tankers, tyred compactors, etc.) may take 2 or 3 times as much time as that needed for actual work. The output of the binder transport machines must not allow the machines to stand idle. Finally, the accessibility of the road section concerned must be ensured, as construction will require rather heavy machines. Both in preparation and at some other stages of stabilization, the grader can render useful assistance, being adaptable for the development of the earth-road profile, building of low embankments, and even the mixing of materials necessary for mechanical stabilization.

Today mainly mechanized or self-propelled graders are used, as against the horse-drawn units once employed, when there was a much lower level of agricultural mechanization (Fig. 281).

The hauled grader of today has a twin-shaft, with an axial distance of 4.5–6.5 m, and the blade between the two shafts, readily adjustable both horizontally and vertically, and easy to rotate in these directions even under operational conditions. Generally, the blade is set with its front edge plough at a depth of 30 cm, though this depends on the cohesion of the soil. The angle included by the blade and the shaft is set according to the soil type and the operation required. Cutting is done at the lowest speed (2–3 km/h), while levelling and transport by the second and third speeds, respectively (10–20 km per hour).

The daily output of the machine when grading earth roads is 12 000–15 000 m². In stabilization, then many processes: loosening the soil in 3 or 4 runs, crushing it in 4–6 runs by pushing the surface material, shifting the required additive, that is, another soil type used for improvement, flattening the surface in a further 4–6 runs, and finally mixing the soil in 7 or 8 further runs, will reduce the daily output considerably. The working phases of earth road grading are presented in Fig. 282, while Fig. 283 illustrates the grader application when it removes the

FIG. 281. Horse-drawn grader used in early earth-road maintenance

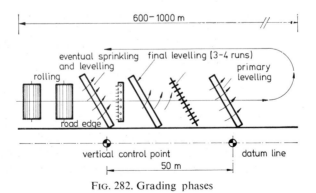

FIG. 282. Grading phases

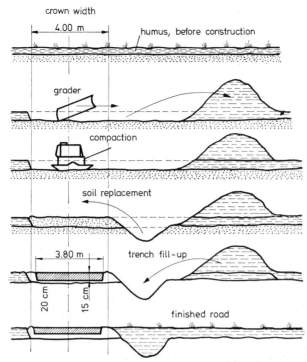

FIG. 283. Earthwork by a grader from a pit for earth-road construction

FIG. 284. Modern self-propelled grader

top humus layer laterally and then, after compacting the base, lifts enough soil for stabilization from the trench onto the crown. Modern graders are self-propelled, like that shown in Fig. 284.

The height of the road to be constructed is set by driving poles at 20–50 m intervals into the bank, about 1.5 m from the edge of the layer to be stabilized, whose top will then indicate the height of the road. The depth of treatment must also be marked on these poles.

9.4.2 Pulverization

Pulverization consists of two stages: loosening up the soil to the desired depth, then disintegration of the clogs to the degree demanded by stabilization. Certain soil types, like fine dry sand or fine Mo, do not require any of these operations, but in other cases this is the most difficult and delicate job of the whole project, as an insufficient pulverization may cause extremely low strength figures (see 4.4). The soil can be loosened up by a special machine or, for example, by using the multirow plough referred to Section 9. Up-to-date machines perform the two operations together, in a single run. An example is the rotary scraper which crushes the soil, if the moisture content exceeds the desired level. The soil is then dried, and the binder admixed. The essential part of these machines is the milling mechanism mounted to a horizontal shaft, performing 200–250 revolutions per minute, which cuts up the soil with its blades, spreads it forward, and mixes it. The best types are equipped with spray heads, to feed water and liquid binders which ensure a much better mixture. Depending on the soil type, these scrapers can complete pulverization and dry or wet mixing in 3–8 runs.

After the Howard units the world markets show a general preference for the Seaman and Ringhoffer machines (see their principal engineering data in Table 48), though Skoda is manufacturing similarly very good scrapers. Figures 285–288 show these machines in operation.

The milling drum is moved vertically by a hydraulic jack, and is driven by the tractor itself via a universal-joint shaft. Other machine types have a separate motor for driving the drum. Rotating the drum requires 16 to 25 HP, while traction needs 26–40 HP, depending on the heaviness of the soil. The operational speed of 3–6 km/h is governed by the type of tractor used.

The thickness of the stabilized layer is usually 15 cm. Design, as shown above, consists of specifying the amount of stabilizer needed for the required strength and degree of compaction. The 15-cm thickness is that of the finished pavement, so the required depth of pulverization should be determined on the basis of a calculation illustrated in Fig. 289.

Figure 289 illustrates the changes in the top layer of the road during the stabilization process, where the work started from original soil. Corresponding to the produced, loosened, and mixed and compacted conditions after the admixture of additives, the figure describes the quantitative variation of the individual com-

Fig. 285. UNIMIX scraper by Howard

Table 48

Scraper data

Manufacturer	Hauled		Self-propelled		
	Ringhoffer		Seaman Andwall Co.		
Type	R-100	D-47	DMS-67	DS-47	DMT-47
Engine output, HP	100/132	138	200	138	138
Width, cm	190	213	213	213	213
Mixer shaft dia, cm	88	68.6	83.8	68.6	68.6
Speed, rpm	160–320	180–282	1 ... 75 2 ... 148 3 ... 278 4 ... 488	215–350	215–350
Speed, km/h	2–6	2–6	2–6	1.4–8	0.9–6.4
Weight, Mp	3.6	3.4	4.2	4.7	6.0
Length, m	4.91	5.93	7.70		
Turning radius	—	—	—	6.10	6.10

FIG. 286. Hungarian pulverizer

298

FIG. 287. Lime stabilization by a Ringhoffer pulvetizer

ponents. At the beginning, the water content and density of the soil are known, so that the s, l, and v figures can also be calculated ($s_1 + v_1 + l_1 = 100\%$). While loosening the soil, V_s does not change, V_v will decrease as a result of drying, and V_l will increase significantly ($s_2 + v_2 + l_2 = 100$). Admixture of the additive is a new element and, in addition, the water content must be increased to the level required by the optimum moisture content of compaction. During the compaction process itself only the air content will change, while the layer thickness must assume the specified figure. If this thickness is h_4, as shown in Fig. 289, then the required loosening depth h_1 can be calculated from the following equation:

$$\frac{h_1}{h_4} = \frac{s_1 + v_1 + l_1}{s_1 + a + v_3 + l_4}$$

in practice, instead of the density a, the amount of additive to be admixed is usually specified in the dry weight percentage of the soil. If this is $p\%$, then the following relation will exist:

$$p = \frac{a\,\gamma_a}{s_1\,\gamma_s}$$

299

FIG. 288. Self-propelled Ringhoffer pulverizer (SV-180) tested under particularly unfavourable operational conditions. Its 172 HP Deutz-engine can loosen up and pulverize a limestone soil, frozen to a depth of 1 m, down to as much ars 30 cm at an ambient temperature of $-12\,^{\circ}\mathrm{C}$

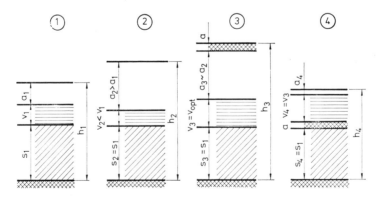

FIG. 289. Changes in the top layer of a stabilized road during the stabilization process. 1 — soil; 2 — loosened soil; 3 — soil mixed with stabilizer and water; 4 — compacted stabilized original soil

where γ_a is the specific weight of the stabilizer. Thence we get

$$a = p \frac{\gamma_0}{\gamma_a}$$

where γ_0 is the dry density of the produced soil. The value of v_3 can be calculated by working from the fact that, in this phase, the mixture must have the experimentally determined optimum water content. If this is w_{opt}, then

$$v_3 = w_{opt} s_1 \frac{\gamma_s}{\gamma_v}$$

The air content l_4 can be obtained from the information on the saturation of the compacted soil. If, under optimum conditions, this is S_{opt}, then

$$l_4 = (1 - S_{opt})(l_4 + v_3)$$

giving

$$l_4 = \frac{1 - S_{opt}}{S_{opt}} v_3$$

Thus all the values on the right-hand side of the expression h_1/h_4 are known, and since h_4 is given, h_1 can be calculated without difficulty. Since $s_1 + v_1 + l_1 = 1$, the following formula may be written:

$$\frac{h_1}{h_4} = \frac{1}{s_1 + a + v_3 + l_4}$$

Numerical example

Silty fine sand is stabilized with cement. According to the preliminary investigations, the water content of the soil is $w = 13\%$, its void ratio is $n = 43\%$, and its specific gravity amounts to $\gamma_s = 2.67$ p/cm³. In this case the volume percentages (see Eqs 6 and 7) will be

$$s_1 = 1 - n = 0.57$$

$$v_1 = w_{s1} \frac{\gamma_s}{\gamma_v} = 0.13 \cdot 0.57 \cdot \frac{2.67}{1.00} = 0.198$$

$$l_1 = 1 - (0.57 + 0.198) = 0.232$$

while the dry density of the soil produced is

$$\gamma_0 = s\gamma_s = 0.57 \cdot 2.65 = 1.51 \text{ p/cm}^3$$

The specific gravity of the cement is: $\gamma_a = 3.15$ p/cm³, and the quantity specified is 8 weight per cent, thus

$$a = p \frac{\gamma_0}{\gamma_a} = 0.08 \frac{1.51}{3.15} = 0.048$$

If the optimum water content is $w_{opt} = 17\%$, then

$$v_3 = w_{opt} \, s_1 \frac{\gamma_0}{\gamma_v} = 0.17 \cdot 0.57 \cdot \frac{2.67}{1.00} = 0.259$$

Experiments have shown that $S_{opt} = 0.92$ therefore

$$l_4 = \frac{1 - S_{opt}}{S_{opt}} \, v_3 = \frac{0.08}{0.92} \cdot 0.259 = 0.022$$

Thus if the compacted layer must have a thickness of 15 cm, then the depth of loosening should be

$$h_1 = h_4 \frac{1}{s_1 + a + v_3 + l_4} = \frac{15}{0.57 + 0.048 + 0.259 + 0.022} \cong 17 \text{ cm}$$

9.4.3 Stabilizer addition

The solid stabilizer is spread over the pulverized soil surface, then admixed by further runs of the pulverizer machine until it is uniformly distributed. The quantity to be admixed is usually determined during dimensioning, as a weight per cent value ($p\%$) related to dry weight. This may then be converted to m³ of the compacted layer:

$$P = \frac{1000 \, \gamma_0 p}{100 + p} \text{ (kp/m}^3\text{)}$$

where γ_0 is the dry density of the compacted mixture. Thus the cement to be admixed per m² of the soil surface under stabilization will be

$$\bar{P} = hP \text{ (kp/m}^2\text{)}$$

If the stabilizer is delivered to the site in bags, then the spacings of the rows of bags must also be calculated. Along a single-track (3.30–3.50 m wide) road there should be two bag rows distributed and on double-track roads three or four. If the width of the stabilized road is k (m), the number of lengthways rows n, and the quantity to be admixed is P, then the spacings of the crosswise rows (Fig. 290) will be

$$l = \frac{nq}{Pk}$$

where q is the weight of one full bag. The lengthways rows are placed at a distance of $k/2n$ from the edge of the pavement, with spacing k/n.

The bags are positioned by means of knotted ropes, torn up, then the material is spread uniformly. After spreading, the shortest possible period of time should

302

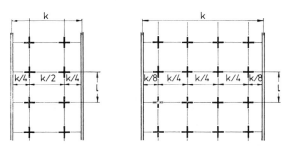

Fig. 290. Stabilizer spreading along single-track and double-track roads

elapse before admixture starts, otherwise the additive may absorb water and become lumpy. Mixing must be continued until the mixture assumes a uniform colour. Scrapers should be used for both mixing and pulverization.

Still more uniform distribution is ensured by the machines designed specifically for this purpose. In this case the powdered bulk material is best delivered in tankers, from which the binder can be transferred pneumatically to the spreader, via a hose, during operation. The quantity to be spread may be controlled by the travelling speed, the rpm of the shaft, or by changing the sprocket-driven gears built into the spreader. At a travelling speed of 0.5 km/h, the quantity thus broadcast may be varied between 5 and 35 kp/m².

Figure 291 shows the Hungarian spreader "KÖZGÉP", while Figs 292 and 293 show a Ringhoffer unit, recharged by a truck-mounted silo during operation.

In order to transform the soil to be stabilized into the optimum consistency for compaction, water must usually be added. This water addition is best performed from tankers under pressure. To determine the amount of water to be admixed, the water content of the soil in a condition corresponding to that when pulverization had been completed must be known. If the stabilized width is k, the compacted thickness h, the length of the section under treatment l, and the dry density to be achieved γ_0, then a single fill-up of the tanker capacity V/m^3 and a uniform distribution of this water along the entire length of the section will increase the water content of the soil by

$$\Delta_w \% = \frac{100 V_{\!_\ast}}{khl\gamma_0}.$$

In determining this amount of water, it must be remembered that the addition of a dry binder (lime, cement) will reduce the water content of the mixture by about 1 per cent compared to the original value, and that in sunny or windy weather the evaporation loss of a 15 cm pavement will represent another 1 per cent Δ_w.

The number of tankers should enable water addition to be completed within 1 or 1 1/2 h. With the operational cycle time of one tanker calculated. this figure

FIG. 291. KÖZGÉP additive spreader. Spreading width: 1.8 m, weight: 300 kp, tank capacity: 500 kp, and spreading output per run: 5–35 kp/m²

can be readily obtained. The following numerical example clearly illustrates this calculation (after Springenschmied):

Let the tanker capacity be 4000 litres. The tank is filled up from a creek at a distance of 6 min, by means of a 5 litre/sec output pump. The individual times are:

— travel to the creek		6	min
— fill-up	$4000/5 \times 60 =$	13.5	min
— travel back to the site		6	min
— discharge at a speed of 1.5 km/h, by 2 runs along the 200 m section	$2 \times \dfrac{0.2 \times 60}{1.5} =$	16	min
— turning and waiting time		5.5	min
	Total	21.5	min

If a full tank is already at the site before starting the first run, then for two charges

— one fill-up and two travelling times	25.5	min
— two discharge times	43	min
that is, a total of	68.5	min
are needed.		

FIG. 292. Ringhoffer machine, recharged during operation by a truck or trailer-mounted silo

Let us assume that the water content of the soil is 5 per cent, although the optimum is 14%. In this case the water to be added will be:

- difference of the two water contents, $14 - 5 =$ 9%
- absorption by the dry additive   1%
- evaporation loss   1%

                                        Total   11%

Spreading the contents of one tank (4 m³) will increase the water content by

$$w = \frac{4 \times 100}{190 \times 6.90 \times 0.15 \times 1.82} = 1.1\%$$

which means that a total of 10 tanks of water will be needed, some of which should be added before, after the admixture of the binder, and the rest.

Further practical rules of water addition include:

- the tanker should travel at a uniform speed (2 − max 3 km/h);
- the tap should be closed before the vehicle stops;
- no water should be permitted to accumulate or flow off in the wheel ruts. This can be achieved either by having the tanker tow a harrow, or by the mixer following the tank car closely.

20 Kézdi: Stabilized

FIG. 293. Ringhoffer machine

Both water and liquid stabilizers (bitumen cut-back or tar) are best added by spray heads on a bridge mounted to the scraper, during the process of admixture. The quantity may then be adjusted by the speed of the machine or by spray-head settings.

9.4.4 Compaction and levelling

Considering the linear character of construction, the requirements set to surface finishing, the thickness of the layer to be compacted, etc., then of all the available compacting implements, the tyred compactor is the most suitable. In Hungary, platform trucks loadable up to 26 t are widely used in earthwork, and perform successful compaction with a maximum width of 2.2 m (see Fig. 267). Their disadvantage is an excessive turning area requirement. Compactors which turn easily in a narrow strip are considered to be more advantageous. For example, see Figs 294 and 295 (Albaret Co).

Compaction must always be started by such machines, and continued until a static- or vibro-roller, can move along the surface. The smooth rollers are the best choice for levelling, but in this case lighter machines will also suffice.

It is essential that the output of compactors should be co-ordinated with that of the mixer or scraper, in order that compaction should follow mixing immedi-

Fig. 294. Small tyred compactor of easy manoeuvreability

ately. This way no problems can be caused by a shower or wind and the resulting strength will be favourable.

After compaction, any eventual surface irregularity should be eliminated by graders. Stabilizations with solid additives must be wet post-treated for at least seven days, again by tankers equipped with devices auxiliary spraying. The soil is kept wet by covering the surface with straw, and this with earth, and then irrigating the latter periodically. Moisture evaporation can also be prevented by a bituminous treatment of the surface, that is, by 0.5–0.7 kg/cm^2 bitumen cut-back of HB-0 or HB-1. It is important that the surface should be moist enough during application.

The green pavement must be protected from traffic, so on the day after construction only light, tyred vehicles should be permitted access. However, when constructing the junctions, it is impossible to prevent graders and other self-propelled machines from turning on the newly constructed section. In such cases, for the protection of the pavement, the turning area should be constructed within the first 10–15 m stretch of the finished section, which a 15 cm earth layer should be spread, containing rocks of size 70 mm maximum.

The clearances must be formed with particular care. The method of constructing the junctions is exampled in Fig. 296.

20*

Fig. 295. The ISOPACTOR units of Albaret compact a cement-stabilized foundation. A special feature of these machines is that the weight per wheel is constant for all positions

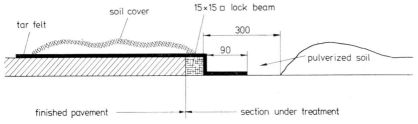

FIG. 296. Clearance at the junction of two construction sections

9.4.5 Construction by a moving plant

The most up-to-date machinery of soil stabilization is represented by a moving plant which performs loosening-up, pulverization, mixing, wetting, and levelling in a single run. The requirements of its application include completed earthwork, sufficient compactness of the latter, no loose or wet areas over which the stabilizer unit has to pass, and which might be destroyed by subsequent traffic.

Of the machines used to stabilize the soil over the road bed, the best known units are the *P* and *H* Single Pass, the Howard Single Pass Train, and the Vögele type moving soil stabilization plant. Since the present volume is not aimed at discussing engineering details, only the last type will be described, but briefly since the structure of this mechanism has not connection with the problems of soil physics, apart from that explained so far.

The machine consists of a caterpillar tractor and the stabilization equipment supported, to some extent by the former. When travelling, the rear part is hydraulically jacked, causing the machine to roll on a total of 9 tyres, and it will be able to turn within a 6 m radius. The working width is 2 m, and if more is needed, then stabilization is performed in several connected bands. It is best to schedule the daily job and determine the length of the section to be stabilized so that the entire width may be finished on one day. To connect perfectly the individual strips, it is best that the machine cuts into the earlier strip when producing the new one. The machine structure ensures strict adherence to the layer thickness specified. The water required for stabilization is usually taken from the tanker travelling parallel with the machine, then fed by the machine via an adjustable gauge. The cement or other powdered stabilizer may be fed to the road surface from bags, as described in connection with the agricultural machinery. A more modern solution than this is to use a separate feeder which can then be hauled and charged up as the trailer of a truck.

The pulverized, wetted, and mixed material is compacted by a vibration-type finisher. The 2 m wide board is actuated by a 14 HP motor, with 4500 vibrations per minute, and an amplitude of 2.5–3.0 mm depending on the attenuation effect of the soil. Acceleration is 30–35 g, the weight of the board 400 kg, so dynamic forces of 12–14 t will be produced. Separate movement of the board is employed to increase compaction efficiency further by its additional mean frequency.

309

The ripper, pulverizer and mixer mechanisms are hydraulically driven continuously. If the mixer encounters too much resistance, the machine stops automatically, so that fracture of the ripper and mixer is not tweatened.

The machine is equipped with an automatic level gauge to ease the building of horizontal surfaces, but it cannot compensate for uneven sections exceeding the total length of the machine.

Liquid stabilizers like bitumen or tar can be fed to the unit from a tanker travelling alongside. Thus, via the feeder, the material will be fed to an adjustable spray unit, and from these to the pulverized soil surface in front of the mixer.

Efficient mixing is done by agitator shafts rotating in opposite directions. The mixing mechanism itself is a positive operation-type unit, completely closed in any working position of the machine, equipped with relatively displaced mixing blades. The rpm can always be adjusted to take into account the soil type: a coarser soil requires a lower speed, while a fine-grain soil needs a higher speed. The mixing chamber fill-up, too, can be adjusted, readily providing adequate coating of the particles by binder can be readily provided for.

9.4.6 In-situ control

The stabilized road can only have the designed quality if adherence to the specifications is continuously checked upon by in-situ measurements throughout the construction period. This is such an extremely important requirement that, if neglected, premature destruction of the stabilized road must definitely be expected. Any deviation from the plan and design will have a detrimental effect: the quality. In conclusion, therefore, let us list the data to be controlled and the measurements that must be made:

— quality of the soil produced or the finished fill-up (water content, void ratio and, perhaps, grain distribution as well as the consistency limit figures);
— ploughing depth;
— degree of pulverization;
— water content of the pulverized soil;
— compaction characteristics;
— amount of water added;
— the compactness achieved;
— thickness of the finished pavement;
— the stabilizer quantity admixed;
— the strength obtained, and other soil physics properties.

The above activities demand a field laboratory. Changes in the weather conditions require further measurements, if they are to be taken into account. Finally, the soil physical characteristics of the soil, too, must be given continuous attention.

Bibliography

ABC des Teerstraßenbaus. Essen: Beratungsstelle der Verkaufsvereinigung für Teererzeugnisse (VfT-Aktiengesellschaft). 5th ed., 1963.

ABRIKOSOVA, I. I.—DERYAGIN, B. V.: Direct measurement of molecular attractive force between solids (in Russian), Moscow: Zhur. Exp. Teor Fiz. (1956) 3.

ÁCS, P.—BOROMISZA, T.—GÁSPÁR, L.: Útépítési geotechnikai vizsgálatok (Geotechnical examinations in road construction). Budapest: Útügyi Kutató Intézet **36**, 1965.

AICHHORN, W.: Bituminöser Oberflächenschutz mechanisch stabilisierter Tragschichten. Essen: VfT-Mitteilungen **1**, 1956.

AICHHORN, W.: Entwicklung der Bodenstabilisierung in Österreich. Straße und Verkehr **6** (1963a).

AICHHORN, W.: Grundlagen der Bodenstabilisierung. Wien: Forschungsgesellschaft für das Straßenwesen im Öst. Ing.-Arch.-V. Arbeitsgruppe "Untergrundforschung". **23** (1963b) 7/21.

AICHHORN, W.: Bituminöse Stabilisierung von Sand- und Kiesböden für Tragschichten, Konferenzbericht der Internazionalen Diskussionstagung über Bodenmechanik im Straßenbau. Wien: Öst. Ing.-Arch.-V. 1964.

Altering soil properties with chemicals. Industrial and Engineering Chemistry **47** (1955) 11, 2230–2281. USA.

American Society for Testing and Materials. Compaction of soils. Symposium 1964. Philadelphia, Pa.: The Society 1965. Spec. Techn. Publ. No. 377.

Anleitung für den Bau und die Unterhaltung mechanisch verfestigter Trag- und Verschleißschichten. Wien: Forschungsgesellschaft für das Straßenwesen im Öst. Ing.-Arch.-V. Arbeitsgruppe "Untergrundforschung". 2nd ed. 19, 1957.

Asphalt Emulsion Specifications. Compiled by Bitucote Products St. Louis, Mo. USA, 1964.

The Asphalt Institute, USA. Recommended procedures and specifications for asphalt-treated soil bases. 1964.

BAKER, C. N.: Strength of soil-cement as a function of degree of mixing. Highway Research Board Meeting, Jan. 1954.

BARABÁS, F.: Betonadalékanyag keverési arányának megállapítása grafikus úton (Determination of mixing ratio of concrete fines graphically). Mélyépítéstudományi Szemle **1**, (1951) 5.

BARENBURG, E. J.: Phosphoric acid stabilisation of soils — a review of the literature. Highway Research Board, 42nd Annual Meeting, Jan. 1963.

BAVER, L. D.: Soil physics. New York, N. Y.: John Wiley and Sons, 1948.

BEÉR, F.: Erfahrungen mit Bodenstabilisation in Ungarn (nach Á. Kézdi). VDI-Zeitschrift **99** (1957) 24.

Beiträge zu den Problemen der Bodenmechanik im modernen Straßenbau. Linz/Donau: Landesgruppe Oberösterreich der Österreichischen Gesellschaft für das Straßenwesen 1961.

BEKKER, M. G.: Theory of land locomotion. The mechanics of vehicle mobility. Ann Arbor: University of Michigan Press 1965.

BERNATZIK, W.: Baugrund und Physik. Zürich: Schweizer Druck- und Verlagshaus 1947.

BETHÄUSER, A.—BRAND, W.: Bodenverfestigung mit Kals als rationelle Planungsverbesserung im Eisenbahnbau. Der Tiefbau **4** (1961).

(BEZRUK, V. M.—KNAZYUK, K. A.) Безрук, В. М., Кназюк, К. А: Устройство цементногрунтовых оснований и покрытий. Moscow: Dorizdat 1951.

Bibliography on soil stabilisation. New Delhi: The Indian National Society of Soil Mechanics and Foundation Engineering 1954.

(BIRULYA) Вируля: Проектирование автомобильных дорог. Moscow 1950.

Bodenstabilisierung mit Kalk. Köln: Forschungsgesellschaft für das Straßenwesen e.V. 1958.

Die Bodenstabilisierung mit Kalk. Bielefeld: Straße und Autobahn. 1959, 1960, 1961.

Bodenvermörtelungsmaschine. Joseph Bögele AG. Mannheim (without date).

BOGÁRDI, I.: Einige Anwendungen der Bodenverfestigung im Wasserbau. 2. Donau-Europäische Konferenz, Wien: Öst. Ing.-Arch,—V. (1968) 209–215.

BOGÁRDI, I.—GÁSPÁR, L.: Examinations for seepage-inhibitory layers stabilized by local soils. Vízügyi Közlemények 1966.

BONNENFANT, J. L.: Théorie des chaussées en béton d'argille. Travaux **5** (1946).

BÓRA, Gy.: Mezőgazdasági gépállomások útjainak tervezése (Design of roads of machine and tractor stations). Mélyépítéstudományi Szemle **4** (1954) 3–4.

BOROMISZA, T.: Hazai tapasztalatok a bitumenes talajstabilizálásnál (Experiences with bituminous soil stabilization in Hungary). Mélyépítéstudományi Szemle **15** (1965).

BOROMISZA, T.—FERENCZY, G.: Korszerű pályaszerkezetek (Up-to-date road-ways). Útügyi Kutatóintézet 1964.

BOROMISZA, T.—GÁSPÁR, L.: A bitumenes talajstabilizáció hazai tapasztalatai (Experiences with bituminous soil stabilization in Hungary). Mélyépítéstudományi Szemle **11** 7, (1961) 311–322.

BOROS, J.: Bodenstabilisierung auf einer Tessiner Nationalstraßen-Baustelle. 2. Donau-Europäische Konferenz, Wien: Öst. Ing.-Arch.V. (1968a) 216–219.

BOROS, J.: Autobahnbau bei schwierigen Untergrundverhältnissen. 2. Donau-Europäische Konferenz. Wien: Öst. Ing.-Arch.-V. (1968b) 220–224.

BRAND, W.: Systematik der Bodenverfestigung und Technologie der Bodenstabilisierung mit Kalk. Straße und Autobahn **10** (1960).

BRAND, W.: Der Einfluß von Kalziumhydroxid auf die Eigenschaften schluffiger Böden im Straßenbau. Dissertation; Rheinisch-Westfälische Technische Hochschule, Aachen 1962.

BRANDL, H.: Die Scherfestigkeit kalk- und zementstabilisierter feinkörniger Böden mit besonderer Berücksichtigung der Frosteinwirkung. 2. Donau-Europäische Konferenz, Wien: Öst. Ing.-Arch.-V. (1968) 203–206.

BRUNAUER, S.—COPELAND, L. E.: The chemistry of concrete. Scientific American **4** (1964) 81–92.

BUÓCZ, T.—CSÁGOLY, J.: Talajstabilizáció hígított bitumennel (Soil stabilization with diluted bitumen). Mélyépítéstudományi Szemle **11** (1961) 6.

Calcium Chloride Institute: Calcium chloride for stabilisation of bases and wearing courses. Washington, D. C.: 1953.

CATTON, D. M.: Laboratory investigations of soil-cement mixtures for subgrade treatment in Kansas. Washington, D. C.: Proc. Highway Research Board 1939.

CATTON, D. M.: Soil-cement: A construction material. Proceedings of the conference on soil stabilisation. Cambridge Mass.: Massachussetts Institute of Technology 1952.

CATTON, D. M.: Bodenverfestigung mit Zement in den USA. In: Beton, Herstellung und Verwendung, H. **9**. Düsseldorf: Beton-Verlag GmbH 1958.

312

CHADDA, L. R.—RAJ HEM: Role of detrimental salts in soil stabilization with and without cement. II. Effect of sodium carbonate. The Indian Concrete Journal, India **29** (1955) 12, 401–402.

CHADDA, L. R.: Effect of moisture on the compressive strength of soil-cement mixtures. The Indian Concrete Journal, India **30** (1956) 4.

CHAPMAN, D. L.: A contribution to the theory of electrocapillarity. Philosophical Magazine and Journal of Science. Series G. **25** (1958) 6.

CLARE, K. E.: The waterproofing of soil by resinous materials. Journal of the Society of Chemical Industry **68** (1949) 69–76.

CLARE, K. E.: The use of stabilized soil for road construction in the U.S.A. London: Road Research Techn. Paper 29, 1954a.

CLARE, K. E.: Some problems in mixing granular materials used in road construction. London: Public Works and Municipal Services Congress 1954b.

CLARE, E.—CRUCHLEY, A. E.: Laboratory experiments in the stabilization of clays with hydrated lime. Geotechnique **7** (1957) 97–111.

CORRENS, W. C: The experimental chemical weathering of silicates. Clay Minerals Bulletin **4** (1961) 26.

DALLAVALLE, J. M.: Micromeritics. The technology of fine particles. New York: Pitman Publishing Corp. 1948.

DAVIDSON, D. T.: Soil stabilization with chemicals. Ames, Iowa: Iowa Highway Research Board, Bulletin 22, 1960.

DAWSON, R. F.: Special factors in lime stabilization. Washington, D. C.: Highway Research Board, Bulletin 128, 1956.

DERYAGIN, B. V.: The force between molecules. Scientific American **7** (1960).

DIAMOND, S.—KINTER, E. B.: Surface areas of clay minerals as derived from measurements of glycerol retention. Urbana, Ill.: Proceedings, Fifth National Clay Conference 1956.

DOMJÁN, V.: Két- és háromkomponensű rendszerek nyírási ellenállása (Shearing resistance of two- and three-component systems). Budapest: Diplomarbeit, Technical University of Budapest, 1965.

DOS SANTOS, M. P. R.: A new soil constant and its applications. Zürich: Proc. 3rd Int. Conf. Soil Mech. Found. Engg. Vol. I, 1953.

DOS SANTOS, M. P. R.: Prediction of the consistency limits of soils and soil mixtures. Washington, D. C.: Highway Research Board, Bulletin 108, 1955.

DUTILLEUL, M. S.: L'expérience anglaise en matière de sol-ciment. Annales de l'Inst. Techn. Paris. Bâtiments et des Travaux Publ. No. 96, 1955.

EADES, J. M.—NICHOLS, F. O.—GRIM, R. E.: Formation of new minerals with lime stabilization as proven by field experiments in Virginia. Washington, D. C.: Highway Research Board, Bulletin 335, publication 1017, Lime Stabilization 1962.

ERLENBACH, L.: Bodenverfestigung mit Teer im Land-, Siedlungs-Wirtschafts- und Forstwegebau. Essen: VfT-Mitteilungen 1, 1956.

FANTL, K.: Grundlagen und Erfahrungen der Bodenverfestigung (Bodenstabilisierung). Österreichische Ingenieur-Zeitschrift **4** (1961) 10.

FELT, E. I.: Factors influencing the physical properties of soil-cement mixtures. Washington. D. C.: Highway Research Board, Bulletin 108, 1955.

FERENCZY, G.: Aszfaltburkolatok (Asphalt toppings). Budapest: Műszaki Kiadó 1960.

FERET, R.: Sur la compacité des mortiers hydrauliques. Paris: Annales des Ponts et Chaussées. Mémoires 7, Série 4, 1923.

FIEDLER, H. J.—CZERNY, P.: Bodenstabilisierung und -abdichtung durch Zusatz von Chemikalien. Wiss. Z., TU Dresden **11** (1962) 5, 1159–1166.

FILEP, L.: Egyenlő gömbökből álló halmazok (Sets consisting of equiform spheres). Vízügyi Közlemények 1 (1937).

FINDLEY, A.—CAMPBELL, A. N.—SMITH, N. O.: The phase rule and its applications. 9th ed. New York: Dover Publications Inc. 1951.

FINN, F. N.: A Review of the AASHO Road test with interpretations and applications. Brussels: Centre d'Information du Bitume Symposium 1963.

FOSTER, C. R.—TURNBULL, W. J.: Bituminous stabilization. Proceedings of the conference on soil stabilization. Cambridge, Mass.: Massachusetts Institute of Technology, 1952.

FURNAS, C. C.: Grading aggregates I. Mathematical relations for beds of broken solids of maximum density. Industrial and Engineering Chemistry 23 (1931).

FÜLÖP, I.: A talajstabilizáció gazdasági vizsgálata (Economical examinations of soil stabilization). Mélyépítéstudományi Szemle 16 (1966) 9.

FÜLÖP, I.: Talajstabilizációs kísérletek bázikus hatású barnaszénpernyével (Soil-stabilization experiments with basic-effect lignite flue-dust). Mélyépítéstudományi Szemle 17 (1967) 9.

GABOS, GY.: Alkalmazzunk cementtalajt épületek alapanyagául (Application of cement-soil for raw material of buildings). Magyar Építőipar 9 (1959) 10, 505–509.

GÁSPÁR, L.: Helyi és hulladékanyagok felhasználása közutak építésénél (Use of local and waste matter in public-road building). Mélyépítéstudományi Szemle 3 (1953) 4.

GÁSPÁR, L.: Az útügy meteorológiai vonatkozásairól (Meteorology in traffic). Mélyépítéstudományi Szemle 3 (1953) 10, 11, 12.

GÁSPÁR, L.: Talajstabilizáció I—II (Soil stabilization I—II), Budapest: Útügyi Kutató Intézet 8, 1959.

GÁSPÁR, L.: Cementtel stabilizált alapú utakkal kapcsolatos tapasztalatok (Experiences with cement-stabilized roads). Mélyépítéstudományi Szemle 11 (1961) 9.

GÁSPÁR, L.: A cementes talajstabilizáció újabb hazai kísérletei (Newer experiments for soil-cement stabilization in Hungary). Mélyépítéstudományi Szemle 14 (1964a) 6.

GÁSPÁR, L.: Az Izsáki Állami Gazdaságban talajstabilizálással épített kísérleti úthálózat tapasztalatai (Experiences of an experimental road system built by soil stabilization in the Izsák State Farm). Közlekedéstudományi Szemle 14 (1964b) 8.

GÁSPÁR, I..: A talajstabilizáció időszerű kérdései (Current problems of soil stabilization). Mélyépítéstudományi Szemle 14 (1964c) 12.

GILLILAND, J. L.—HUNTER, H. M.: Rapid method for estimating cement content of soil-cement and blended cements. Philadelphia, Pa.: Bull. American Soc. Test. Mater. (1952) (180).

GOUY, G. Sur la constitution de la charge électrique à la surface d'un électrolyte. Journal de Physique 9 (1910) 4.

GRATON, I.. C.—FRAZER, H. J.: Systematic packing of spheres; with particular relation to porosity and permeability. Journal of Geology 43 (1935).

GRIM, R. E.: Clay mineralogy. New York–Toronto–London: McGraw-Hill Book Co., Inc. 1958.

HASHIMOTO, I.—JACKSON, M. L.: Rapid dissolution of allophane and kaolonite-halloysite after dehydration. Proceedings, 7th Conference on Clays and Clay Minerals. London: Pergamon Press 1960.

HAUSER, E A.: Soil stabilization and colloid science. Washington, D. C.: Highway Research Board, Bulletin 108, 1955.

HENKE, K. F.—FENSCH, L.—MEZGER, H.: Zusammenstellung und Auswertung der Literatur über Bodenstabilisierung mit Chemikalien. Bonn: Bundesminister für Verkehr 1962.

HENNIKER, J. C.—MCBAIN, J. W.: The depth of a surface of a liquid. Technical Report No. 6. Stanford, Cal.: Standard Research Institute, 1948.

HERION, E.: Bodenverfestigung mit Teer auf den Deckenlosen S_1 und S_2 der Bundesautobahn Hamburg—Hannover. Essen: VfT.-Mitteilungen. H. 1, 1956.

HERPAY, I.: Erdei utak pályaszerkezetének kiválasztása (Selection of structure of forest roads). Az Erdő 10 (1961) 1, 1–10.

HERPAY, I.: Kalkstabilisation als Tragschicht im leichten Oberbau der Wirtschaftswege. 2. Donau-Europäische Konferenz, Wien: Öst. Ing.-Arch.-V. 1968, pp. 231–239.

HERPAY, I.—PANKOTAI, G.: Mezőgazdasági útépítés (Road building in Agriculture). Budapest: Mezőgazdasági Kiadó 1963.

HERRIN, M.: Drying phase of soil-asphalt construction. Washington, D. C.: Highway Research Board, Bulletin 204, 1958.

HERZOG, A.—MITCHELL, J. K.: Reactions accompanying the stabilization of clay with cement. A paper presented at the 42nd Annual Meeting of the Highway Research Board, Washington, D. C. 1963.

HOOVER, J. M.—DAVIDSON, D. T.: Organic cationic chemicals as stabilizing agents for Iowa loess. Washington, D. C.: Highway Research Board, Bulletin 129, 1956.

IDEL, K. H.: Die Scherfestigkeit rolliger Erdstoffe. Karlsruhe: Veröffentlichungen des Instituts für Bodenmechanik und Grundbau der Technischen Hochschule Fridericiana, No. 2, 1963.

JÁKY, J.: Talajmechanikai vizsgálatok az útépítésre tekintettel (Soil-mechanical examinations for road building). Budapest: Magyarország Útügyi Évkönyve, 1934.

JÁKY, J.: Földmunkák tömörítése (Gathering of earthwork). Budapest: Mérnöki Továbbképző Intézet, II, 7, 1952.

JÁKY, J.—WÁRLÁM, Á.: Az útépítés talajmechanikája (Soil mechanics of road building). Budapest: Kereskedelmi- és Közlekedésügyi Minisztérium kiadványa, 1937.

JÁRAY, J.: Rugalmas burkolatok méretezése (Dimensioning of elastic pavements). Mélyépítéstudományi Szemle 1 (1951) 5, 6.

JÁRAY, J.: Zusammenhang zwischen der gesamten Kornoberfläche und der Fließgrenze von Böden. Gedenkbuch für Prof. Dr. J. Jáky, Budapest: Akadémiai Kiadó 1955.

JENNY, H.: Factors of soil formation; a system of quantitative pedology. New York: McGraw-Hill Book Co. Inc. 1941.

JESSBERGER, H. L.: Grundlagen und Anwendung der Bodenstabilisierung. Düsseldorf: VDI-Verlag GmbH, 1967.

JOHNSON, A. W.—MORELAND, H.—DAVIDSON, D. T.—HANDY, R. L.: Soil stabilization (Section 21). In: WOODS, K. B.—BERRY, D. S.—GOETZ, W. H.: Highway Engineering Handbook. New York: McGraw-Hill Book Co. Inc. 1960.

JOHNSON, J. C.: The place of asphalt stabilization in the expanded highway program. Chicago, Ill.: Presented at the National Convention of American Road Builder's Assoc., Jan. 1957.

KABAI, I.: A szemcseeloszlás és a tömöríthetőség összefüggése (Relationship between grain-size distribution and compactibility). Thesis, Technical University Budapest, 1972.

KARI, W. J.: Asphalt treated bases. American Bitumen and Asphalt Company 1962.

KATTI, R. K.—DAVIDSON, D. T.—SHEELER, J. B.: Water in cutback asphalt stabilization of soil. Washington, D. C.: Highway Research Board, Bulletin 241, 1960.

KERR, P. F.: Discussion of R. E. Grim "Physico-chemical properties of soils: clay minerals". Proc. Amer. Scc. of Civil Engineers Journal, Soil Mech. and Found. Div. Vol. 85, No. SM 2.

KÉZDI, Á.: Cementtalajutak vizsgálata és méretezése (Examination and dimensioning of soil-cement roads). Budapest: Közlekedési Kiadó 1951.

KÉZDI, Á.: Talajmechanika II (Soil mechanics, vol 2) Budapest: Tankönyvkiadó 1954.

KÉZDI, Á.: Kísérleti cementtalajutak tervezése és kipróbálása (Planning and testing of experimental soil-cement roads). Vol. I. Budapest: Építőipari és Közlekedésügyi Műszaki Egyetem Tudományos Közleményei 1955.

KÉZDI, Á.: Cementtalajutak tartóssága (Durability of soil-cement roads). Mélyépítéstudományi Szemle 7 (1957a) 7–8.

KÉZDI, Á.: Erfahrungen mit der Bodenvermörtelung in Ungarn. Straßen- und Tiefbau, Heidelberg 9 (1957b).

KÉZDI, Á.: Bodenstabilisation in Ungarn. VDI-Zeitschrift, Berlin 24 (1957).

KÉZDI, Á.: Beiträge der Spannungsverteilung im Boden. Der Bauingenieur 2 (1958a).

KÉZDI, Á.: Cinq ans de mécanique du sol en Hongrie. Paris: Annales de l'Inst. Techn. du Bât. et des Trav. Publ. (1958b) 127–128.

KÉZDI, Á.: Über Bodenstabilisierung im Straßenbau. Die Straße 3 (1963).

315

Kézdi, Á.: Lectures on soil mechanics. Princeton, N. J.: Publication of the School of Engineering, Princeton University 1964a.

Kézdi, Á.: Bemessung von Straßendecken. Österreichische Ingenieurzeitschrift 12 (1964b).

Kézdi, Á.: Contributions to the investigation of granular systems. Washington, D. C.: Highway Research Record, No. 52, HRB. publ. 1177, 1964c.

Kézdi, Á.: Bodenmechanik. Budapest—Berlin: Akadémiai Kiadó und VEB Verlag für Bauwesen (1964d) vol. 1-2.

Kézdi, Á.: Új eredmények a talajfizikában (New results in soil physics). Mélyépítéstudományi Szemle 16 (1966a) 6.

Kézdi, Á.: Some characteristics of packings. In: Rheology and soil mechanics. IUTAM — Symposium, Grenoble, 1964. Berlin—Heidelberg—New York: Springer Verlag 1966b.

Kézdi, Á.: Kohéziós talajok nyírószilárdsága (Shearing strength of cohesion soils). Mélyépítéstudományi Szemle 17 (1967a) 1.

Kézdi, Á.: A talajstabilizáció néhány fizikai és kémiai tulajdonsága (Physical and chemical properties of soil stabilization). Ép. Közl. Tud. Közl. (1967b) 2, 179–204.

Kézdi, Á. Festigkeit von stabilisierten Erdstoffen. 2. Donau-Europäische Konferenz, Wien: Öst. Ing.-Arch.-V. (1968a), 240–242.

Kézdi, Á.: Distribution of grains and voids according to their volume. Acta techn. Acad. Sci. hung. 63 (1968b) 1–4, 125–131.

Kézdi, Á.: Spannungen in Zweiphasensystemen. Acta techn. Acad. Sci. hung. 69 (1970a) 1–2, 22–39.

Kézdi, Á.: Handbuch der Bodenmechanik. Berlin: Verlag für Bauwesen. Band 1, 1969; Band 2, 1970; Band 3, 1973.

Kézdi, Á.: Fragen der Bodenphysik. Düsseldorf: VDI-Verlag 1976.

Kézdi, Á.—Brahma, S.: The strength of soil cement. Madras, India: Seminar on Engineering Materials. Industrial Scientific Research Association Indsearch 1966.

Kézdi, Á.—Nagyváti, B.: Strength of stabilized soils. Acta techn. Acad. Sci. hung. 62 (1968) 1–2, 75–95.

Kézdi, Á.—Nagyváti, B.: Einfluß von Zusatzmitteln auf die Eigenschaften von stabilisierten Böden. Acta techn. Acad. Sci. hung. 68 (1970) 3–4, 283–291.

Kinze, M.: Spannungen und Verformungen bei der statischen Bodenverdichtung. Berlin: Mitteilungen des Instituts für Wasserwirtschaft H. 26, 1966.

Korbonits, D.: Mezőgazdasági utak építése és fenntartása (Building and maintenance of agricultural roads). Budapest: Útügyi Kutató Intézet 1962.

Körmendi, J.: Útfenntartás kisgépesítése (Mechanisation of maintenance of roads with small machines). Budapest: Útügyi Kutató Intézet 1960.

Koženy, J.: Über Grundwasserbewegung. Wasserkraft und Wasserwirtschaft 22 (1927).

Lambe, T. W.: The effect of polymers on soil properties. Zürich: Proc. 3rd Int. Conf. Soil Mech. Found. Engg. 1953.

Lambe, T. W.: Civil engineering need for soil chemicals. Industrial and Engineering Chemistry 47 (1955) 2234–2239.

Lambe, T. W.: The modification of frost-heaving of soils with additives. Washington, D. C.: Highway Research Board 1956.

Lambe, T. W.: The structure of compacted clay. Proc. Amer. Soc. of Civil Engineers. Journal of the Soil Mech. and Found. Div., Vol. 84, No. SM 2, 1958.

Lambe, T. W.: Soil stabilization. In: Foundation engineering, ed. by G. A. Leonards, New York: McGraw-Hill Book Co. Inc. 1962.

Lambe, T. W.—Michaels, A. S.: Altering soil properties with chemicals. Chemical and Engineering News 32 (1954) 488–497.

Lambe, T. W.—Michaels, A. S.—Moh, Z. C.: Improvement of soil-cement with alkali metal compounds. Washington, D. C.: Highway Research Board, Bulletin 241, 1960.

Larnach, W. J.: The strength of soil-cement mixtures. Civil Engineering and Public Works Review 55 (1960) H. 1648.

LAWRANCE, A. E.: Soil stabilization in relation to modern road construction. Slough: British Bitumen Emulsions Ltd., Technical Report 1948.

LEADABRAND, J. A.—NORLING, L. T.: Simplified methods of testing soil-cement mixtures. In: Highway Research Board, Bulletin 122. Washington, D. C. 1956.

LEHOCZKY, K.: Az útépítés kézikönyve (Handbook for road building). Budapest: Műszaki Kiadó 1955.

LEONARDS, G. A.: Engineering properties of soils. In: Foundation engineering, ed. by G. A Leonards, New York: McGraw-Hill Book Co. Inc. 1962.

LEUSSINK, H.—KUTZNER, CH.: Laboratoriumsversuch zur Feststellung der dichtesten. Lagerung körniger Erdstoffe. Karlsruhe: Veröffentlichungen des Instituts für Bodenmechanik und Grundbau, No. 8, 1962.

LIFSHITZ. E. M : Intermolecular forces of attraction between solid bodies (in Russian). Moscow: Zhur. Exp. Teor. Fiz. **29** (1956) 94

Lime stabilization of roads. Washington, D. C.: National Lime Association, Bulletin 323, 1954.

Lime stabilization construction manual. Washington, D. C.: American Road Builders Association Technical Bulletin 243, 1959.

LINEMANN, K. (ed.): Erdstabilisierung in Theorie und Praxis. Berlin: VEB Verlag für Bauwesen 1966.

LOW, P. F.: Condition of water in soil systems and its response to applied force fields. Washington, D. C.: Highway Research Board, Spec. Report 40, 1958.

LYONS, J. W.: Stabilizing a problem soil — cheaply. Engineering New Record 1957.

MAINFORT, R. C.: Soil stabilization with resins and chemicals. Washington, D. C.: Highway Research Board, Bulletin 108, 1955.

MARKWICK, A. H.: The basic principles of soil compaction and their application. London: The Institution of Civil Engineering 1945.

MARSHALL, T. J.: Some properties of soil treated with portland cement. Australia: Symposium on Soil Stabilization 1954.

MATEOS, M.—DAVIDSON, D. T.: Lime and fly ash proportions in soil, lime and fly ash mixtures, and some aspects of soil lime stabilization. Washington, D. C.: Highway Research Board, Bulletin 335, Lime Stabilization 1962.

MEHRA, S. R.—CHADDA, L. R.—KAPUR, R. N.: Role of detrimental salts in soil stabilization with and without cement. I. Effect of sodium sulphate The Indian Concrete Journal **29** (1955) 10.

MEHRA, S. R.—UPPAL, H. L.: Use of stabilized soil in engineering construction. Journal, Indian Roads Congress, Vol. **14**, 1949; Vol. **15**, 1951.

MÉSZÁROS, J.—SITKEI, GY.: A mezőgazdasági gépek vizsgálata (Tests for agricultural machines). Budapest: Akadémiai Kiadó 1965.

MICHAELS, A. S.: Altering soil-water relationships by chemical means. Proceedings of the Conference on Soil Stabilization. Cambridge, Mass.: Massachusetts Institute of Technology 1962.

MICHAELS, A. S.—PUZINAUSKAS, V.: Additives as aids to asphalt stabilization of fine-grained soils. Washington, D. C.: Highway Research Board, Bulletin 129, 1956.

MICHAELS, A. S.—PUZINAUSKAS, V.: Improvement of asphaltstabilized fine-grained soils with chemical additives. Washington, D. C.: Highway Research Board, Bulletin 204, 1958.

MICHAELS, A. S.—TAUSCH, F. W.: Fine-grain soil stabilization with phosphoric acid and secondary additives. Washington, D. C.: Highway Research Board, Bulletin 241, 1960.

MITCHELL, J. K.—FREITAG, D. R.: A review and evaluation of soil-cement pavements. Proc. Amer. Soc. of Civil Engineers. Vol. **81**, No. *SM* 6, 1959.

MITCHELL, J. K.—HOOPER, D. R.: The influence of time between mixing and compaction on properties of a limestabilized expansive clay. Berkeley, Calif.: Highway Research Board 1961.

MURRAY, G. E.: Soil stabilization by chemical means. Proceedings of the Conference on Soil Stabilization. Cambridge, Mass.: Massachusetts Institute of Technology 1952.

MURRAY, G. E.: Effect of stabilizer structure on preparation and properties of stabilized soil. Washington, D. C.: Highway Research Board 1955.

NAGYVÁTI, B.: Cementtalajutak építése (Construction of cement-soil roads). Mélyépítéstudományi Szemle 8 (1955).

NAGYVÁTI, B.: Rideg anyagok húzószilárdságának kísérleti meghatározása (Versuche zur Bestimmung der Zugfestigkeit von spröden Materialien). Mélyépítéstudományi Szemle 8 (1958) 300–305.

NAGYVÁTI, B.: Homok kátránnyal és trasziiszttel való stabilizálása (Stabilization of sand with tar and pozzuolana meal). Mélyépítéstudományi Szemle 9 (1959) 4 180–185.

NAGYVÁTI, B.: Úrburkolatok alatti szűrőréteg vizsgálata (Examination of filter beds under road pavement). Ép. Közl. Tud. Közl. 1 (1961) 4.

NAGYVÁTI, B.: Cementtalaj-utak építése (Building of soil-cement roads). Mélyépítéstudományi Szemle 15 (1965) 8, 5.

NÜSSBAUM, P. L.–LARSEN, T. J.: Load-deflection characteristics of soil-cement. Skokie, Ill.: Portland Cement Association 1964.

OGILVIE, J. G.—SHEELER, J. B.—DAVIDSON, D. T.: Stabilization of loess with aniline-furfural. Washington, D. C.: Proceedings, Highway Research Board, Vol. 36, 1957.

(OKHOTIN, V. V.) Охотин, В. В.: Лабораторные опыты по составлению дорожных грунтовых смесей наименьшей пористости. Leningrad 1929.

VAN OLPHEN, H.: Chemical treatment of drilling muds. Delft: Tech. Univ. Dix. Farad. Soc. No. 1, 1951.

OREL, M.—GSPAN, M.: Beständigkeit von Bodenverfestigungen gegen Witterungseinflüsse. Zement-Kal-Gips 23 (1970) 1, 44–48.

OTTO, H.: Hinweise zur Beurteilung von Bodenstabilisierungen im Straßenbau. Zürich: Hoch- und Tiefbau, No. 33, 1963.

PANKOTAI, G.: Az erdőgazdasági szállítás jelenlegi helyzete és feladatai a Magyar Népköztársaságban (Present state and tasks of forest-economy transport in Hungary). Erdészettudományi Közlemények (1960).

PATTON, J.—REEDER, W.: New indicator for titration of calcium with (ethylene-dinitrilo)-tetra-acetate. Analyt. Chem. 28 (6) (1955), 1026–1028.

PÄTZHOLD, H.: Über die Stabilisierung von Sanden durch Zumischung von Teer. Essen: VfT-Mitteilungen, H. 1, 1956.

PÄTZHOLD, H.: Bituminöse Stabilisierung im Straßen- und Wegebau. Essen: VfT-Mitteilungen, H. 2, 1957.

PÄTZHOLD, H.: Bodenverfestigung mit bituminösen Bindemitteln. Straßenbau und Bautenschutz mit Steinkohlenteer, H. 1, 1960.

PCA: Soil primer. Chicago Ill.: Portland Cement Association 1962.

PETRASOVITS, G.: Talajok stabilizálása műgyantákkal (Soil-stabilization with artificial resins). Építéstudományi Műszaki Egyetem Közleményei. Budapest, 1965.

PIETSCH, P. E.—DAVIDSON, D. T.: Effects of lime on plasticity and compressive strength of representative Iowa soils. Washington, D. C.: Highway Research Board, Bulletin 335, publication 1017, Lime Stabilization, 1962.

Proceedings of the Conference on Soil Stabilization. Cambridge, Mass.: Massachusetts Institute of Technology 1952.

PRUŠKA, L.: Die optimale Verdichtungsenergie. Proceedings, Conference on Soil Mechanics and Foundation Engineering. Budapest: Akadémiai Kiadó 1963.

PUZÍNAUSKAS, V.—KALLAS, B. F.: Stabilization of fine-grained soils with cutback asphalt and secondary additives. Washington, D. C.: Highway Research Board, Bulletin 309, 1961.

QUÍRICO, D.: A cementstabilizáció kivitelezésével kapcsolatos újabb kísérletek és tapasztalatok (New experiments and experiences concerning cement stabilization). Mélyépítéstudományi Szemle 3 (1953) 9.

Rázsó, I.: Szántóföldön lefolyó gördülési jelenségek és mezőgazdasági vonatkozásaik (Rollings at fieldlands and their agricultural relations). Budapest: MTA Műsz. Tud. Oszt. Közl. II. — 1, 1951.

Regele, Z.: Experiments with carbamide-resin grouts for soil stabilization. Lodz: Proceedings of the Seminar on soil mechanics and foundation engineering. 1964.

Reinhold, F.: Elastic behavior of soil-cement mixtures. Washington, D. C.: Highway Research Board, Bulletin 108, 1955.

Robinson, D. J.: British studies on the incorporation of admixtures with soil. Proceedings of the Conference on Soil Stabilization. Cambridge, Mass.: Massachusetts Institute of Technology 1952.

Rotfuchs, G.: Zusammenhänge zwischen der Kornzusammensetzung und der Dichtigkeit von Mörtel und Betonmischungen. Bitumen 1935.

Ruiz, C. L.: Osmotic interpretation of the swelling of expansive soils. Washington, D. C.: Proceedings, Highway Research Board, Vol. 40, 1961.

Schoefield, R. K.—Samson, H.: Flocculation of kaolinite due to the attraction of oppositely charged faces. Discussions of the Faraday Society, No. 18, 1954, p. 135.

Scott, R. F.: Principles of soil mechanics. Reading, Mass.: Addison-Wesley-Publishing Co. Inc. 1963.

Seed, H. B.—Chan, C. K.: Compacted clays. Proceedings, Amer. Soc. Civil Engineers, Journal of the Soil Mech. and Found. Div., Proc. 2216, 1959.

Seed, H. B.—Woodward, R. J.—Lundgreen, R. Fundamental aspects of the Atterberg limits. Proceedings, Amer. Soc. Civil Engineers, Journal of the Soil Mech. and Found. Div., Vol. 90, No. SM 6, 1964.

Shell: Design charts for flexible pavements. London: Shell Oil Company. Asphalt Sales Department. Shell International Petroleum Company Limited 1963.

Sherwood, P. T.: Soil stabilization by the use of chemical admixtures — a review of the present position. Roads and Road Construction. April 1961.

Sitkei, Gy.: Futóhomok talajainak hordóképessége (Carrying capacity of wind-blown sand). Járművek, Mezőgazdasági Gépek 13 (1966) 2.

Sitkei, Gy.: A mezőgazdasági gépek talajmechanikai problémái (Soil-mechanical problems of agricultural machines). Budapest: Akadémiai Kiadó 1967.

Sjaastad, G. D.: The effect of vacuum on the shearing resistance of ideal granular systems. Ph. D. thesis, Princeton Univ., Dept. of Civil Eng. 1963.

Slichter, C. S.: Theoretical investigation of the motion of ground water. U. S. Geol. Survey, 19th Ann. Report, Part 2, 1899.

Smith, J. C.: Mixing chemicals with soil. Industrial and Engineering Chemistry 47 (1955) 2240–2244.

Smith, W. O.: Capillary flow through an ideal uniform soil. Physics 3 (1932) 139—146.

Soil and Soil-aggregate Stabilization. A Symposium. Washington, D. C.: Highway Research Board, Bulletin 108, 1955.

Soil-cement Laboratory Handbook. Chicago, Ill.: Portland Cement Association 1959.

Soil-cement Roads. Bombay: The Concrete Association of India 1948.

Soil Cement Construction Handbook. Chicago, Ill.: Portland Cement Association (without date).

Soil Cement Stabilization. Chicago, Ill.: Pettibone Mulliken Corp. (without date).

Soil Mechanics for Road Engineers. Department of Scientific and Industrial Research, Road Research Laboratory. London: Her Majesty's Stationary Office 1952.

Soil-stabilization Methods. Bulletin 25. Milwaukee. Wis. U.S.A.: Seaman Motors (without date).

Sowers, G. F.—Vesić, A. B.: The study of stresses in a flexible pavement system. Atlanta, Ga.: The State Highway Department of Georgia in cooperation with the Bureau of Public Roads 1960.

Springenschmid, R.: Einige grundlegende Betrachtungen über Bodenverfestigung mit Zement im Straßenbau. Die Bauwirtschaft 37 (1957).

319

SPRINGENSCHMID, R.: Beanspruchung und Prüfung von Bodenverfestigungen mit Zement. Straßen- und Tiefbau **3** (1960).

SPRINGENSCHMID, R.: Praktische Hinweise für den Bau von Bodenzementverfestigungen mit Mehrgangmischern. Düsseldorf: Beton-Verlag GmbH 1961.

Straßenbau von A-Z. Bearbeitet für die Forschungsgesellschaft für das Straßenwesen e. V. Vol. IV. Bielefeld 1958.

Tagungs-Berichte der Arbeitsgruppe "Untegrundforschung 1960–1961". Wien: Forschungsgesellschaft für das Straßenwesen im Öst. Ing.- und Arch.-V. H. 20, 1962.

TAILLEBOT, A.: Emploi de résines synthétiques dans les travaux publics. — Consolidation des fouilles de la centrale hydro-électrique de Bergerac. Travaux **52** (1969), 409, 217–220.

TAYLOR, H. F. W.: The chemistry of cement hydration. Chapter in "Progress in ceramic science", ed. by J. E. Burke, London: Pergamon Press 1961.

Tickness Design — Asphalt Pavement Structures for Highways and Streets. Chicago, Ill.: The Asphalt Institute. 7th ed. 1963.

(TOKIN, A. N.—YAKOVLEVA, V. A.) Токин, А. Н. Яковлева, В. А: Олеотермальная обработка цементогрунта. Строит. и архит. **2** (1969) 6, pp. 84–87.

UPPAL, I. S.—KAPUR, B. P.: Role of detrimental salts in soil stabilization with and without cement. III. Effect of Magnesium Sulphate. The Indian Concrete Journal **31** (1957) 7.

VALLERGA, B. A.: Emulsified petroleum oils and resins in reconstituting asphalts in pavements. Washington, D. C.: Proceedings, Highway Research Board 1963.

VÁSÁRHELYI, B.: Útépítéstan (Road construction). Budapest: Tankönyvkiadó 1963.

VERSTRAETEN, J.: Determination des contraintes et des déformations dans les systèmes multicouches. Bruxelles: Centre de Recherches Routières 1962.

VESIĆ, A. B.: Validity of layered soil theories for flexible pavements. Ann Arbor, Mich. International Conference on the Structural Design of Asphalt Pavements 1963.

Vorlaufiges Merkblatt für Bodenverfestigung mit bituminösen Bindemitteln. Köln: Forschungsgesellschaft für das Straßenwesen e. V. 1958.

WÁRLÁM, Á.: Földutak (Earth roads). Budapest: Építési Zsebkönyv 1938.

WESSEL, H.: Zur Theorie der Bodenverfestigung mit Spezialzement. 2. Donau-Europäische Konferenz, Wien: Öst. Ing.-Arch. V. 1968, pp. 266–269.

WHITE, H. E.—WALTON, S. F.: Particle packing and particle shape. Journal American Ceramic Society **20** (1937).

WIŁUN, Z.: Verdichtbarkeit und physiko-mechanische Eigenschaften der aufgeschütteten vereichteten Böden. 2. Donau-Europäische Konferenz, Wien: Öst. Ing.-Arch.-V. 1968, pp. 270–274.

WINTERKORN, H. F.: Principles and practice of soil stabilization. In: J. Alexander: Colloid Chemistry, Theoretical and Applied. New York, N. Y.: Reinhold Publishing Corporation 1946.

WINTERKORN, H. F.: Macromeritic liquids. American Society of Testing Materials. Philadelphia: Symposium on Dynamic Testing of Soils 1953.

WINTERKORN, H. F.: The science of soil stabilization. Washington, D. C.: Highway Research Board, Bulletin 108, 1955a.

WINTERKORN, H. F.: Probleme der Bodenstabilisierung. Linz/Donau: Tagung des Österreichischen National-Komitees der Internationalen Gesellschaft für Grundbau und Bodenmechanik 1955b.

WINTERKORN, H. F.: Soil stabilization. Mimeographed lecture notes Princeton, N. J.: Princeton University 1963.

WINTERKORN, H. F.: Soil stabilization. In: Foundation Engineering Handbook (ed. by Winterkorn, H. F. and Hsai-Yang Fang). Van Nostrand Reinhold Co., New York 1975.

WINTERKORN, H. F.—AICHHORN, W.: Grundlagen der Bodenstabilisierung im Straßen- und Wegebau. Wien: Forschungsgesellschaft für das Straßenwesen im Öst. Ing.-Arch.-V. Arbeitsgruppe "Untergrundforschung" 1960.

WOODS, K. B.—BERRY, D. S.—GOETZ, W. H.: Highway engineering handbook. First ed. New York—Toronto—London: McGraw-Hill Book Co. Inc. 1960.

WOODS, K. B.—PICONE, C. E.: Soil stabilization. Rio de Janeiro: Proceedings, 1st Pan-American Engineering Congress 1949.

Woods, K. B.—Yoder, E. J.: Stabilization with soil, lime or calcium chloride as an admixture. Proceedings of the Conference on soil stabilization. Cambridge, Mass.: Massachusetts Institute of Technology 1952.

Wooltorton, F. L. D.: Relation between the plasticity index and the percentage of fines in granular soil stabilization. Washington, D. C.: Proceedings, Highway Research Board, Vol. **27**, 1947.

Wooltorton, F. L. D.: Engineering pedology and soil stabilization. Washington, D. C.: Highway Research Board, Bulletin 108, 1955.

Zvetkov, W. S.—Liberman, M. A.—Sestoperov, S. W.: Peculiarities of mixing soil and cement (in Russian) Avtom. dor. **33** (1970) *1*, 12–13.

Index